MUSE

THE GUITAR SONGBOOK

First published by Faber Music Ltd in 2013
Bloomsbury House
74 – 77 Great Russell Street
London WC1B 3DA

Printed in England by Caligraving Ltd

ISBN10: 0-571-53774-X
EAN13: 978-0-571-53774-7

ASSASSIN

Words and Music by Matthew Bellamy

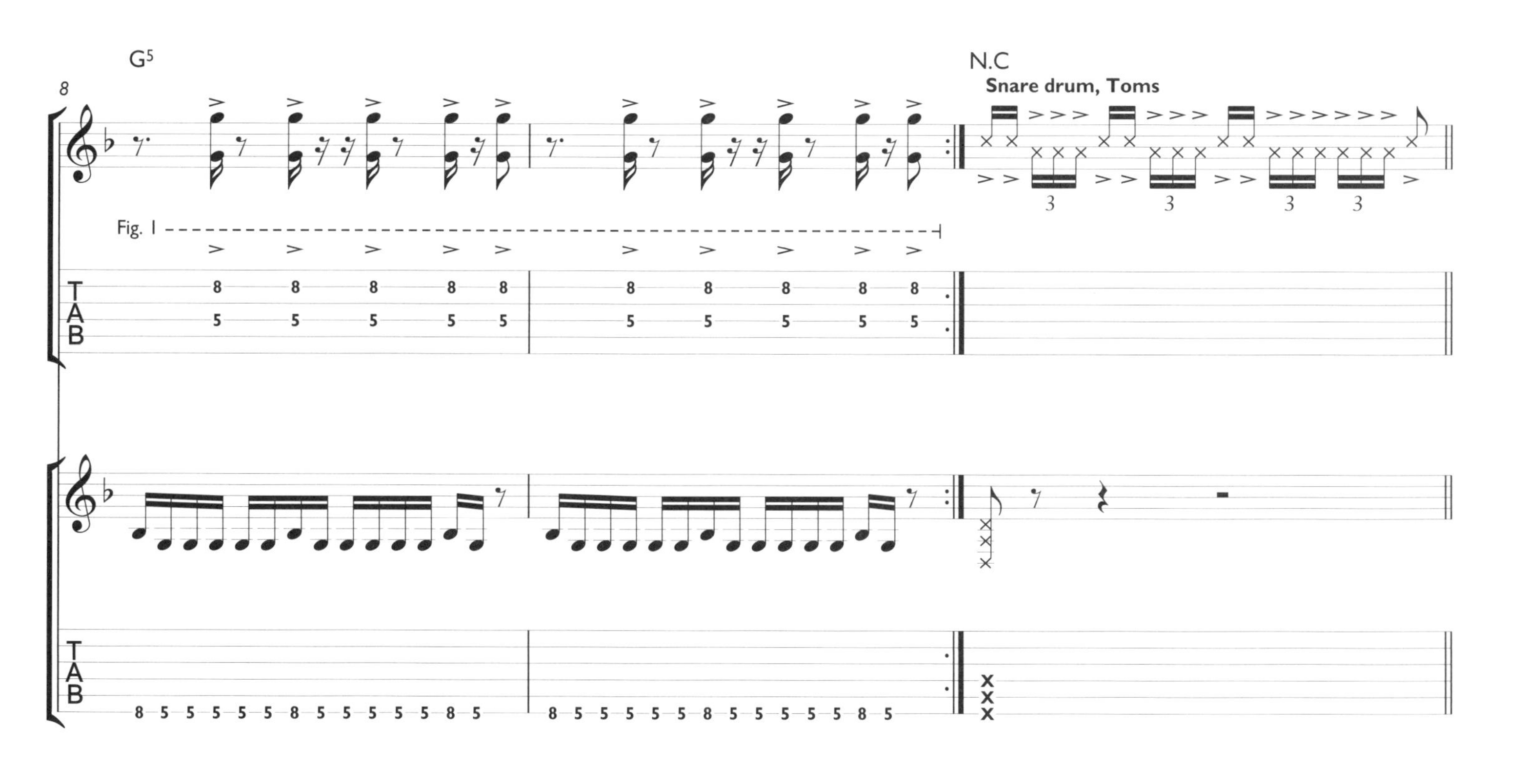
G5
8
N.C
Snare drum, Toms
Fig. 1

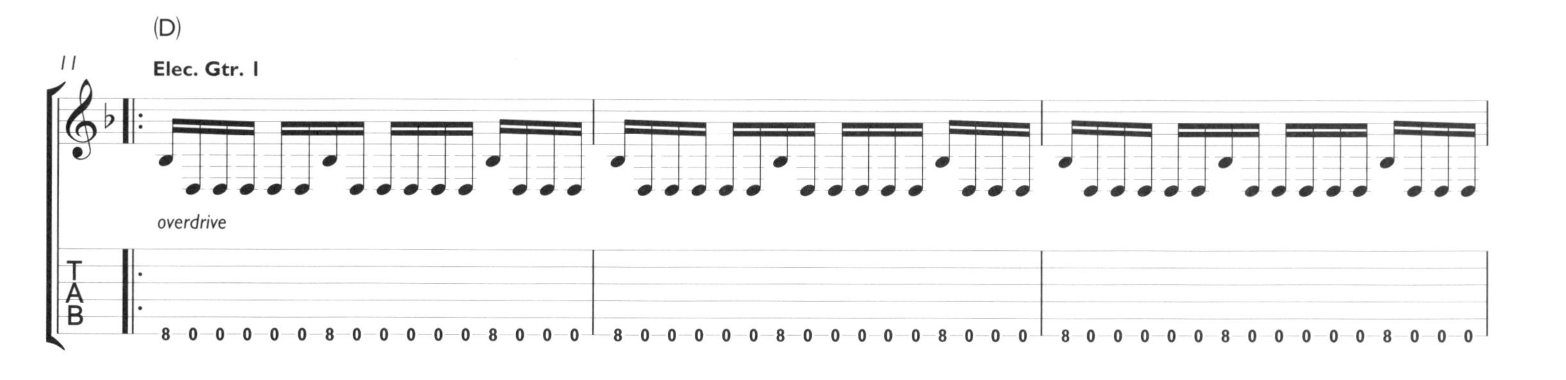
(D)
11
Elec. Gtr. 1
overdrive

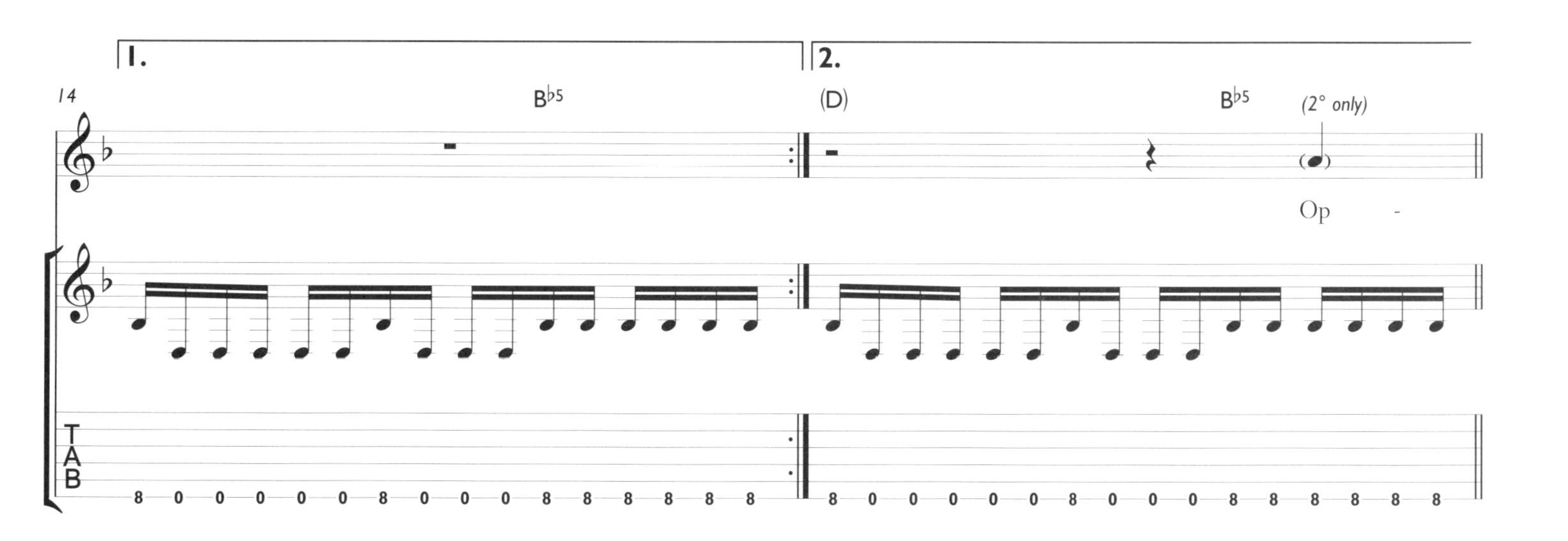
1.
2.
14
B♭5
(D)
(2° only)
Op -

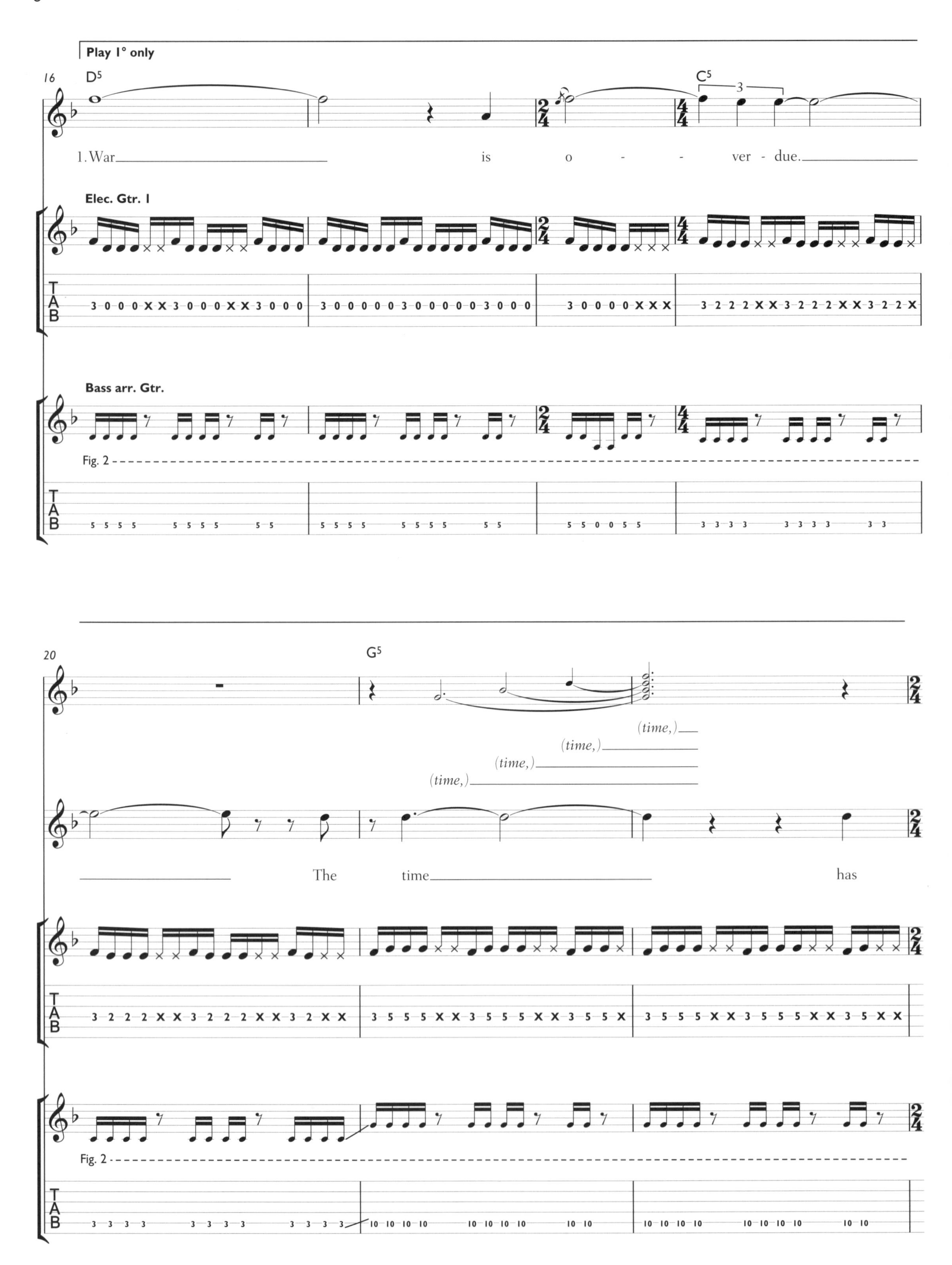
Play 1° only
16
D5
C5
3
1. War is o - - ver - due.
Elec. Gtr. 1
Bass arr. Gtr.
Fig. 2
20
G5
(time,)
(time,)
(time,)
(time,)
The time has
Fig. 2

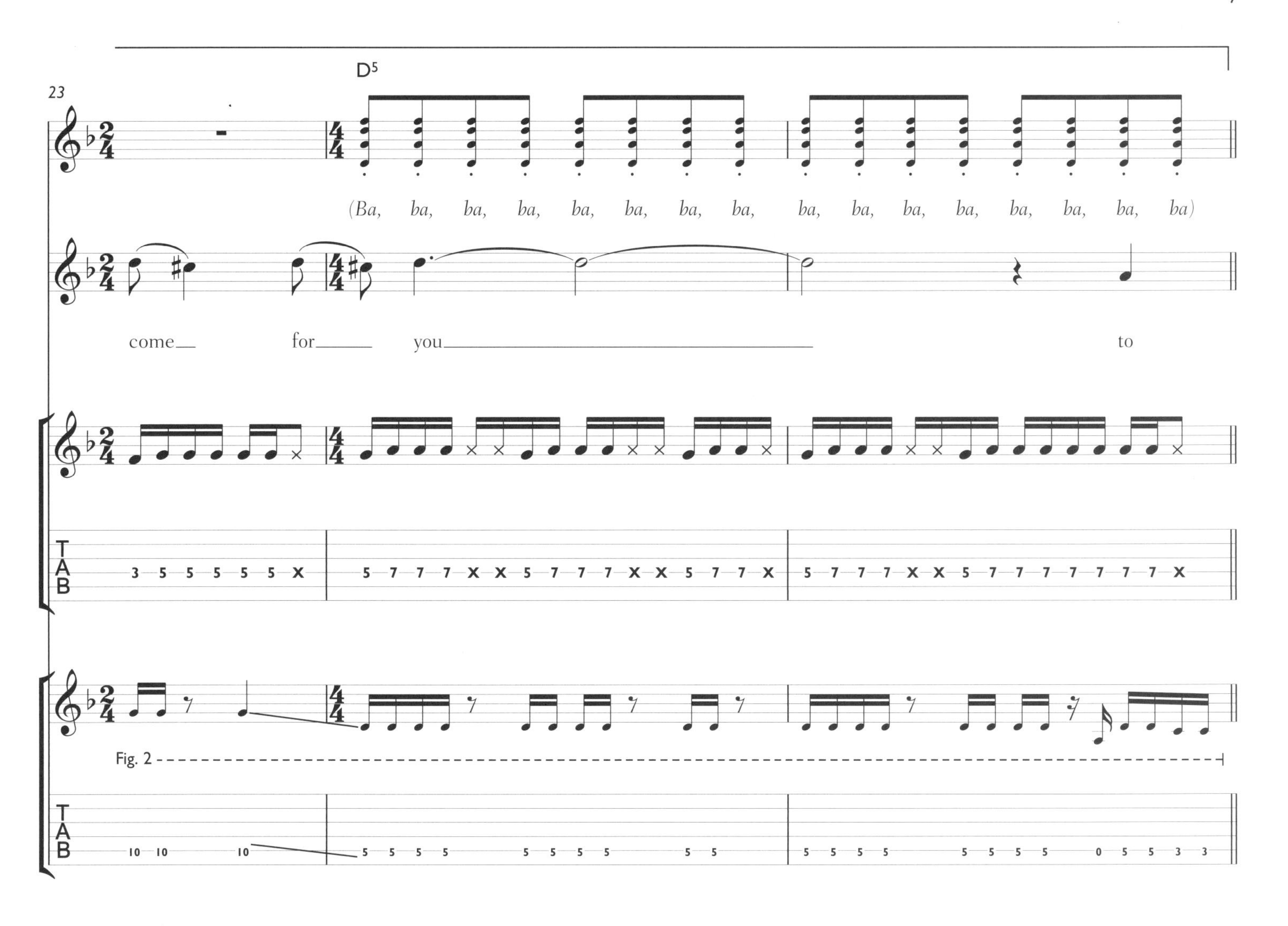
23
D5
(Ba, ba, ba, ba, ba, ba, ba, ba, ba, ba, ba, ba, ba, ba, ba, ba)
come for you to
Fig. 2

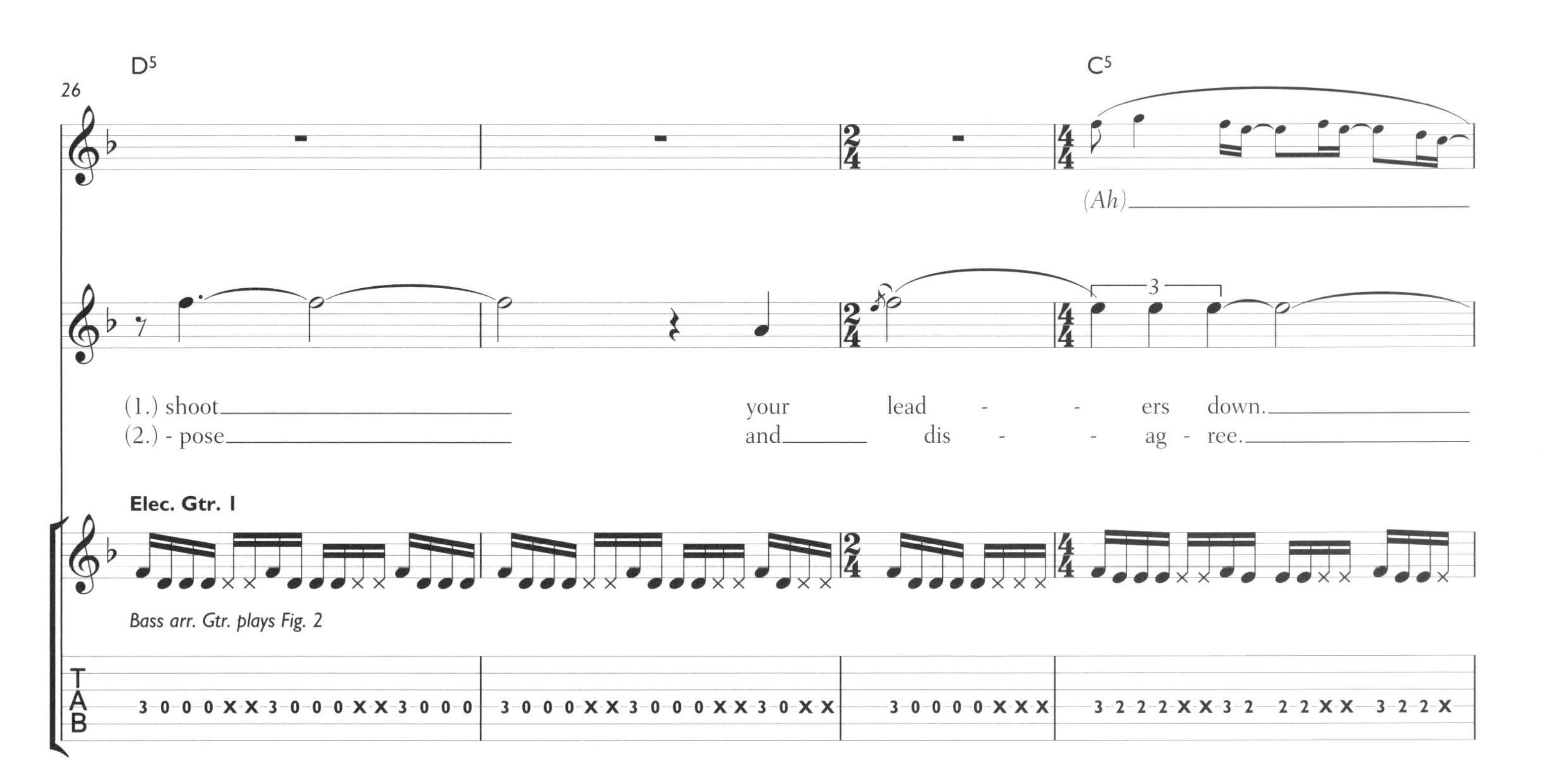
26
D5
C5
(Ah)
(1.) shoot your lead - - ers down.
(2.) - pose and dis - - ag - ree.
Elec. Gtr. 1
Bass arr. Gtr. plays Fig. 2

G5
(1./2.) (for/des - ces/ - troy,)
(1./2.) (for/des - ces/ - troy,)
(1./2.) (for/des - - - ces/ - troy,)
Join for - - - - - - - ces
Des - troy de - mon -
D5
(Ba, ba, ba, ba, ba, ba, ba, ba, ba, ba, ba, ba, ba, ba, ba, ba)
un - der - ground.
- oc - ra - cy.
F5
Bass arr. Gtr.
3fr
cont. sim.
(Lo - sing con - trol,
Lose con - trol, at in - creas - ing
Elec. Gtr. 1

C5
3fr
G5
5fr
cont. sim.
39
in - creas - ing pace, warped and be -
pace, warped and be - witched, in
D5
5fr
F5
3fr
cont. sim.
42
- witched, time to e - rase, what -
time to e - rase what - ev - er they
C5
3fr
45
- ev - er they say, peo - ple are
say, these peo - ple are torn,

G5
5fr
cont. sim.
48
torn,
wild
and
be -
wild
and
be - - reft,
ass -
D5
Play 2° only
A5
open
50
- reft.
As - sas - sin is born.)
- as - sin is born, yeah.
Elec. Gtr. 2
53
A5
Backing vocals (1° only)
born.
Vocals (1° only)
Woah, woah, woah, woah.
Elec. Gtr. 1
Elec. Gtr. 2 plays Fig. 2
G5

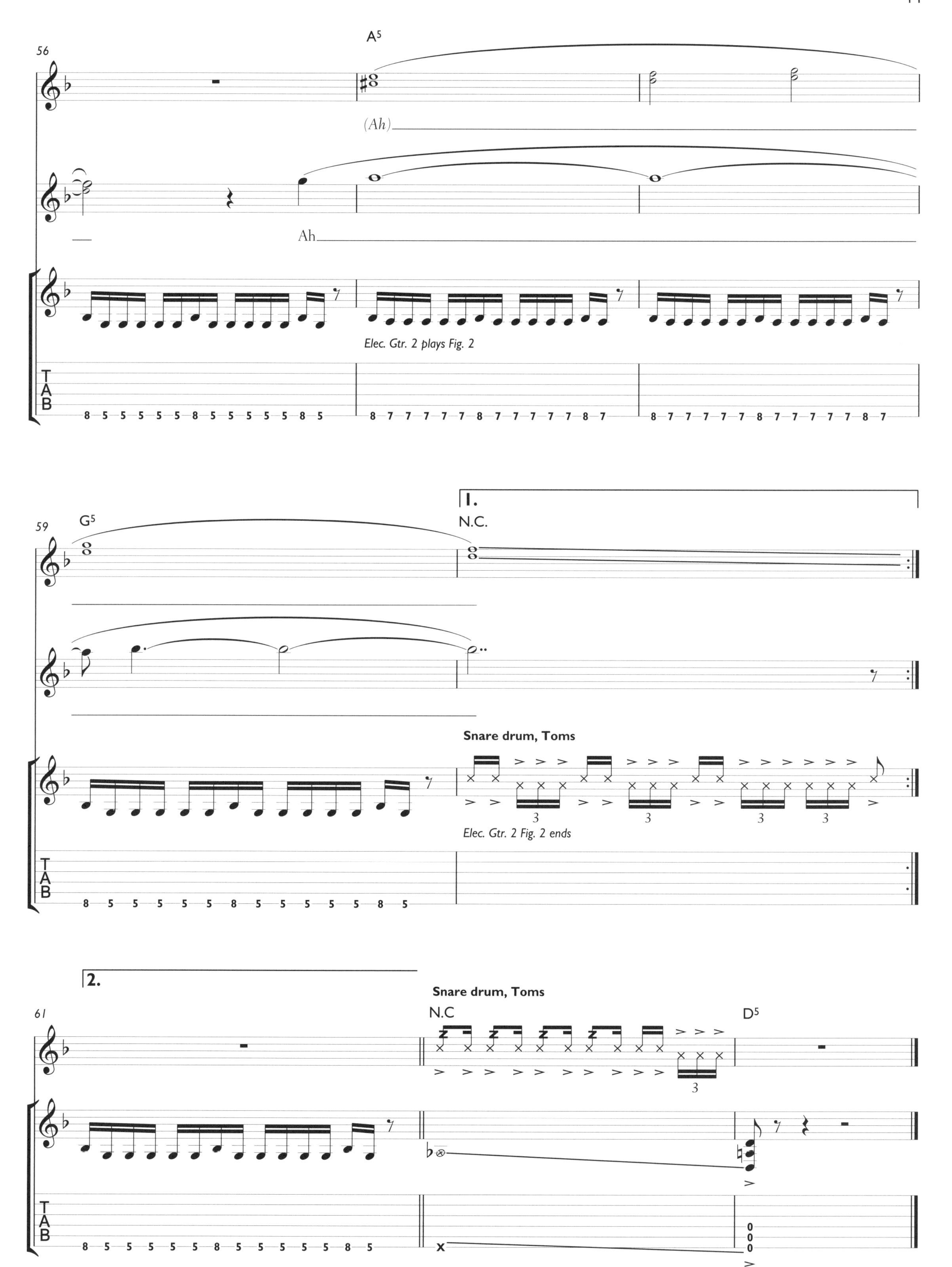
56
A5
(Ah)
Ah
Elec. Gtr. 2 plays Fig. 2
TAB
8 5 5 5 5 5 8 5 5 5 5 5 8 5
8 7 7 7 7 7 8 7 7 7 7 7 8 7
8 7 7 7 7 7 8 7 7 7 7 7 8 7
1.
59
G5
N.C.
Snare drum, Toms
Elec. Gtr. 2 Fig. 2 ends
8 5 5 5 5 5 8 5 5 5 5 5 8 5
2.
Snare drum, Toms
61
N.C
D5
8 5 5 5 5 5 8 5 5 5 5 5 8 5
x
0
0
0

BIG FREEZE

Words and Music by Matthew Bellamy

13
E♭5
E♭7
A♭5
E♭dim
here.) just be - cause I need you? Can we hole
here.) just to prove you're win - ning? Can we hole
T
A
B
16
15
13
14
15
13
13
13
14
13

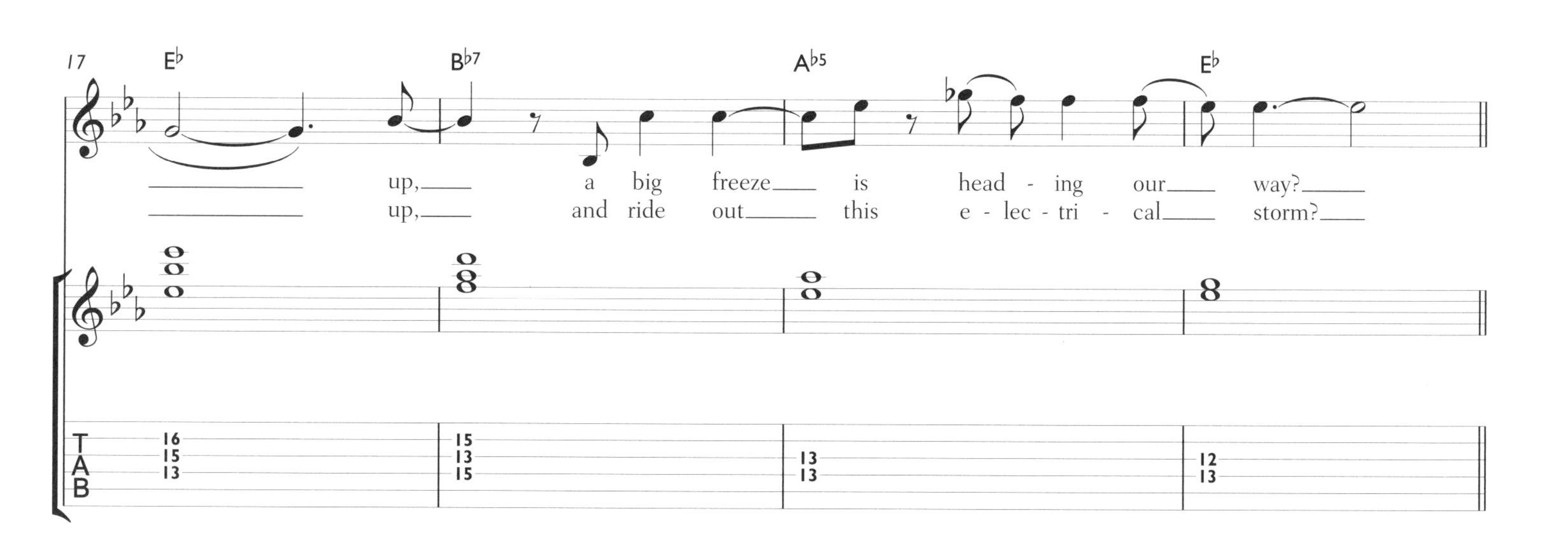
17
E♭
B♭7
A♭5
E♭
up, a big freeze is head - ing our way?
up, and ride out this e - lec - tri - cal storm?
T
A
B
16
15
13
15
13
15
13
13
12
13

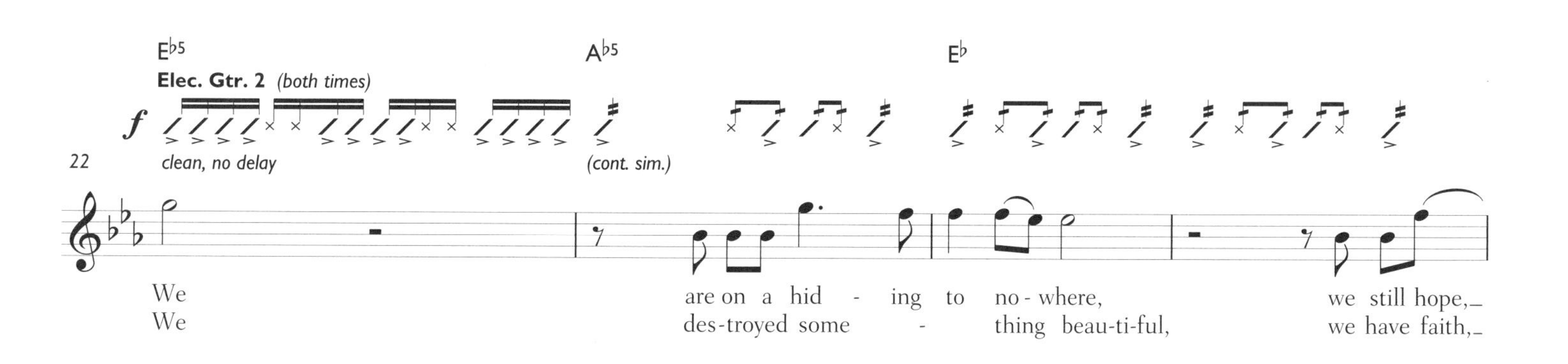
E♭5
A♭5
E♭
Elec. Gtr. 2 (both times)
f
clean, no delay
(cont. sim.)
22
We are on a hid - ing to no - where, we still hope,
We des-troyed some - thing beau-ti-ful, we have faith,

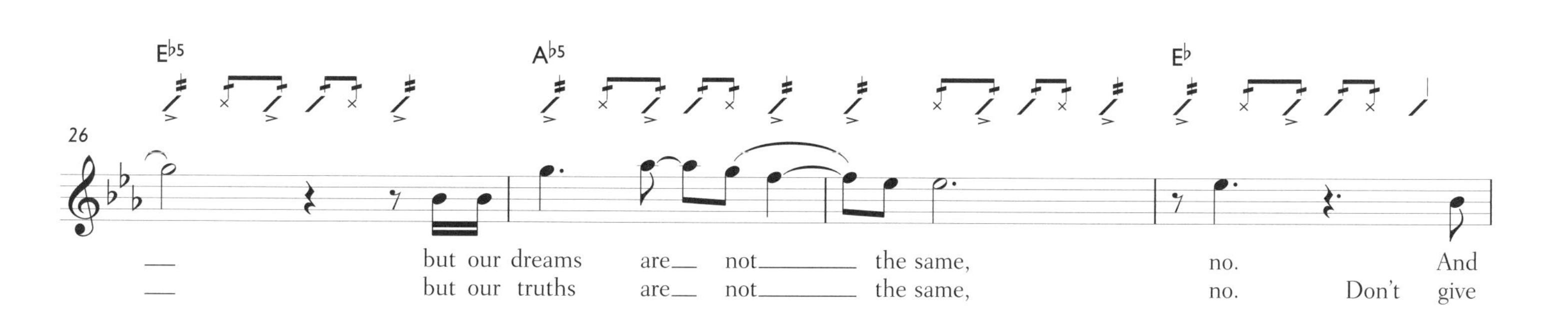
E♭5
A♭5
E♭
26
but our dreams are not the same, no. And
but our truths are not the same, no. Don't give

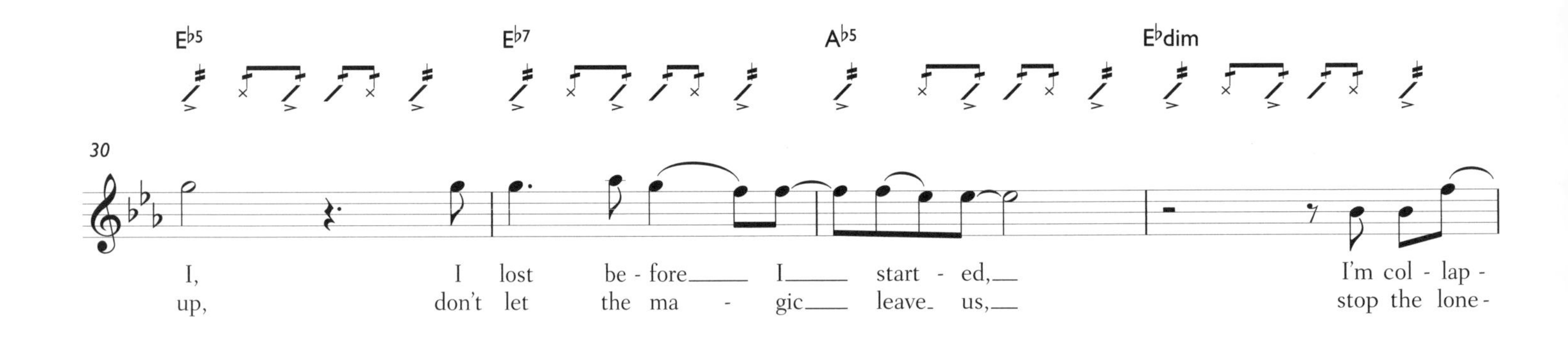
E♭5
E♭7
A♭5
E♭dim
30
I, I lost be - fore I start - ed,
up, don't let the ma - gic leave us,
I'm col - lap -
stop the lone -

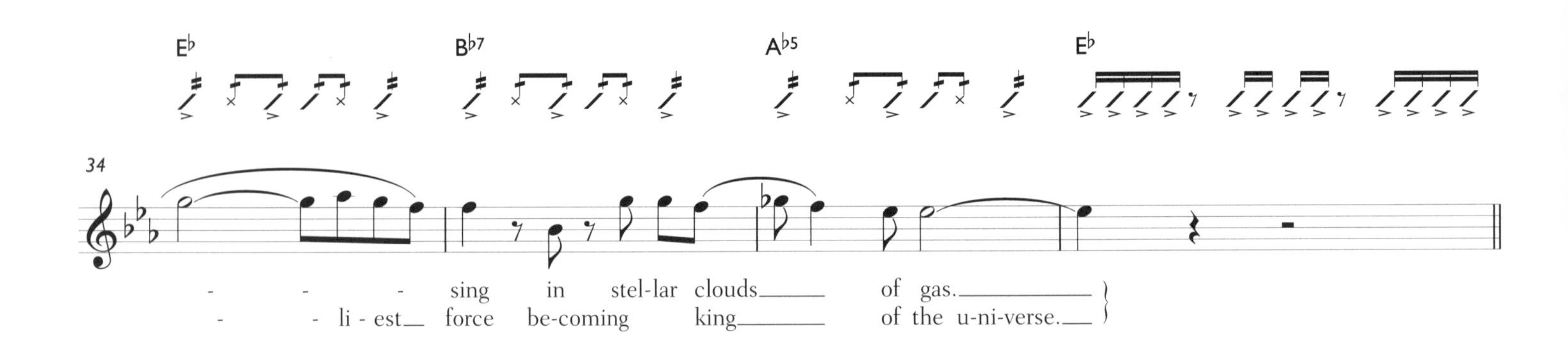
E♭
B♭7
A♭5
E♭
34
- - - sing in stel-lar clouds of gas.
- - li - est force be-coming king of the u-ni-verse.

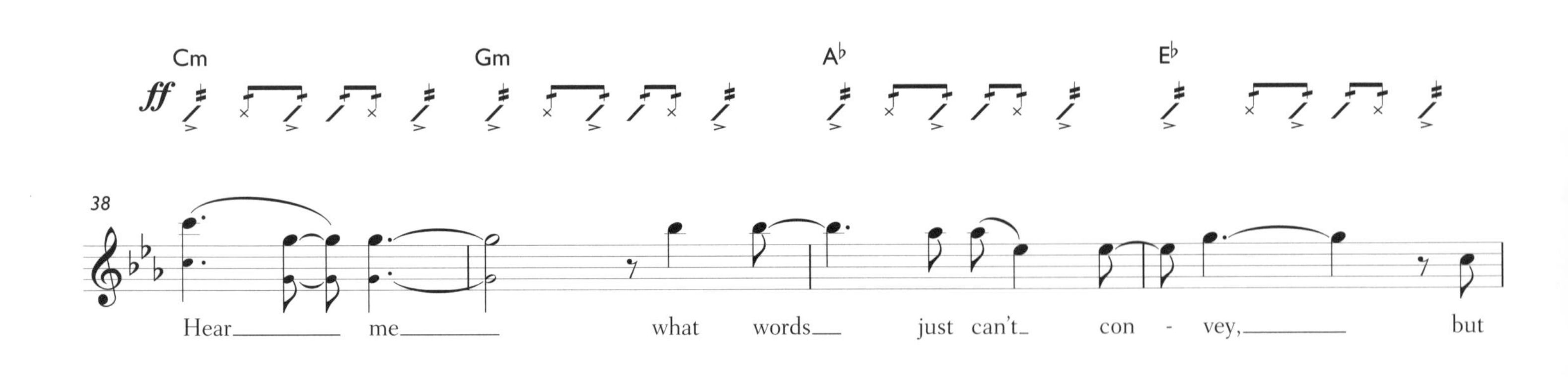
Cm
Gm
A♭
E♭
ff
38
Hear me what words just can't con - vey, but

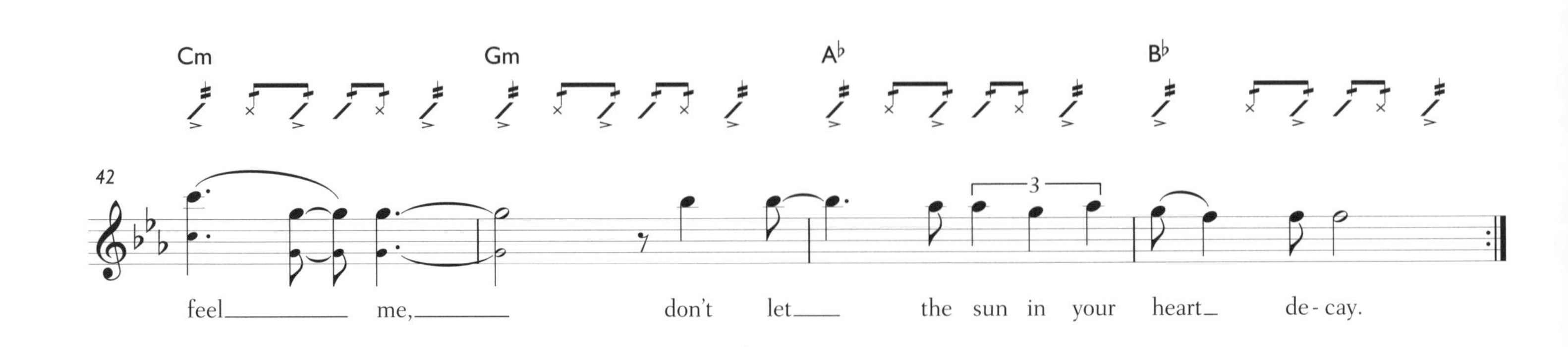
Cm
Gm
A♭
B♭
42
3
feel me, don't let the sun in your heart de - cay.

E♭5
Elec. Gtr. 1
A♭5
E♭
B♭7sus4
(cont. sim.)
mp with crunch & palm muting
rhythmic delay at the 16th
Elec. Gtr. 3
(feedback)
with heavy distortion
(Elec. Gtr. 3)
mf
full
w/bar
1/2
Don't_ give
E♭7
E♭dim
up, don't let the ma - gic___ leave_ us,___ we're col - lap-

61
E♭
B♭7
A♭5
E♭
sing in stel - lar clouds of gas yeah.
full
full
18
18
(18)
x
Cm
Gm
A♭
E♭
Elec. Gtr. 2
66
Oh,
f Fig. 3
1/2
full
11
15
10
13
13
15
16
12

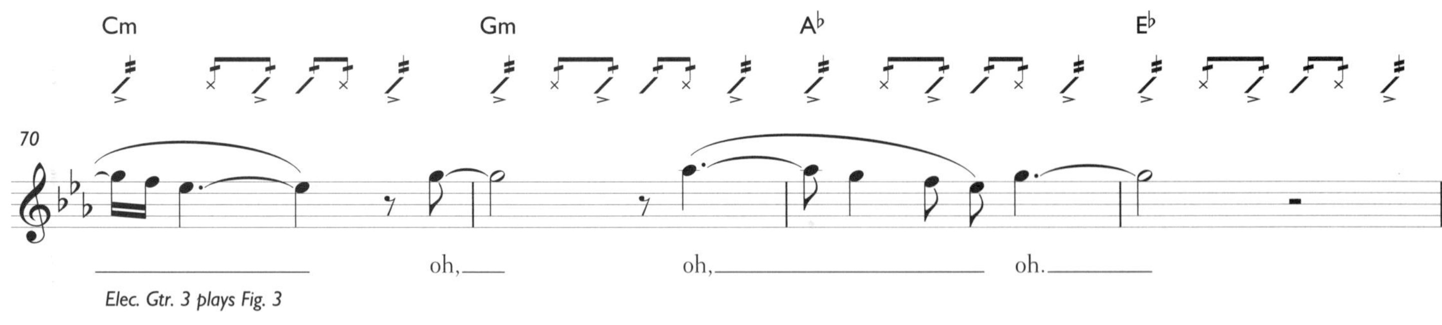
Cm
Gm
A♭
E♭
70
oh, oh, oh.
Elec. Gtr. 3 plays Fig. 3

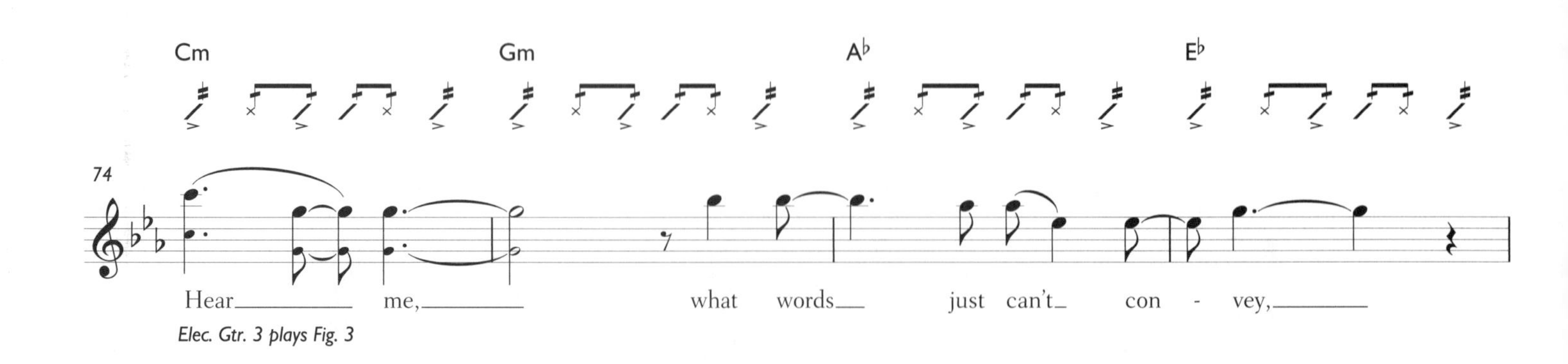
Cm
Gm
A♭
E♭
74
Hear me, what words just can't con - vey,
Elec. Gtr. 3 plays Fig. 3

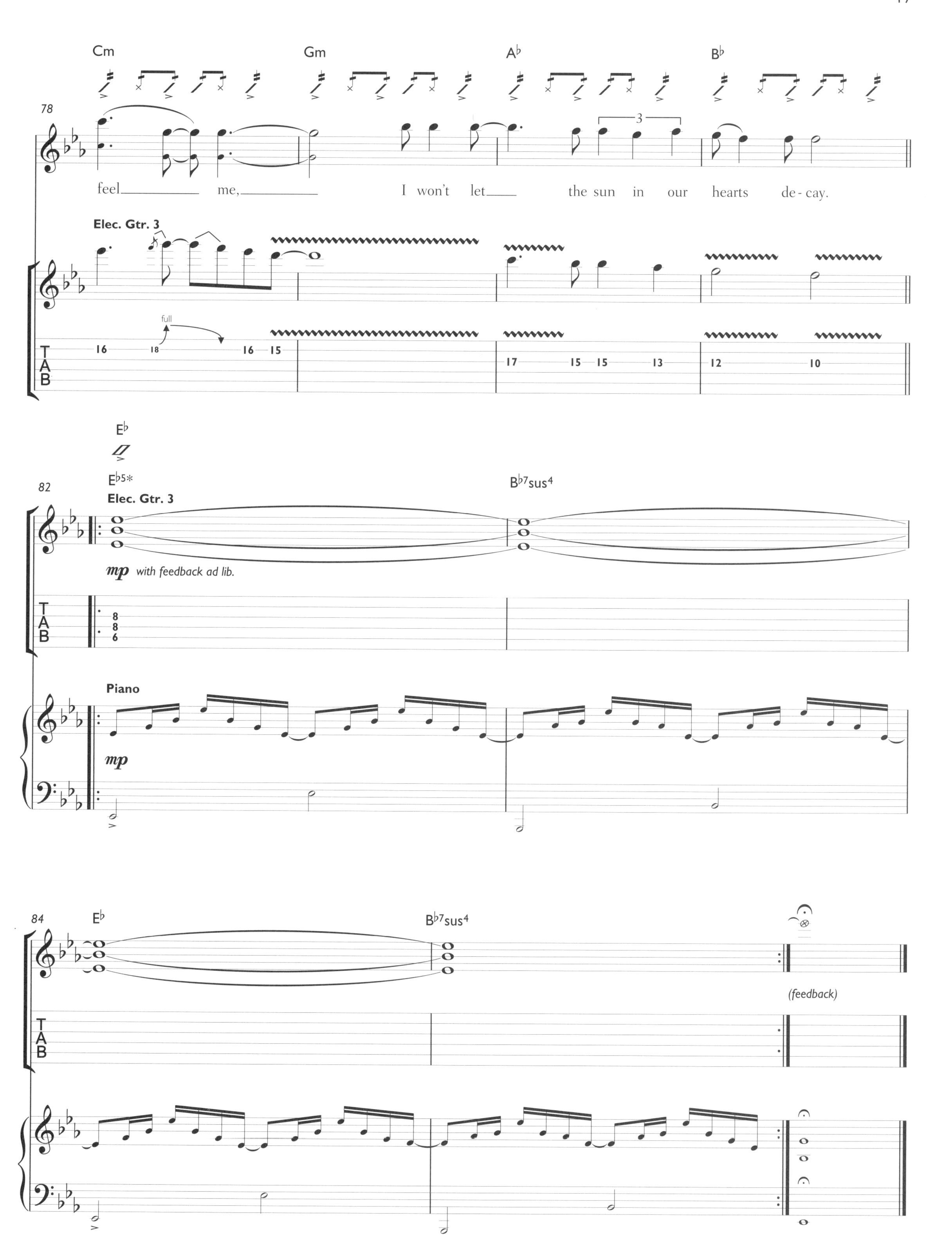
Cm
Gm
A♭
B♭
78
feel me, I won't let the sun in our hearts de - cay.
Elec. Gtr. 3
full
16 18 16 15
17 15 15 13
12 10
E♭
82
E♭5*
Elec. Gtr. 3
B♭7sus4
mp with feedback ad lib.
8
8
6
Piano
mp
84
E♭
B♭7sus4
(feedback)

BLISS

Words and Music by Matthew Bellamy

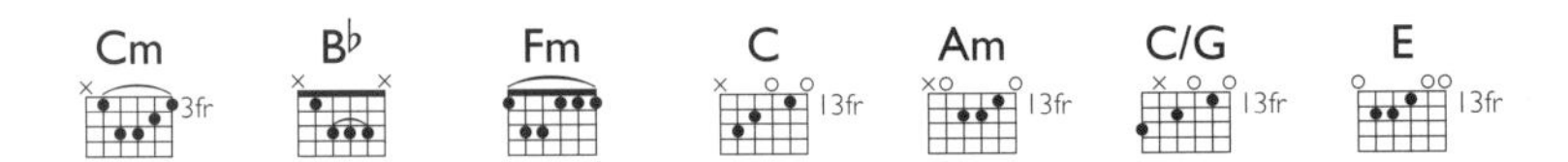

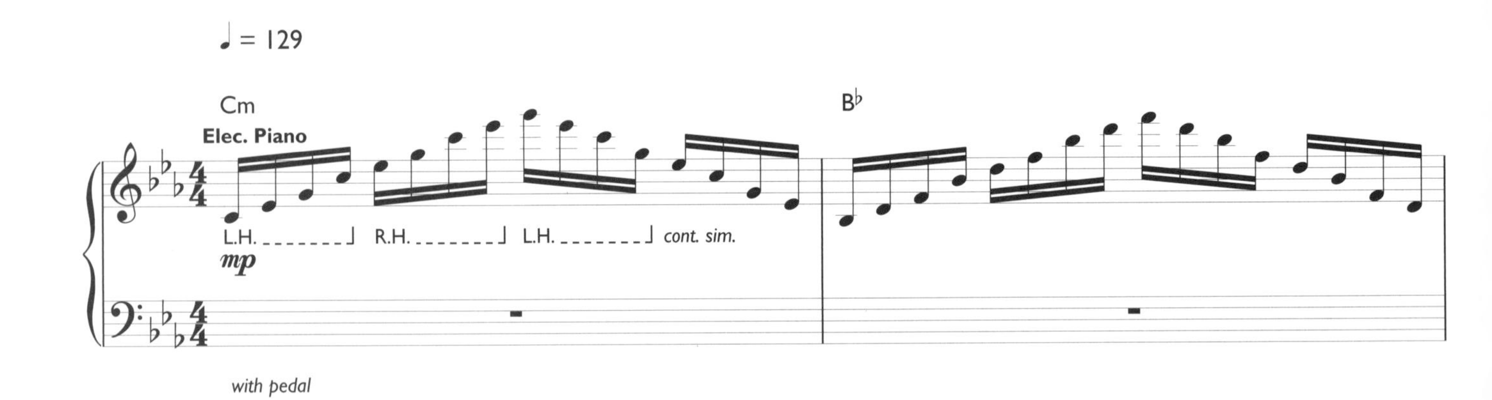

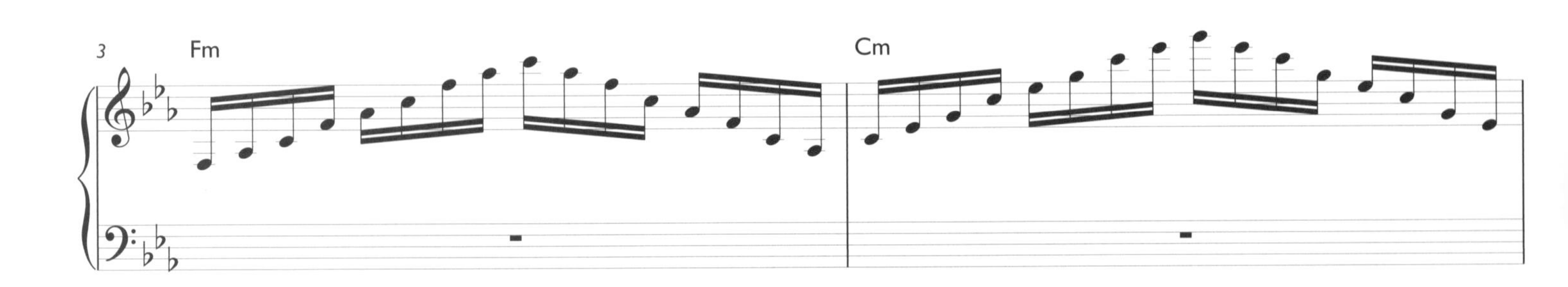

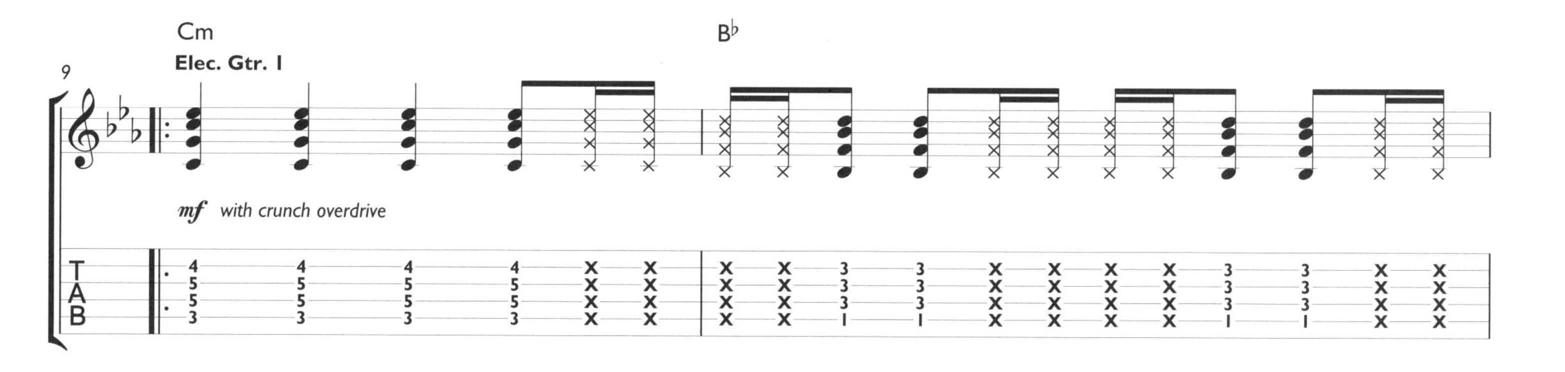
Cm
Elec. Gtr. 1
B♭
mf with crunch overdrive

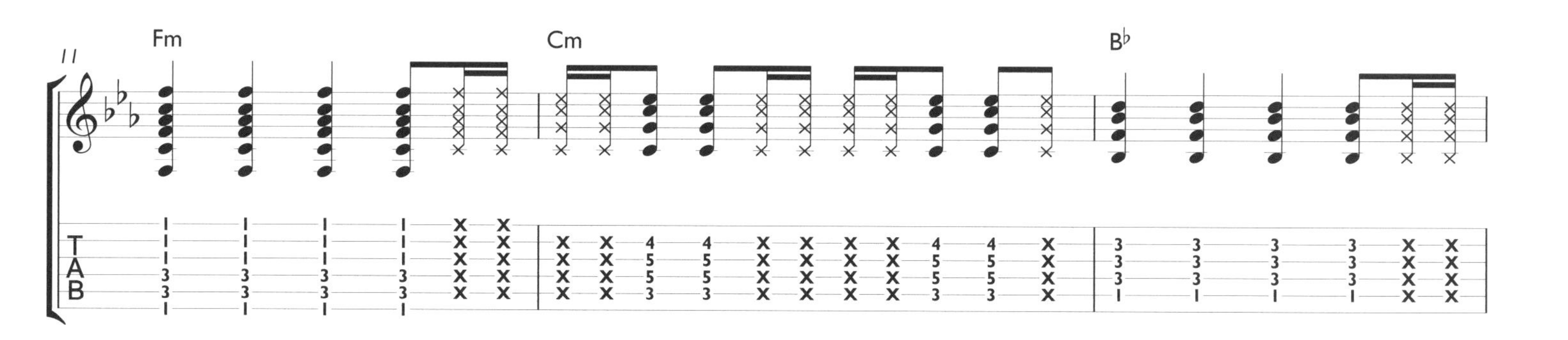
Fm
Cm
B♭

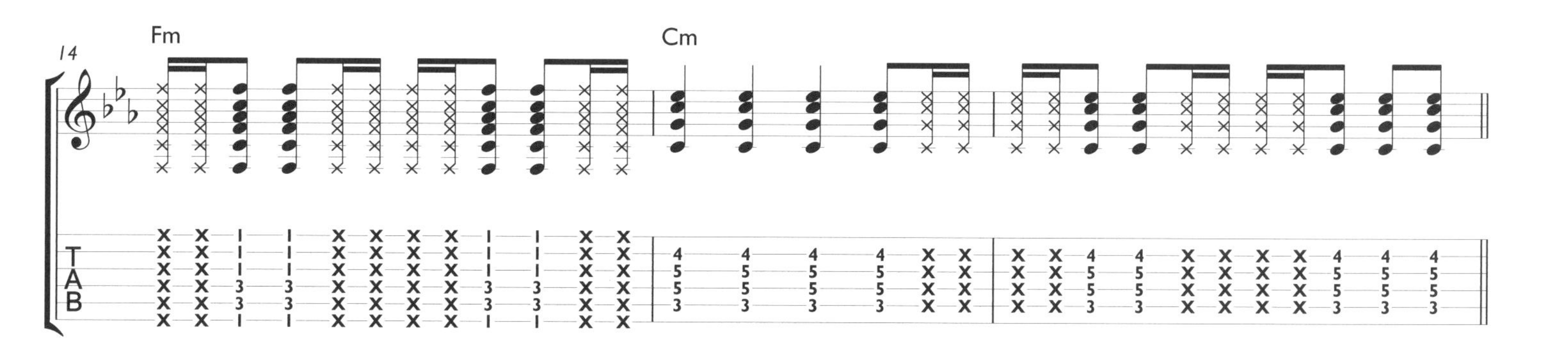
Fm
Cm

Cm
B♭
1. Ev - 'ry - thing a - bout you is how
2. Ev - 'ry - thing a - bout you pains my
Fuzz bass arr. for gtr.

Fm Cm B♭
I'd wan - na be, your free - dom comes
en - vy - ing, your soul can't hate
Fm Cm
na - tural - ly.
a - ny - thing.
B♭ Fm
Ev - 'ry - thing a - bout you re - son - ates hap - pi - ness,
Ev - 'ry - thing a - bout you is so ea - sy to love,
Cm B♭ Fm
no I won't set - tle
they're watch - ing you from

31
Cm
for less.
a - bove.
33
C
Am
C/G
Give me
Gtr. 1
Elec. Pno. with intro arpeggios
36
C
all the peace and
38
Am
E
joy in your mind.

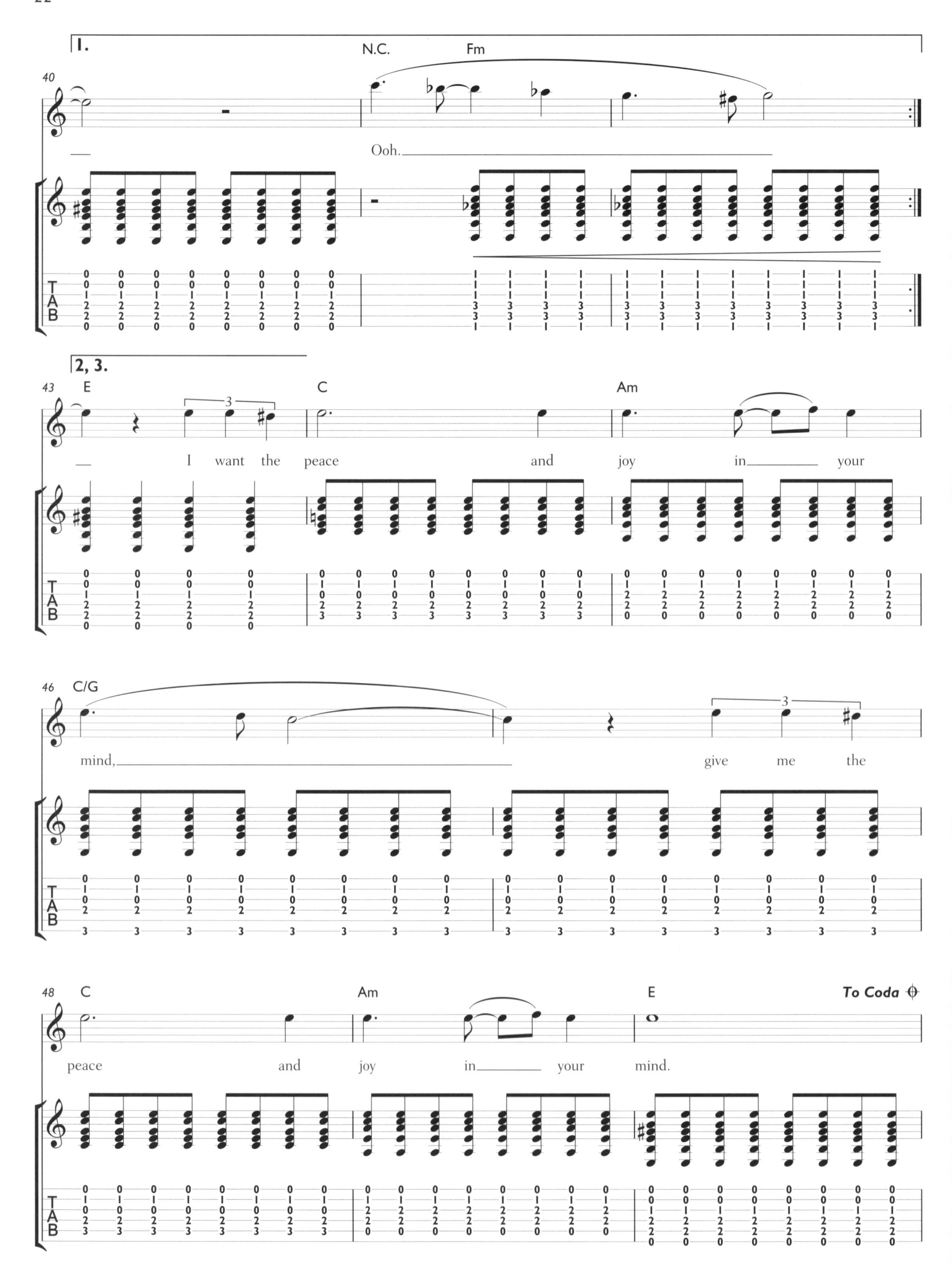
1.
N.C.
Fm
Ooh.
2, 3.
E
C
Am
I want the peace and joy in your
C/G
mind,
give me the
C
Am
E
To Coda
peace and joy in your mind.

N.C.
Fm
51
Ooh.
T
A
B
54
Cm
Synth.
p
B♭
56
Fm
Cm
58
B♭
Fm
60
Cm

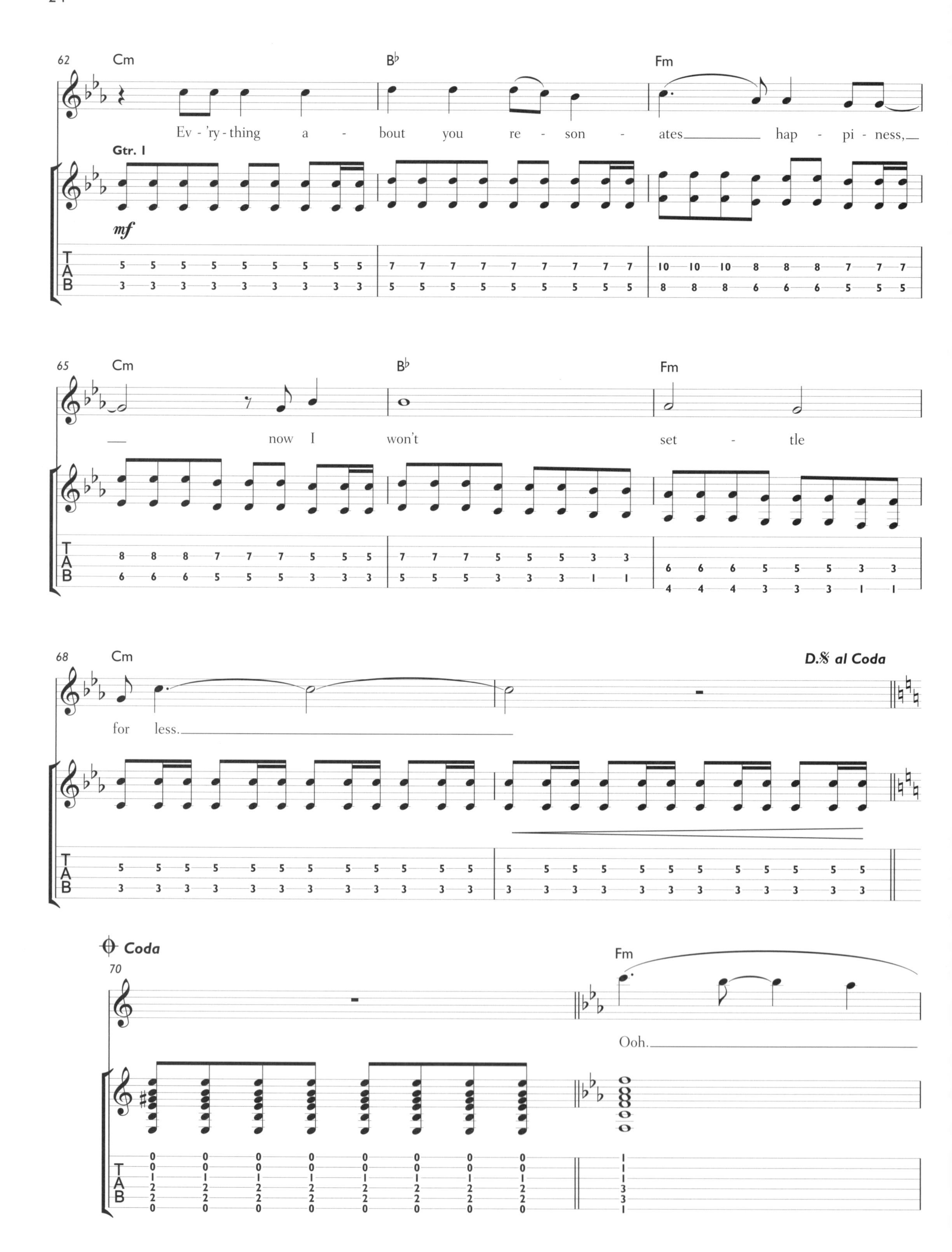
62
Cm
B♭
Fm
Ev - 'ry - thing a - bout you re - son - ates happ - pi - ness,
Gtr. I
mf
65
Cm
B♭
Fm
now I won't set - tle
68
Cm
D.𝄋 al Coda
for less.
Coda
70
Fm
Ooh.

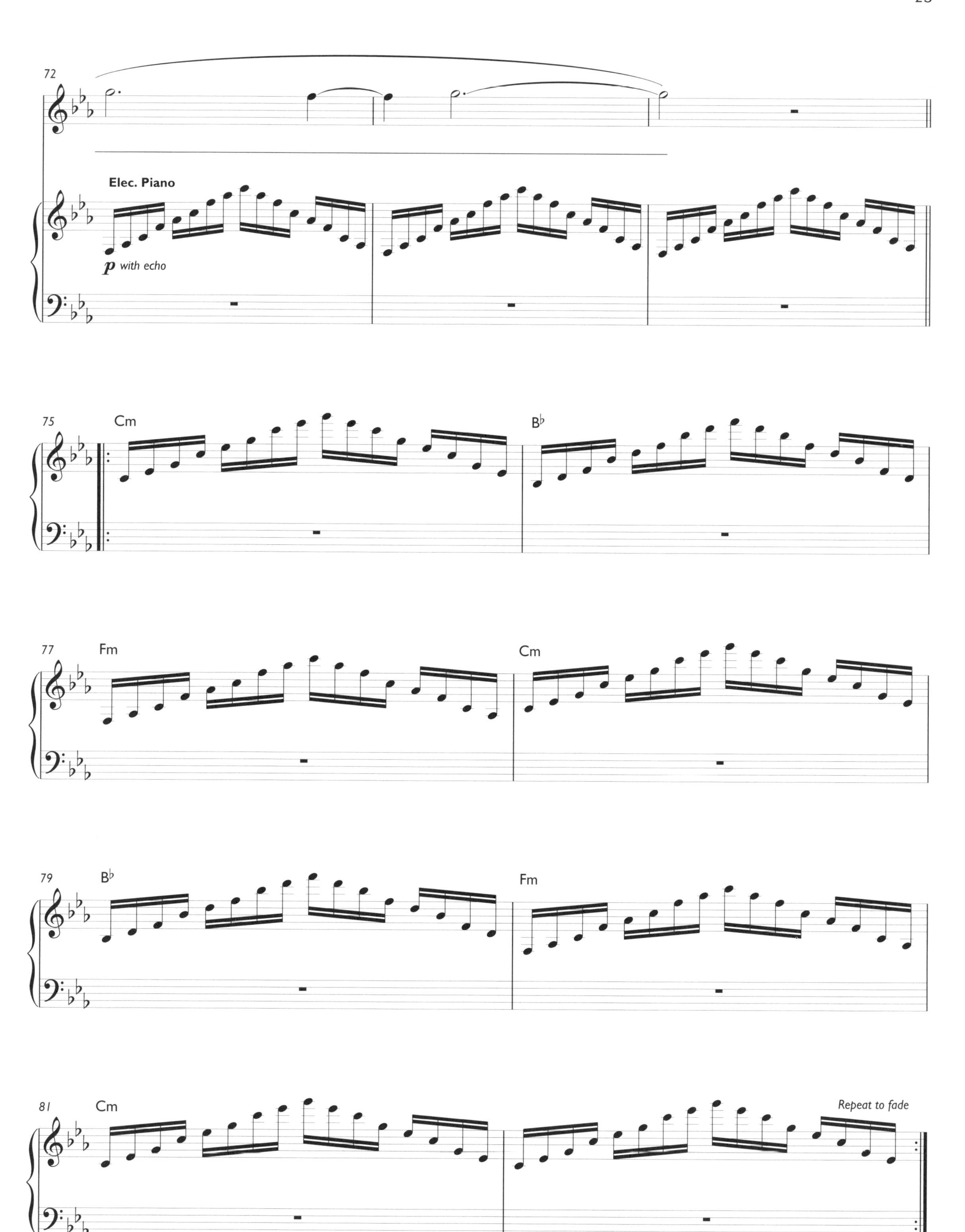
72
Elec. Piano
p with echo
75
Cm
B♭
77
Fm
Cm
79
B♭
Fm
81
Cm
Repeat to fade

CAVE

Words and Music by Matthew Bellamy

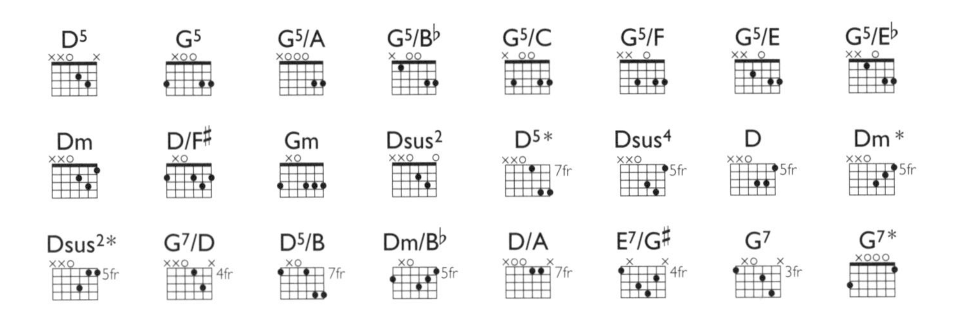

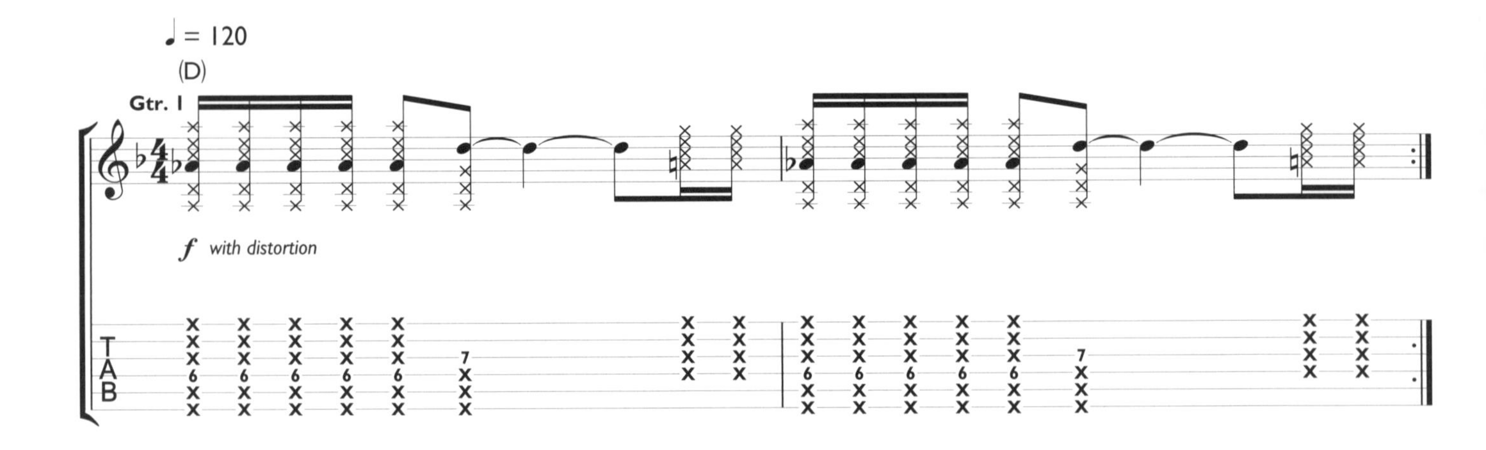

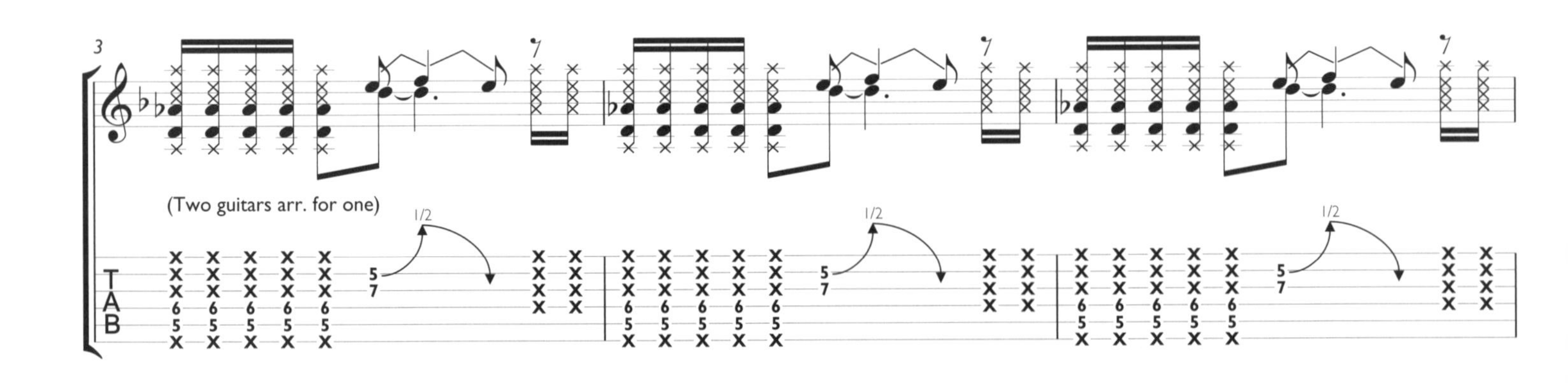

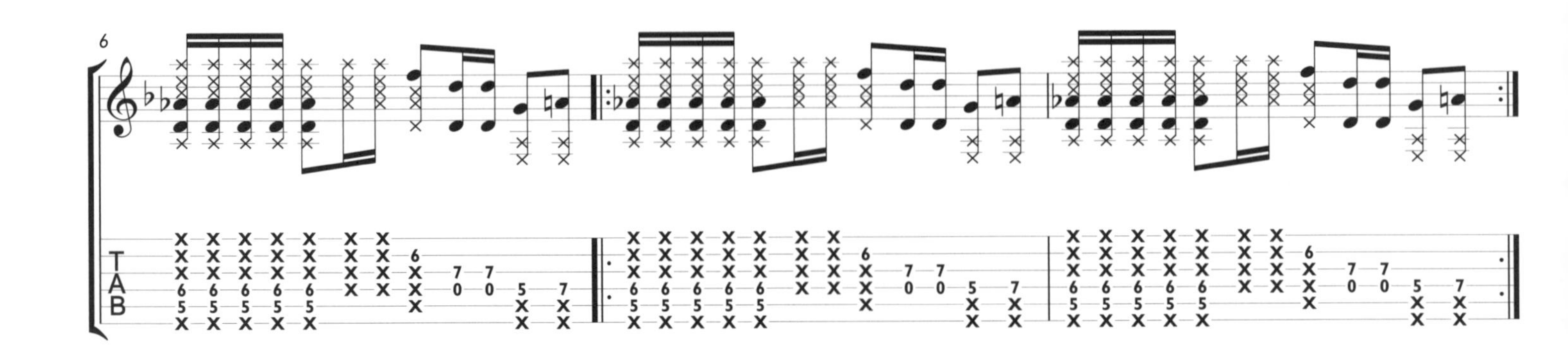

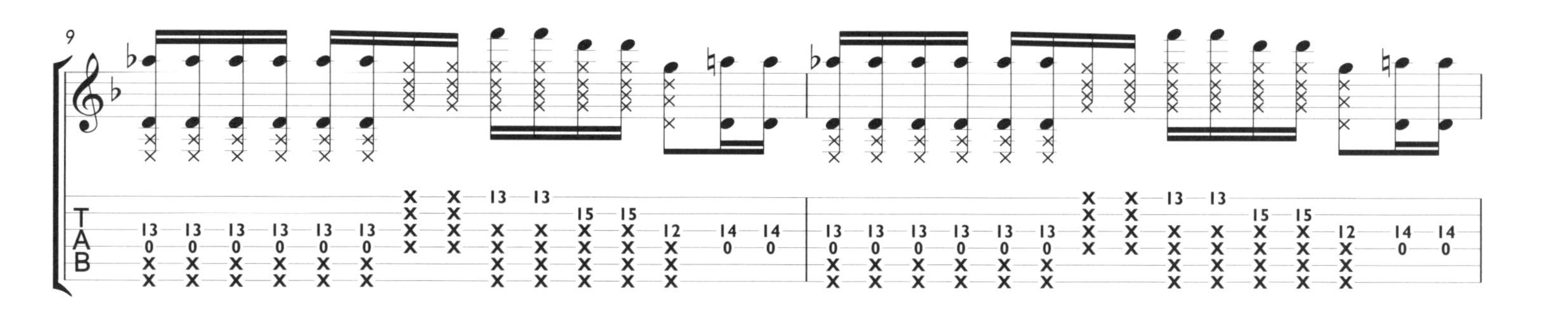

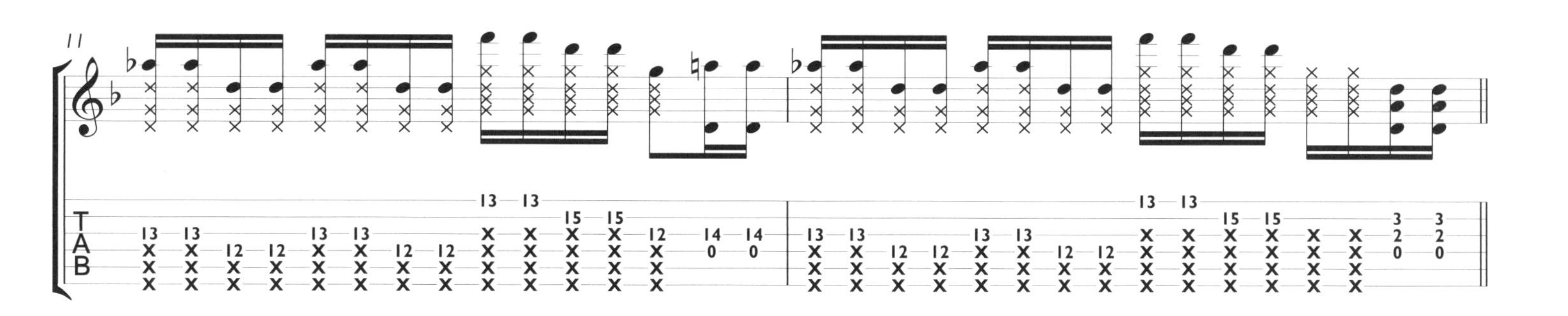

D5
Gtr. 1
1. Leave me a - lone, it's no-thing se - ri - ous. I'll do it my - self,
Bass arr. for gtr.

G5 G5/A G5/B♭ G5/C
it's got no-thing to do with you, and there's no - thing that you

19
G5 G5/F G5/E G5/E♭ (D)
could do.
22
Gtr. 1
25
D5
2. You can see it and you can al-most hear it too, you can al-most taste
4. Leave me a - lone, it's no-thing se - ri - ous, I'll do it my - self,
(Gtr. 1 𝄋)
(Bass arr. for gtr.)
28
G5 G5/A G5/B♭ G5/C
it, it's no-thing to do with you
it's got no-thing to do with you.
and there's still no - thing that you

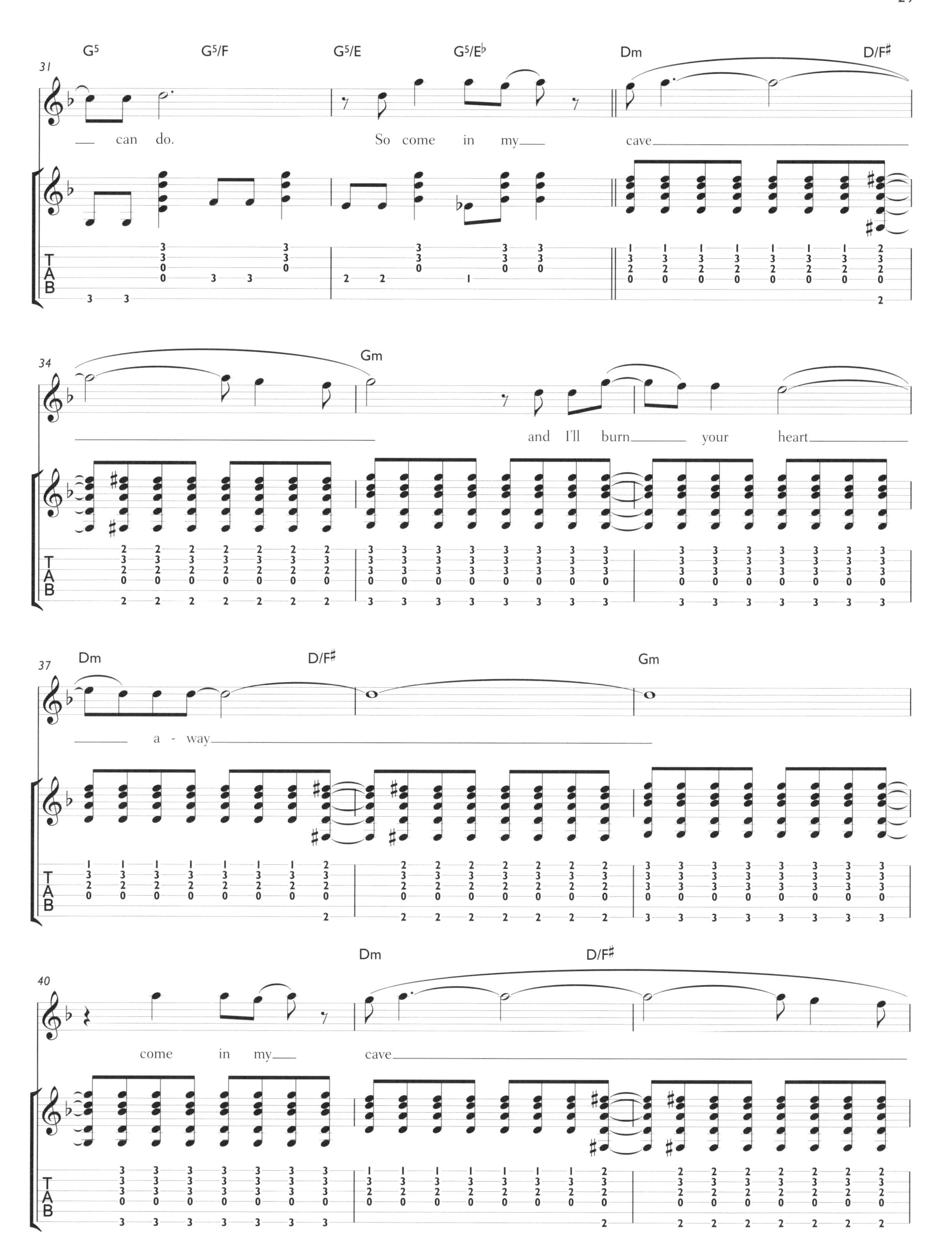
G5
G5/F
G5/E
G5/E♭
Dm
D/F♯
31
can do.
So come in my
cave
34
Gm
and I'll burn your heart
37
Dm
D/F♯
Gm
a - way
40
Dm
D/F♯
come in my
cave
TAB

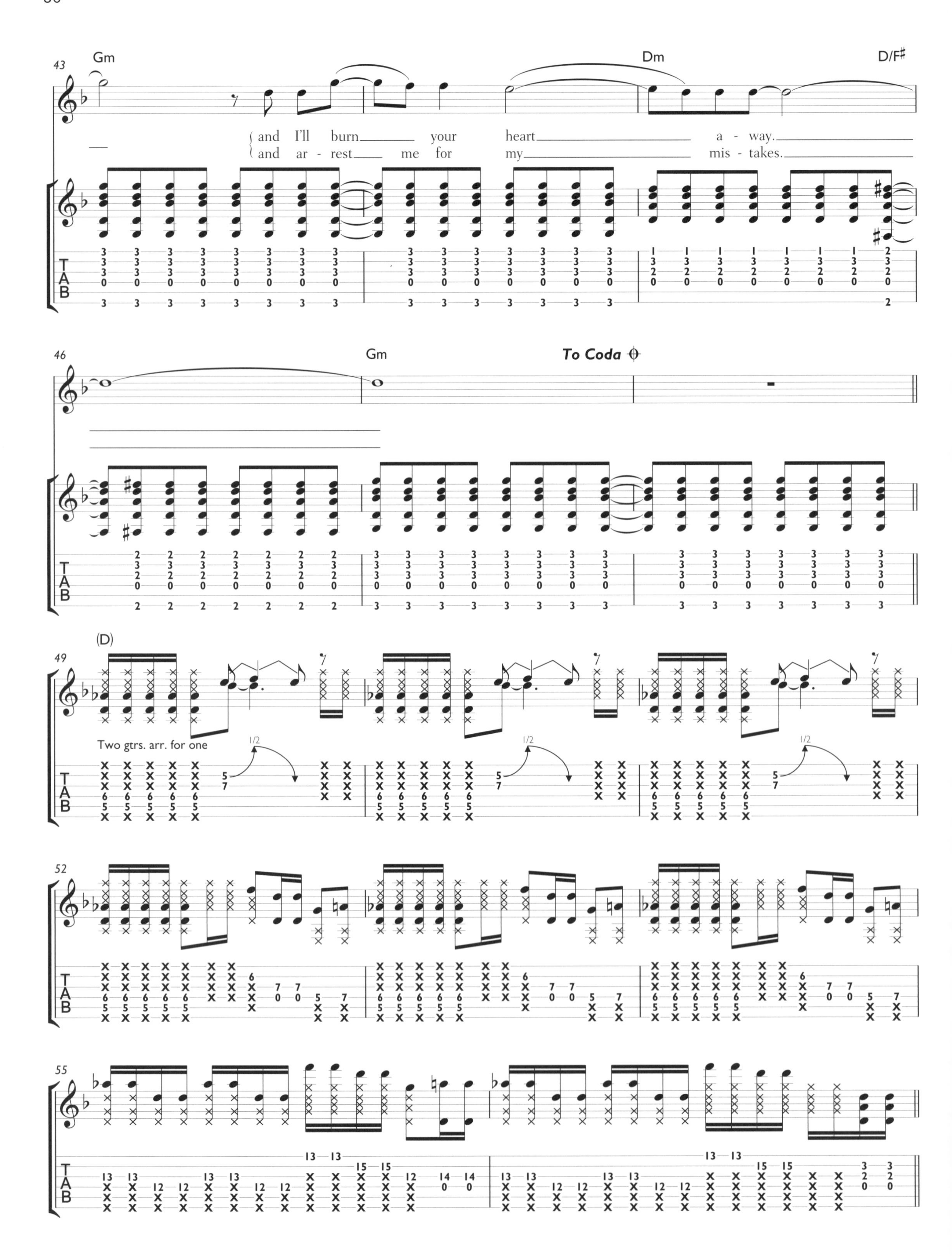
Gm
Dm
D/F♯
and I'll burn your heart a - way.
and ar - rest me for my mis - takes.
Gm
To Coda
(D)
Two gtrs. arr. for one
1/2

D5
Gtr. 1
57
3. Please close your ears and try to look a - way so you'll nev - er hear
Bass arr. for gtr.
1/4
TAB
60
a, a sin - gle word I say
G5
G5/A
G5/B♭
G5/C
and don't ev - er come
63
G5
G5/F
G5/E
G5/E♭
D5
my way.
66
D.𝄋 al Coda

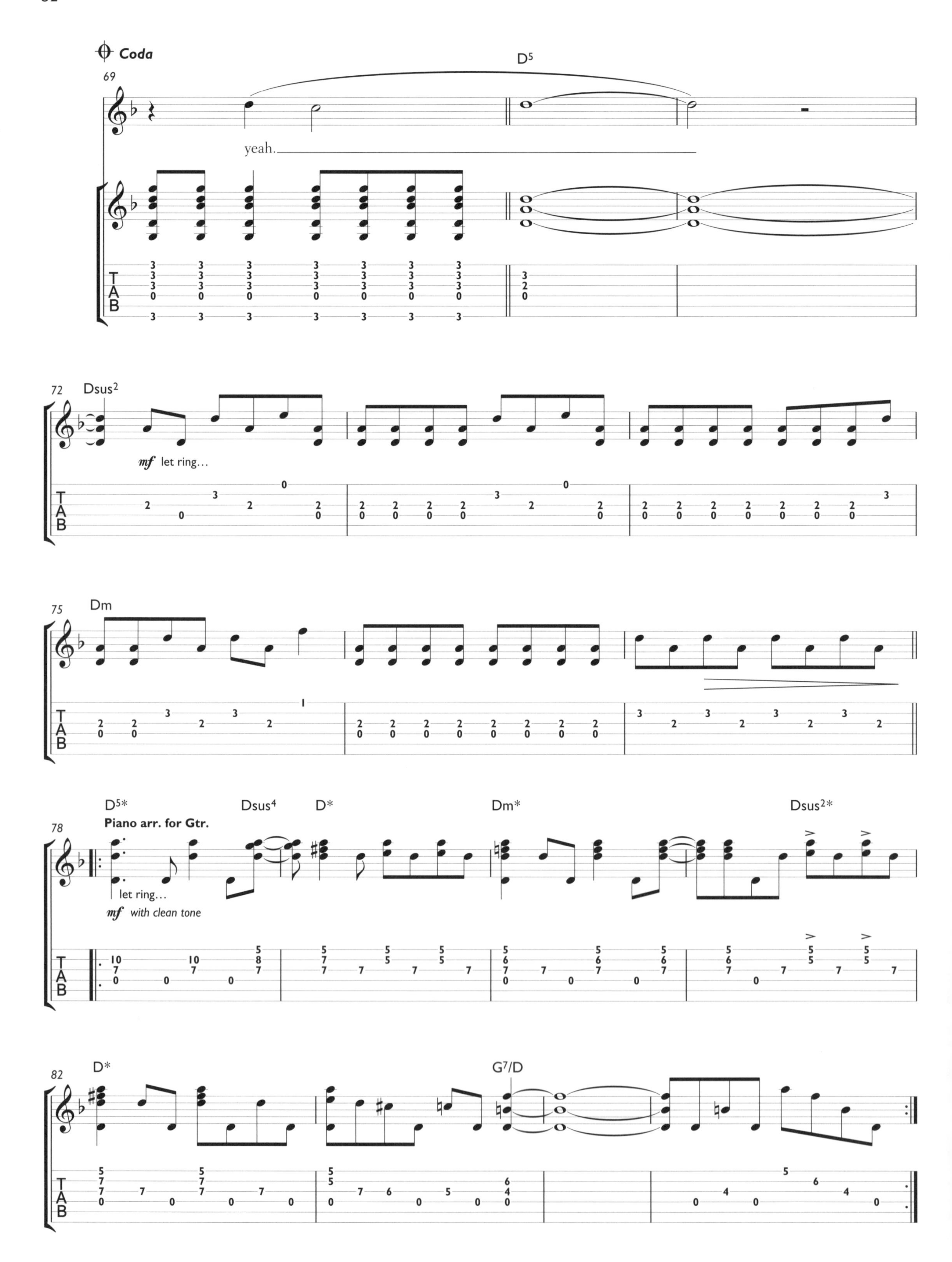
Coda
D5
yeah.
Dsus2
mf let ring…
Dm
D5*
Piano arr. for Gtr.
let ring…
mf with clean tone
Dsus4
D*
Dm*
Dsus2*
D*
G7/D

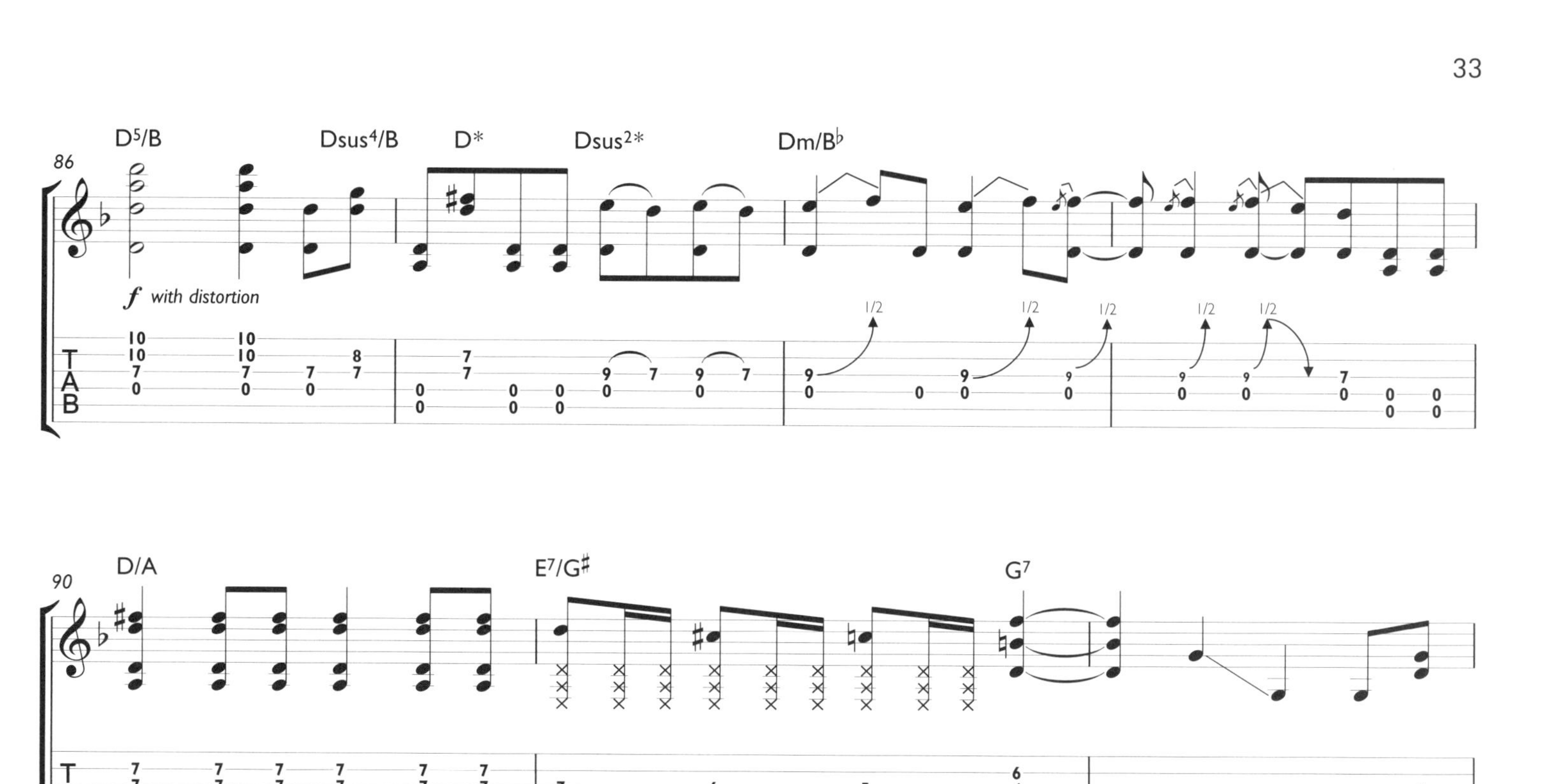
D5/B
Dsus4/B
D*
Dsus2*
Dm/B♭
f with distortion
D/A
E7/G♯
G7

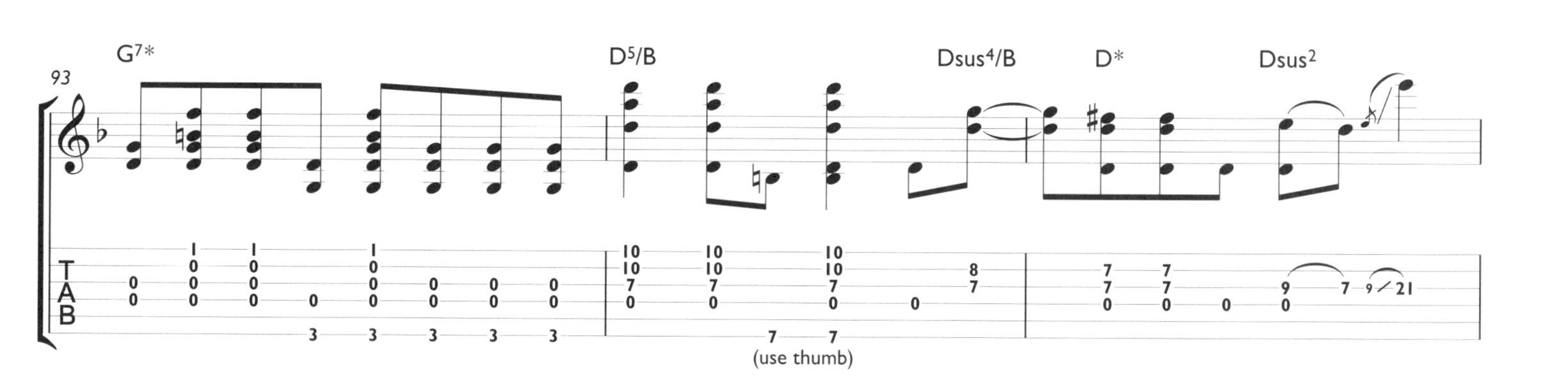
G7*
D5/B
Dsus4/B
D*
Dsus2
(use thumb)

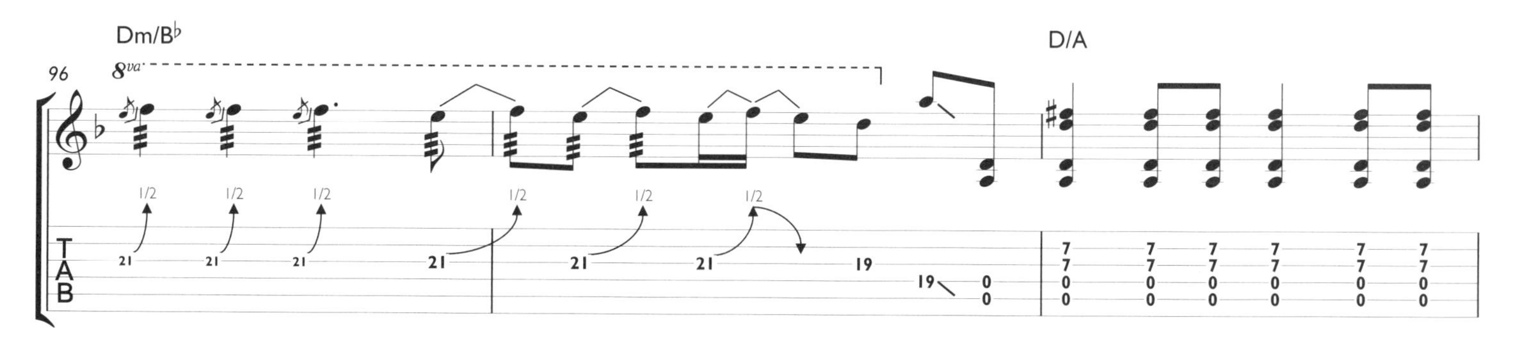
Dm/B♭
8va
D/A

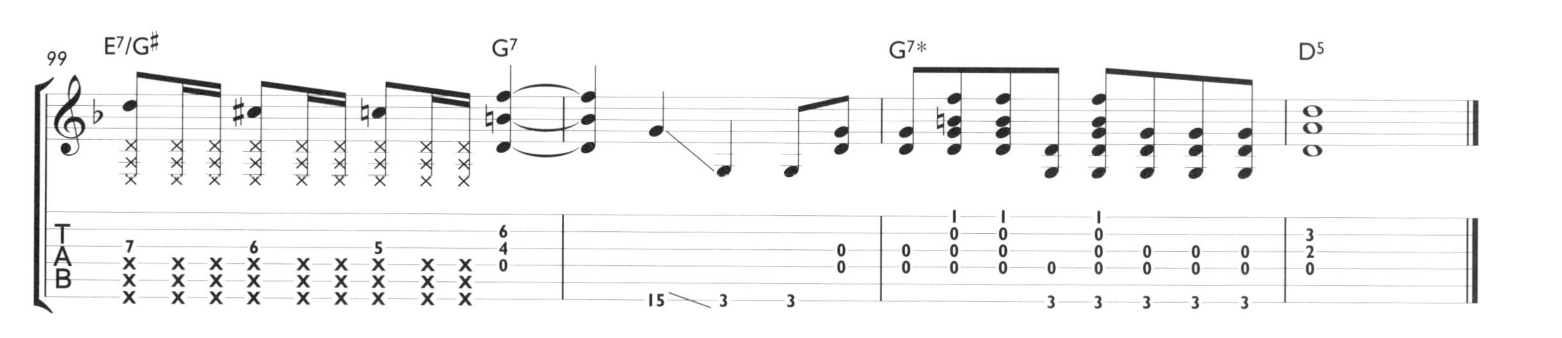
E7/G♯
G7
G7*
D5

CITIZEN ERASED

Words and Music by Matthew Bellamy

2° Gtr. 2
Am
G/A
1. Break me in, teach us to cheat and to lie and cov - er up what should - - n't be shared.
2. Self ex - pressed, exhaust - ing for all to see and to be what you want, and what you need.
1° Elec. Gtr. 2
with distortion
Gtr. 1 with Fig. 1 (x4)
2° play slashes with delay fx. + vol. swell
F/A
E/A
And the truth's un - wind - ing,
cont. sim.

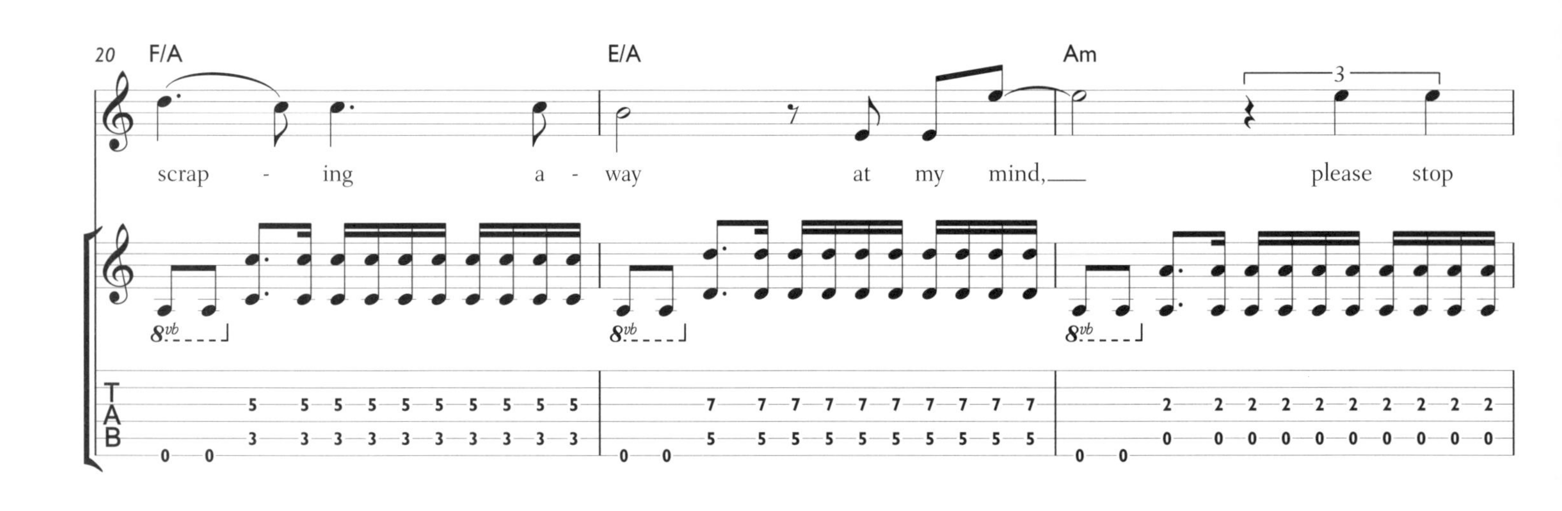
20
F/A
E/A
Am
3
scrap - ing a - way at my mind,
please stop
8vb
T
A
B

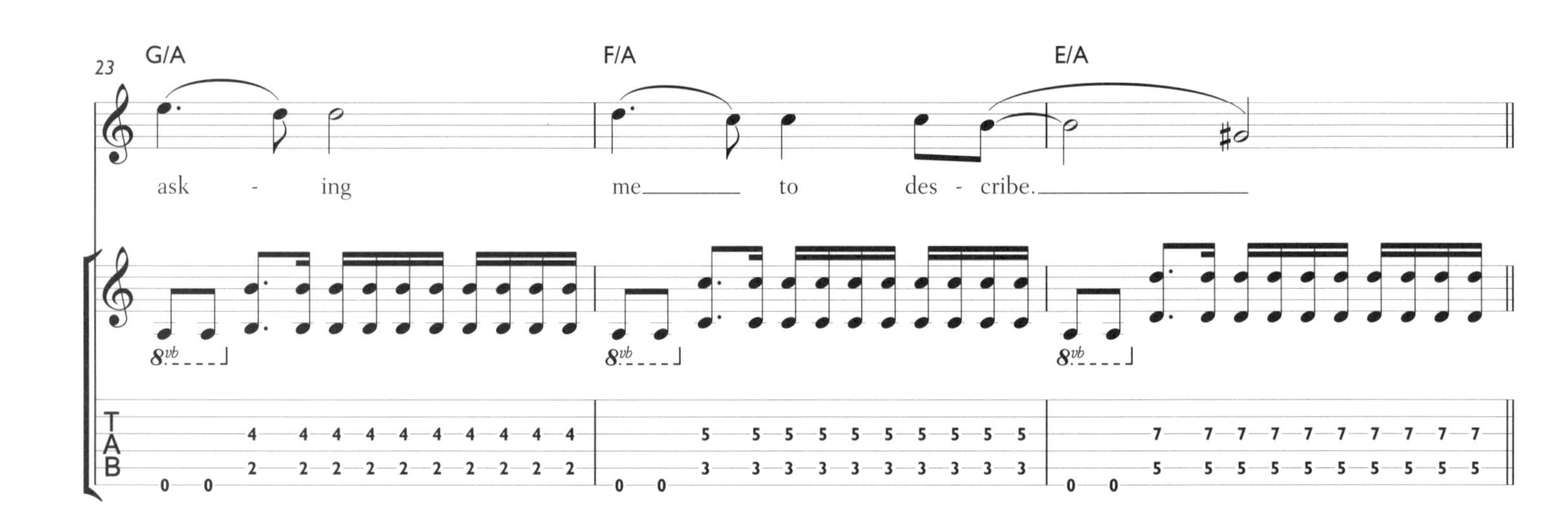
23
G/A
F/A
E/A
ask - ing me to des - cribe.
8vb
T
A
B

Omit 2°
F
C
E
Am*
G
26
Gtrs. 1+2
etc.
Fig. 2
T
A
B

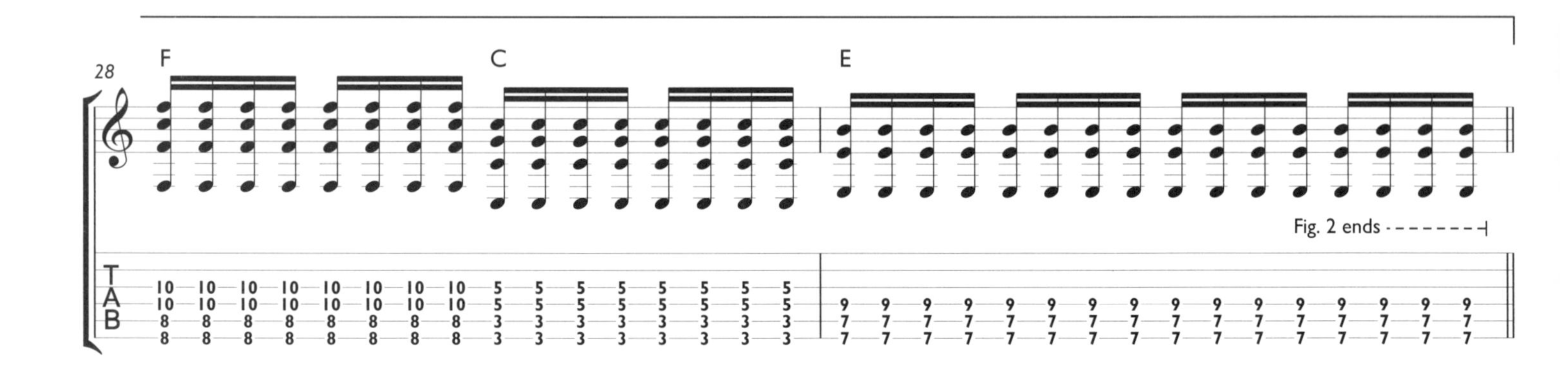
28
F
C
E
Fig. 2 ends
T
A
B

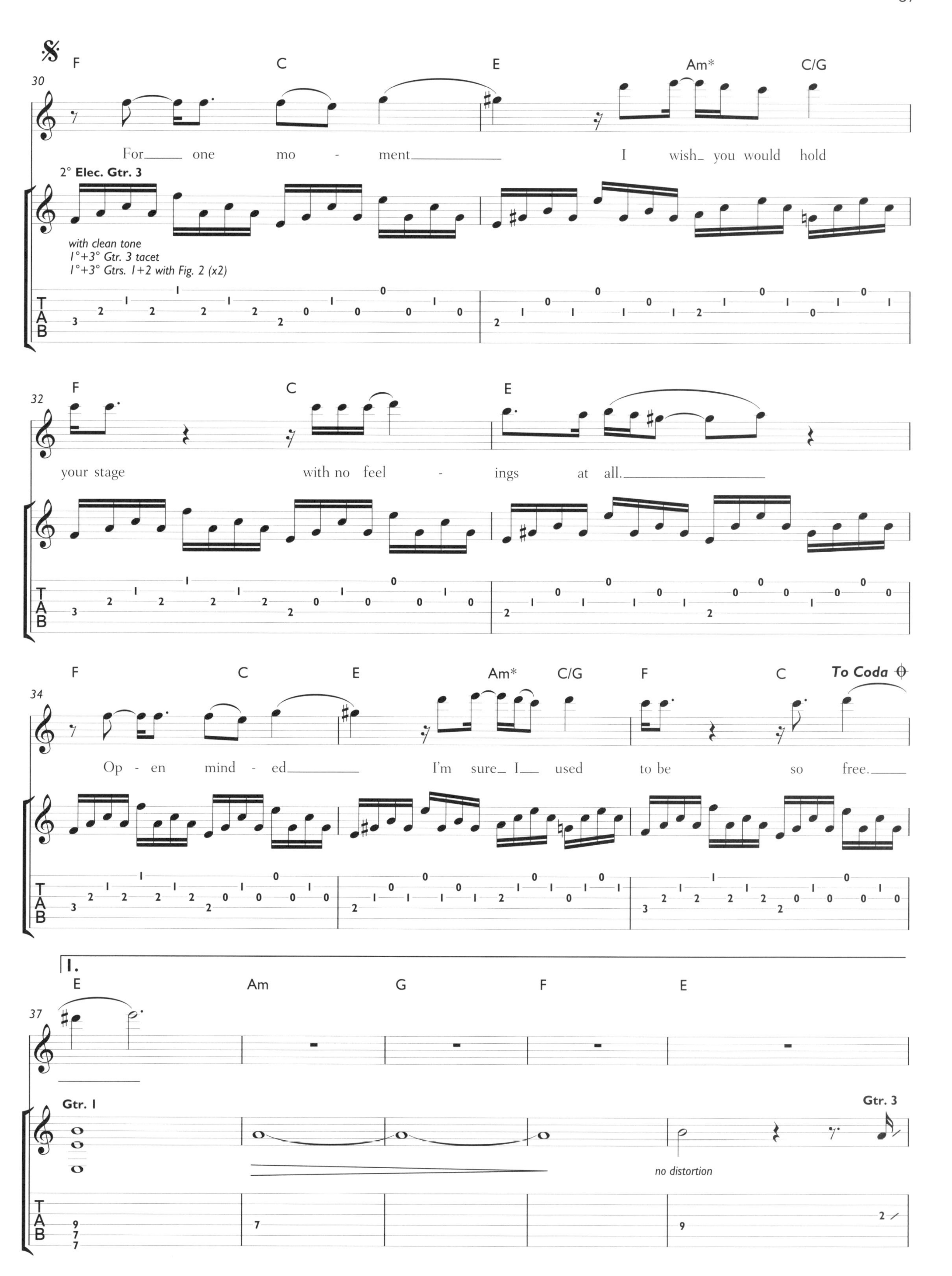
F
C
E
Am*
C/G
For one mo - ment I wish you would hold
2° Elec. Gtr. 3
with clean tone
1°+3° Gtr. 3 tacet
1°+3° Gtrs. 1+2 with Fig. 2 (x2)
your stage with no feel - ings at all.
Op - en mind - ed I'm sure I used to be so free.
To Coda
Am
G
Gtr. 1
Gtr. 3
no distortion

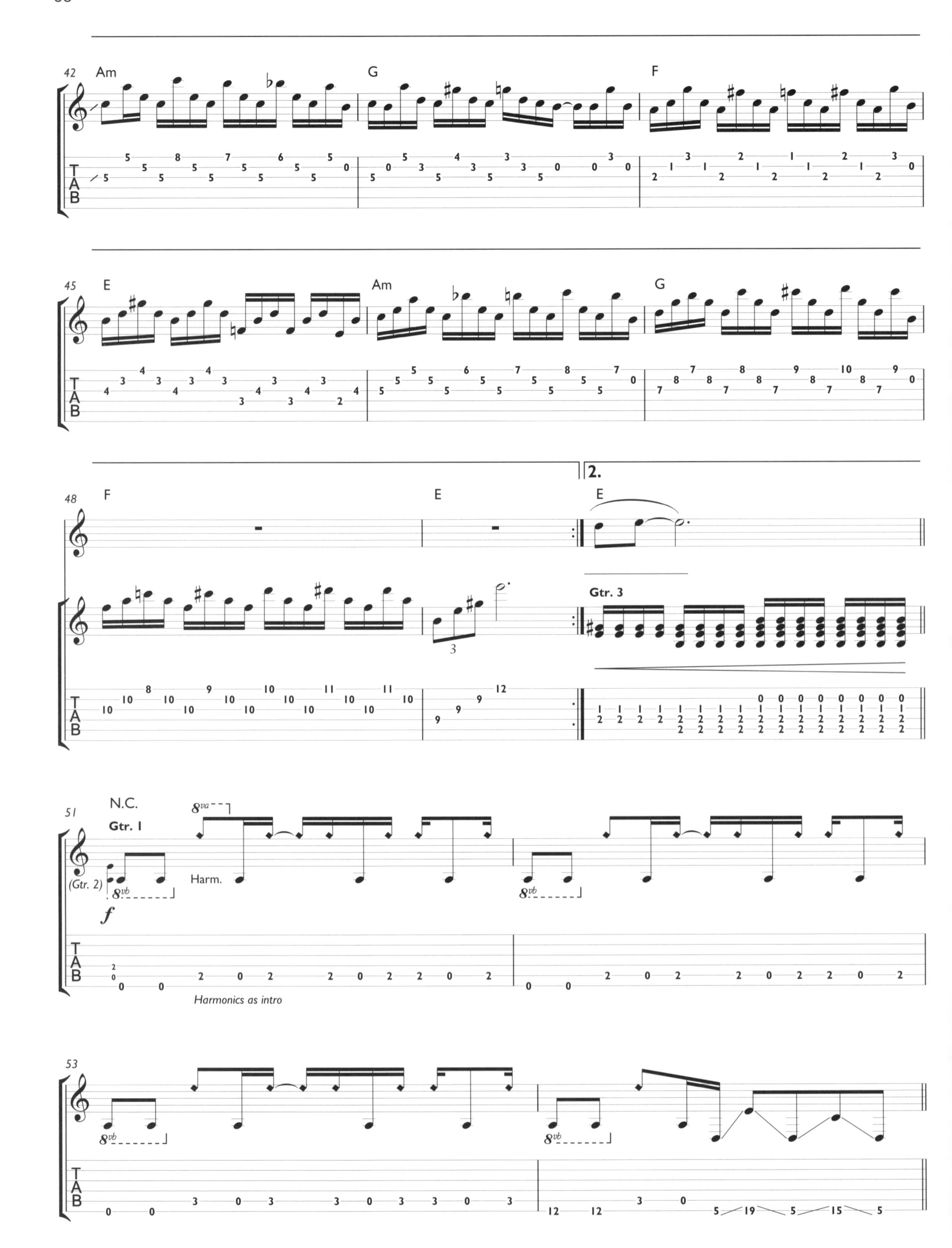

Am
G
F
E
Am
G
F
E
2.
E
Gtr. 3
N.C.
Gtr. 1
(Gtr. 2)
Harm.
Harmonics as intro

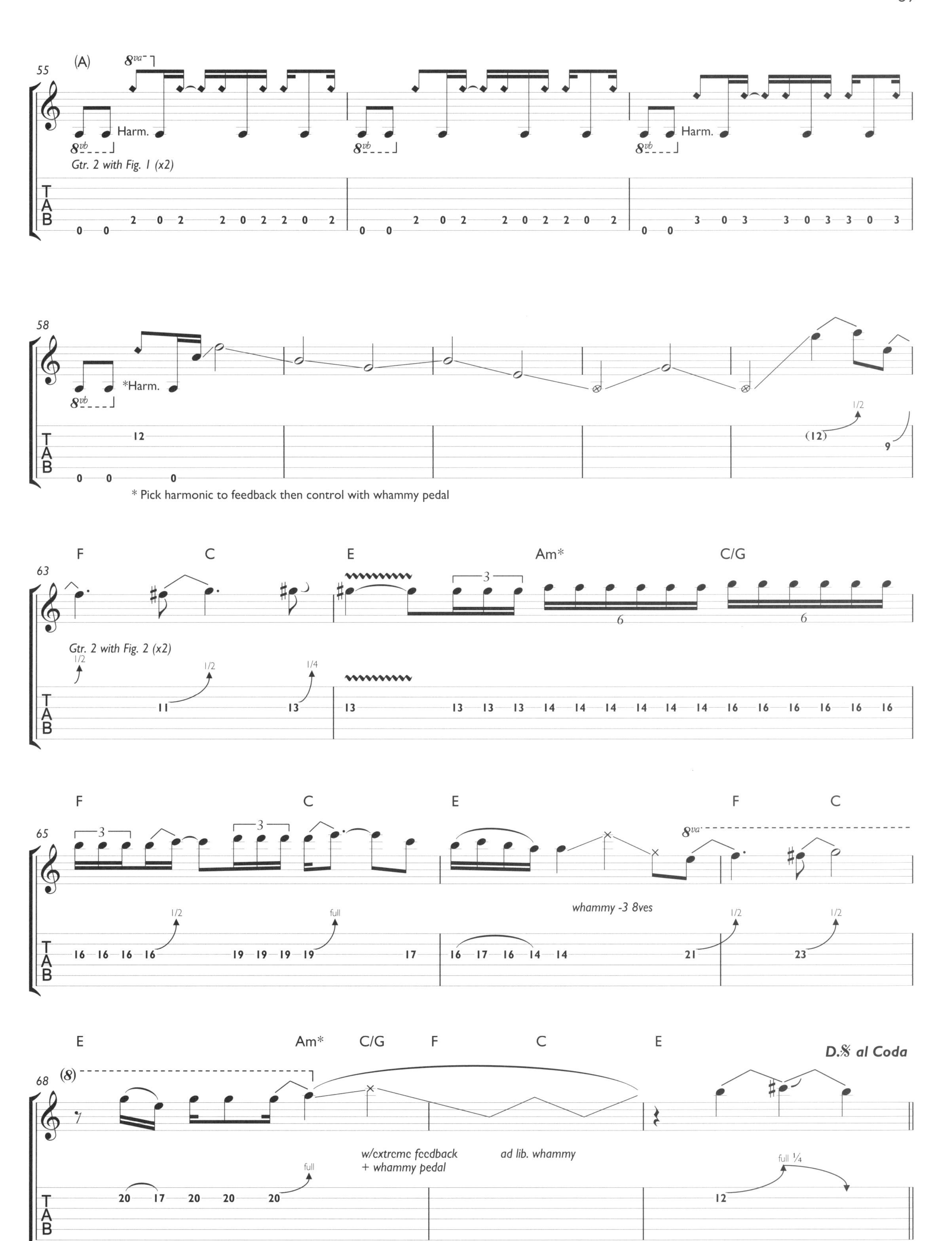
(A)
Harm.
Gtr. 2 with Fig. 1 (x2)
*Harm.
* Pick harmonic to feedback then control with whammy pedal
F
C
E
Am*
C/G
Gtr. 2 with Fig. 2 (x2)
whammy -3 8ves
w/extreme feedback
+ whammy pedal
ad lib. whammy
D.𝄋 al Coda

Coda
♩ = 77
E
Fmaj7
G*
Am**
Gtrs. 1+2
Gtrs. 3
w/bar
p
1/2
1.
2.
E*
G6
C*
cont. sim.

87
C
Am
C/G
2° Wash_ me a - way,___ clean_ your___ bo - dy of me,___
Piano
8vb
90
F
Fm
C
Dm7
___ e - rase___ all the mem - o - ries,___ they'll on - ly___ bring___
(8)
93
Dm/A
Am
C/G
F
Fm
___ us pain.___ And I've_ seen,___ all___ I'll ev - er need.___
8vb
1.
2.
rit.
97
C/G
C
C/G
C
3

DEADSTAR

Words and Music by Matthew Bellamy

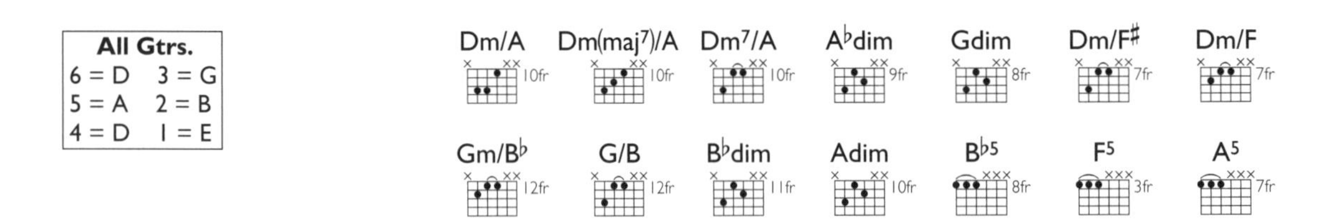

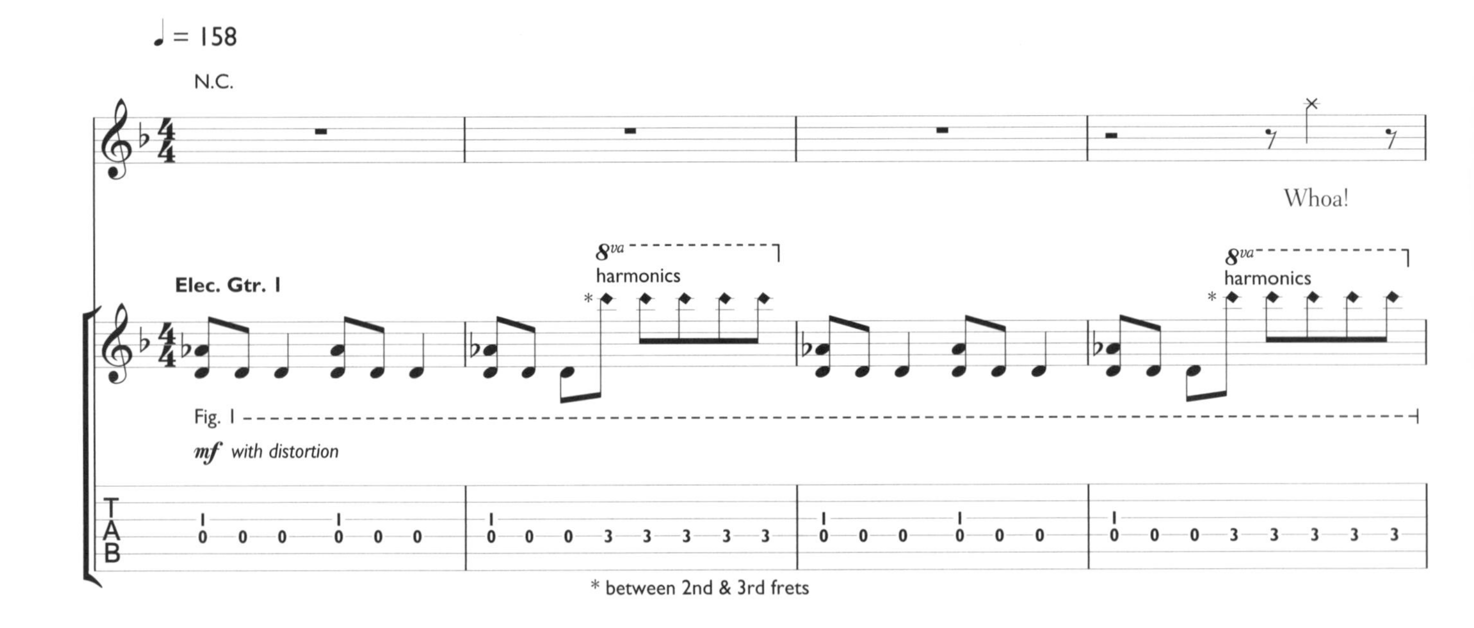

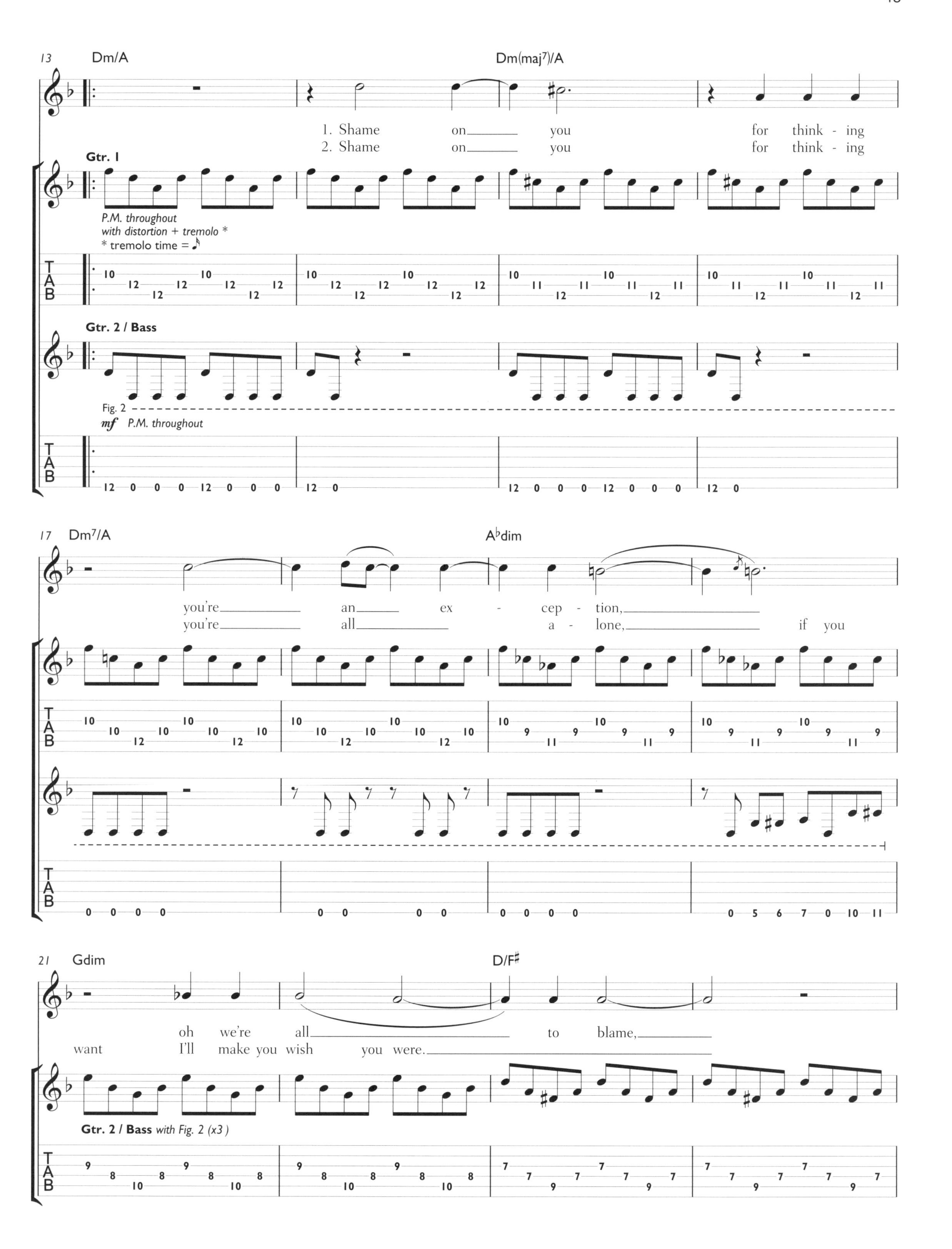
13
Dm/A
Dm(maj7)/A
1. Shame on you for thinking - ing
2. Shame on you for thinking - ing
Gtr. 1
P.M. throughout
with distortion + tremolo *
* tremolo time =
Gtr. 2 / Bass
Fig. 2
mf P.M. throughout
17
Dm7/A
A♭dim
you're an ex - cep - tion,
you're all a - lone, if you
21
Gdim
D/F♯
oh we're all to blame,
want I'll make you wish you were.
Gtr. 2 / Bass with Fig. 2 (x3)

25
Dm/F
D/F♯
crash - ing down to earth.
Fail - ing to im - press.
29
Dm/A
Gm/B♭
Wast - ing and burn - ing out yeah,
Why can't you sleep with
33
G/B
Gm/B♭
fad - ing like a dead star, whoa, whoa.
some - one who'll pro - tect you? Yeah.
37
B♭dim
Adim
Harm is com - ing your way.

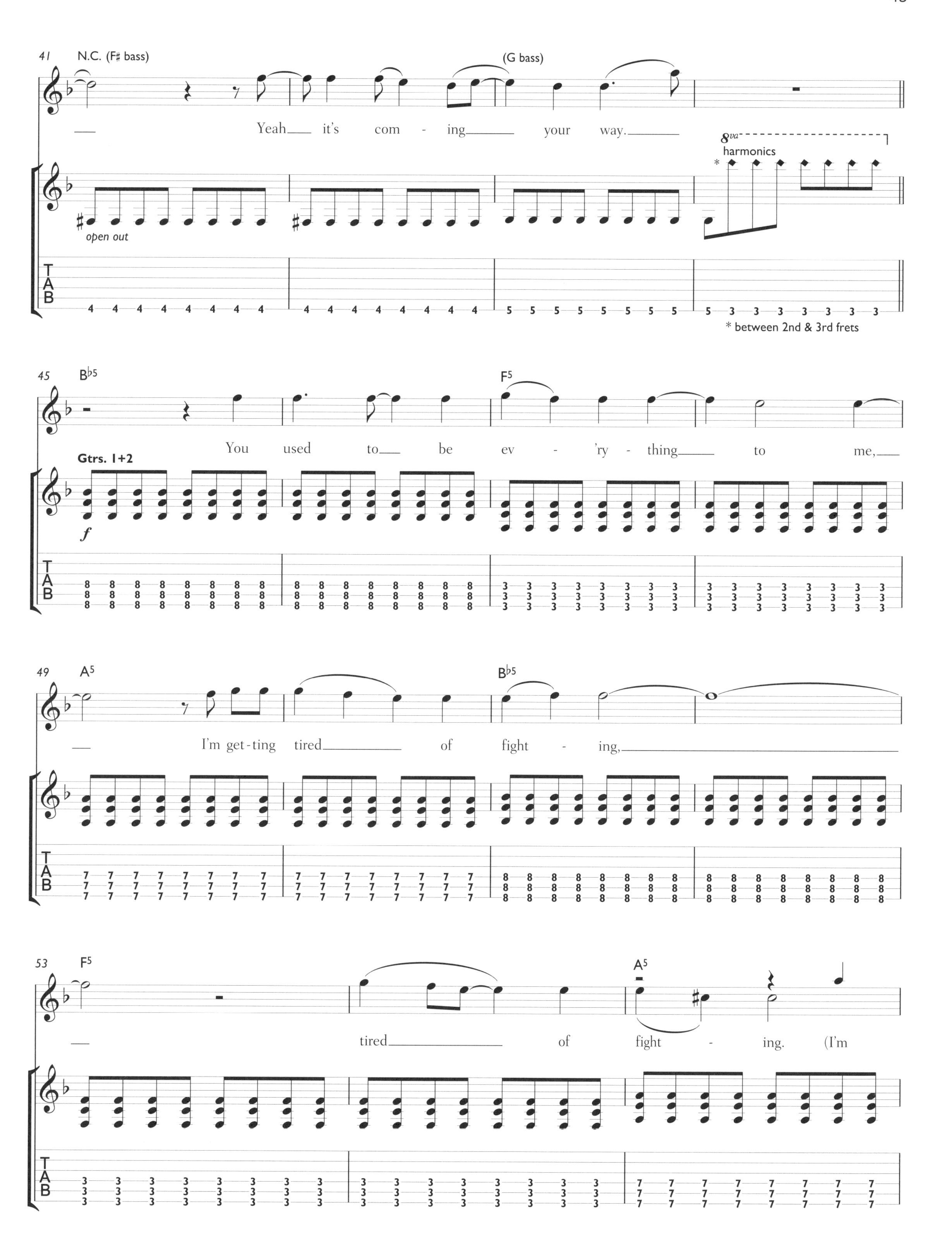
N.C. (F♯ bass)
(G bass)
Yeah it's com - ing your way.
8va
harmonics
open out
* between 2nd & 3rd frets
B♭5
F5
You used to be ev - 'ry - thing to me,
Gtrs. 1+2
A5
I'm get-ting tired of fight - ing,
tired of fight - ing. (I'm

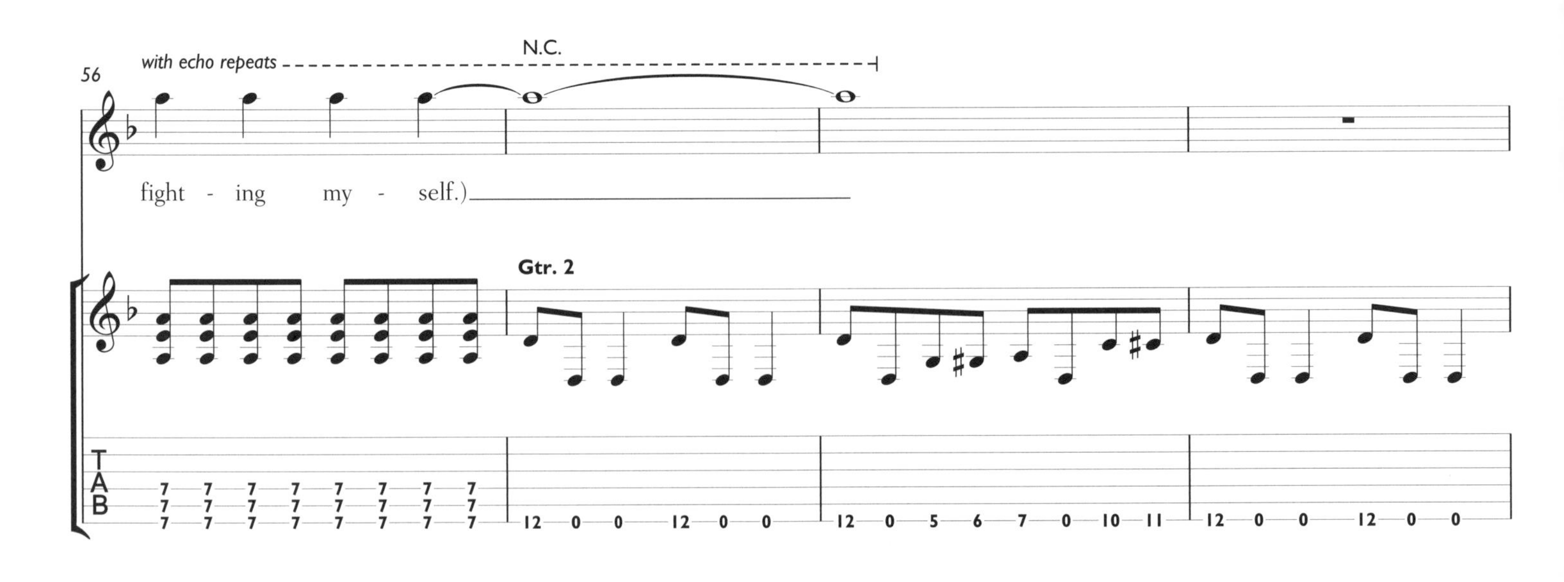
56
with echo repeats
N.C.
fight - ing my - self.)
Gtr. 2
T
A
B
7 7 7 7 7 7 7 7
7 7 7 7 7 7 7 7
7 7 7 7 7 7 7 7
12 0 0 12 0 0
12 0 5 6 7 0 10 11
12 0 0 12 0 0

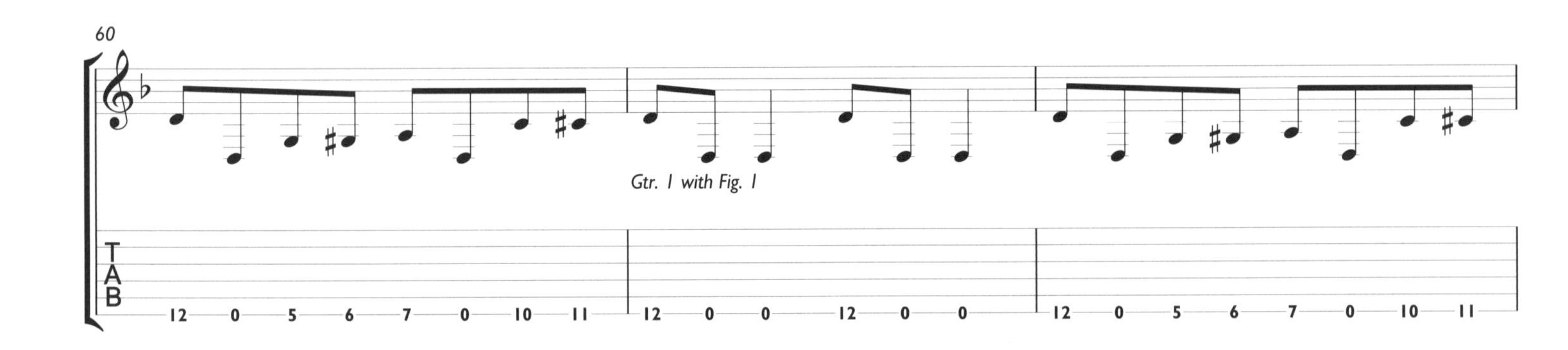
60
Gtr. 1 with Fig. 1
T
A
B
12 0 5 6 7 0 10 11
12 0 0 12 0 0
12 0 5 6 7 0 10 11

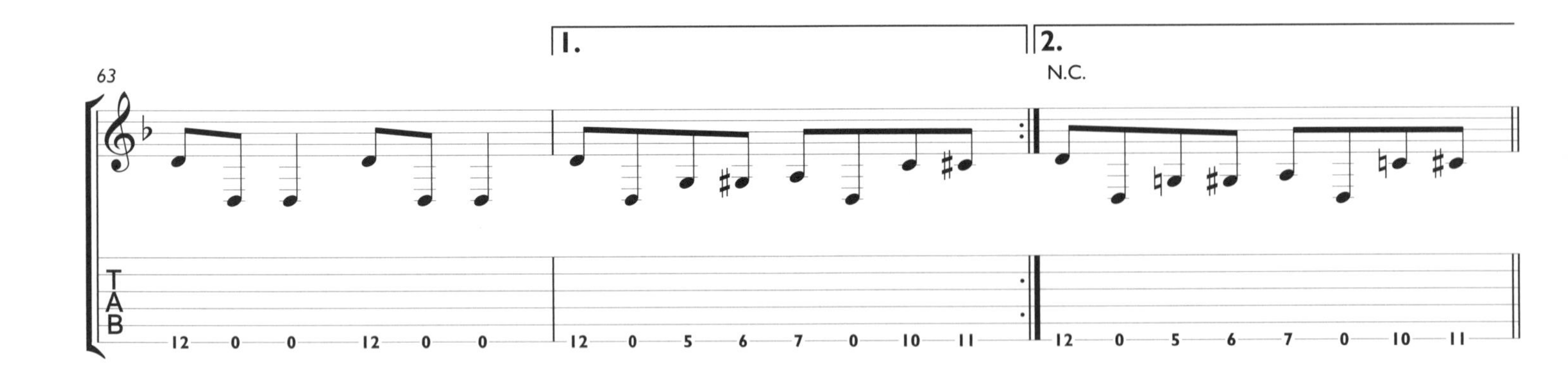
1.
2.
N.C.
63
T
A
B
12 0 0 12 0 0
12 0 5 6 7 0 10 11
12 0 5 6 7 0 10 11

Gtr. 2
66
N.C.
T
A
B
7 7 7 7 7 7 7 7 7 7 7 7 7 7 7 7
7 7 7 7 7 7 7 7 7 7 7 7 7 7 7 7
with whammy pedal
-1 octave
sim.

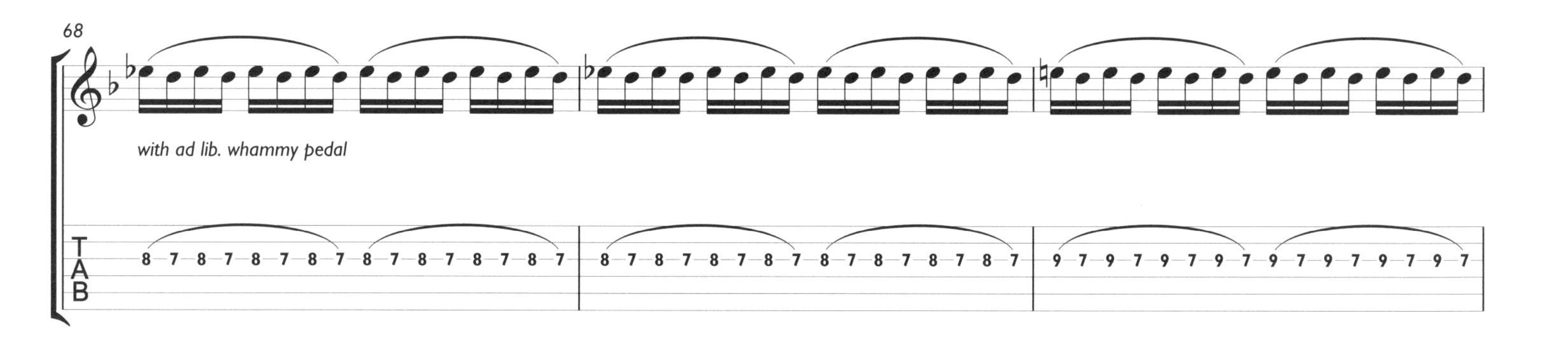
68
with ad lib. whammy pedal
8 7 8 7 8 7 8 7 8 7 8 7 8 7 8 7
8 7 8 7 8 7 8 7 8 7 8 7 8 7 8 7
9 7 9 7 9 7 9 7 9 7 9 7 9 7 9 7

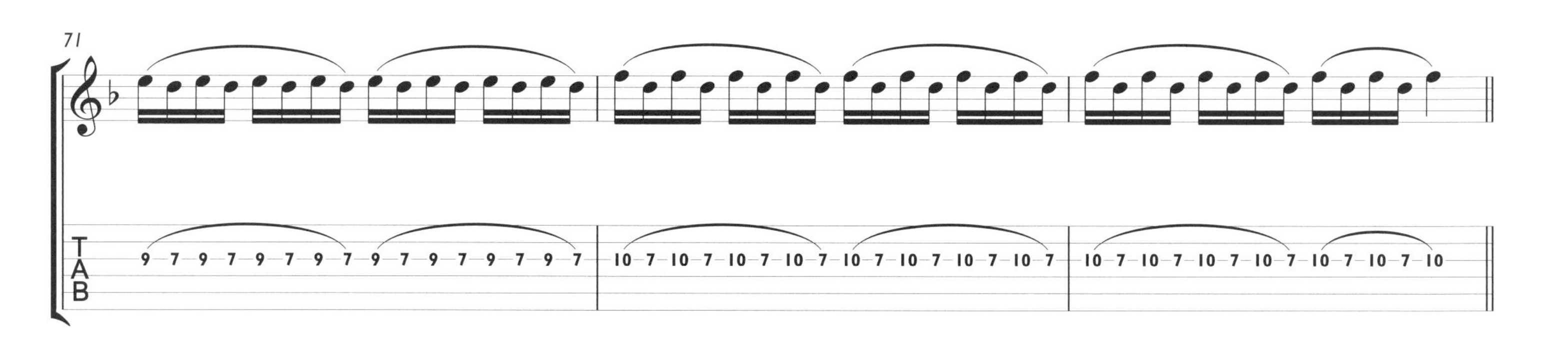
71
9 7 9 7 9 7 9 7 9 7 9 7 9 7 9 7
10 7 10 7 10 7 10 7 10 7 10 7 10 7 10 7
10 7 10 7 10 7 10 7 10 7 10 7 10

74
N.C.
3 & 4° Gtr. 1 with Fig. 1
12 0 0 12 0 0
12 0 5 6 7 0 10 11
12 0 0 12 0 0

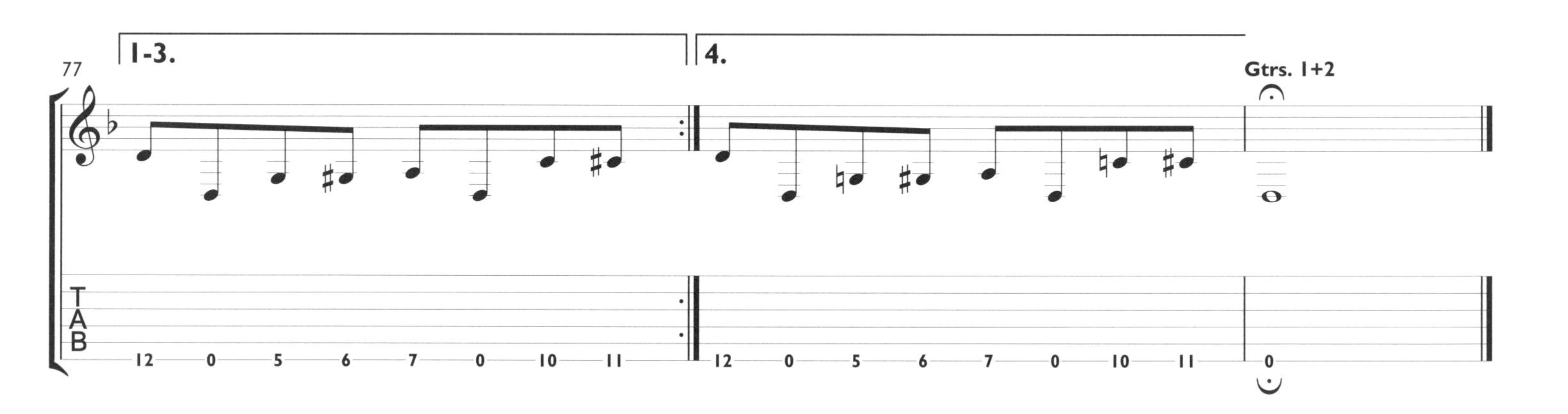
77
1-3.
4.
Gtrs. 1+2
12 0 5 6 7 0 10 11
12 0 5 6 7 0 10 11
0

EXO-POLITICS

Words and Music by Matthew Bellamy

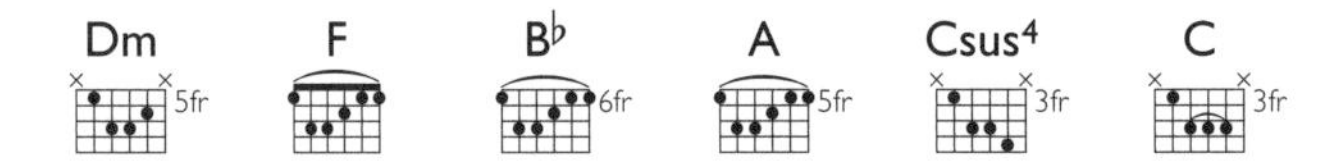

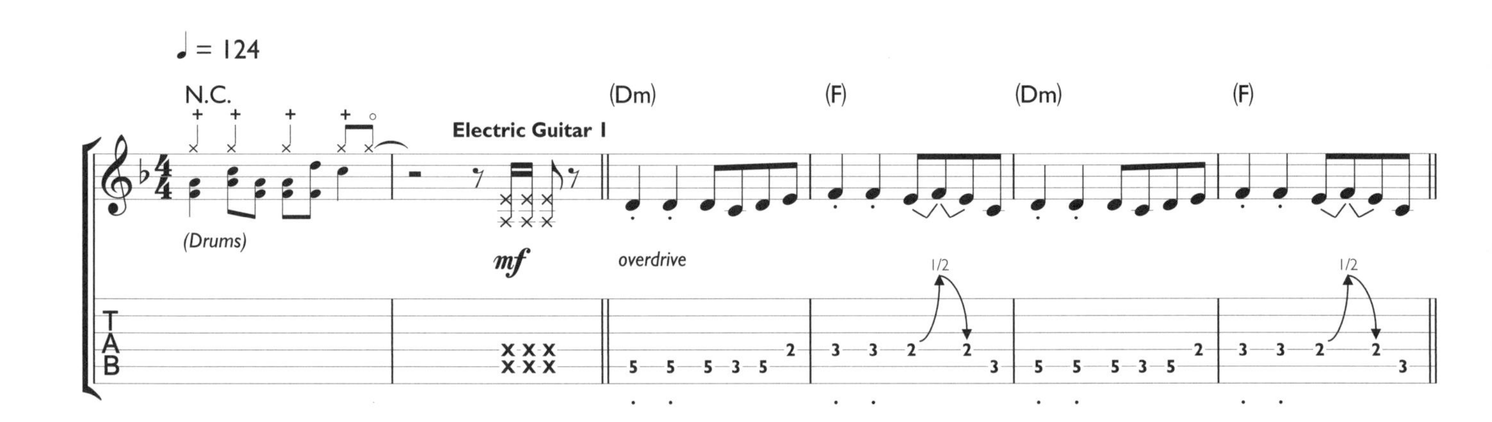

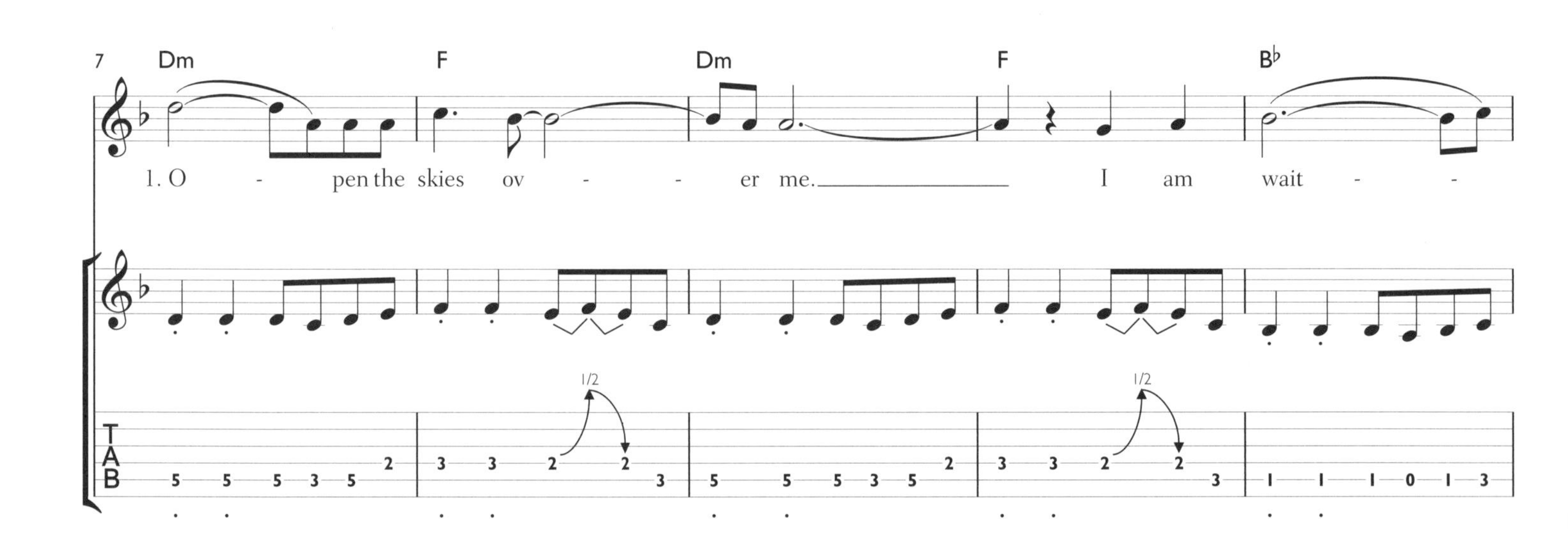

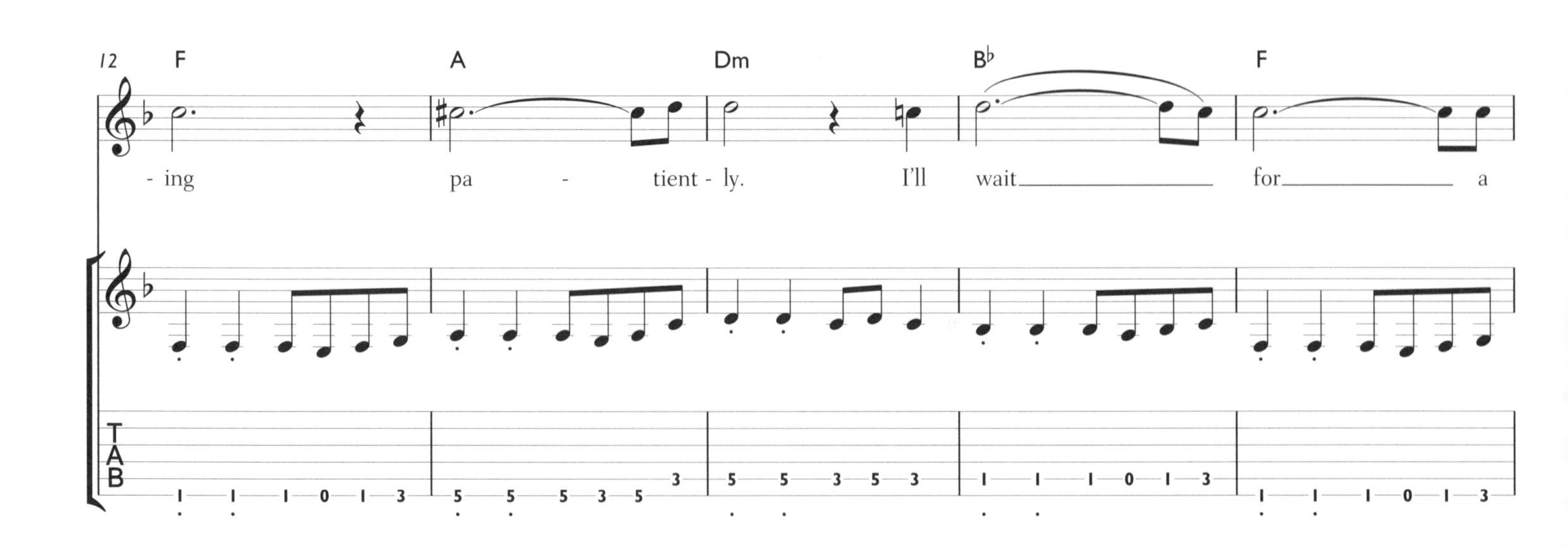

A
Dm
F
Dm
sign.
2. As con - spir - a - cies un - wind,
3. Car - ried through the cent - u - ries,
F
B♭
F
A
Dm
will you slam shut or free your mind, or
sec - rets locked up and load - ed on my back, and it
B♭
F
A
(Dm)
stay hyp - no - tized?
weighs me down.
Tacet 1°
Dm
C
When the Ze - tas fill the skies,
Gtrs. 1 & 2 (composite part)
f overdrive

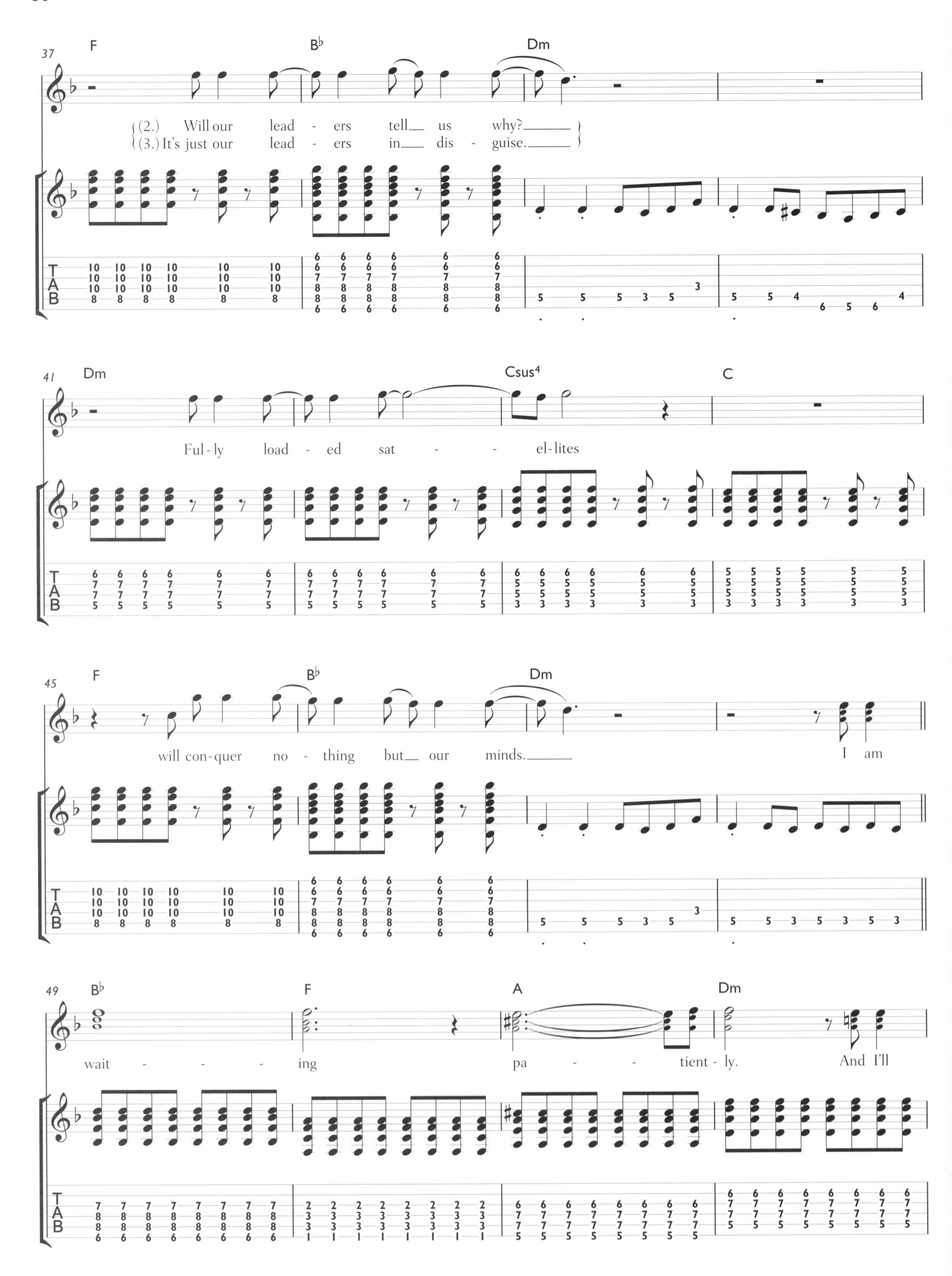
37
F
B♭
Dm
(2.) Will our lead - ers tell us why?
(3.) It's just our lead - ers in dis - guise.
41
Dm
Csus4
C
Ful - ly load - ed sat - - el - lites
45
F
B♭
Dm
will con - quer no - thing but our minds.
I am
49
B♭
F
A
Dm
wait - - - - ing pa - - tient - ly.
And I'll

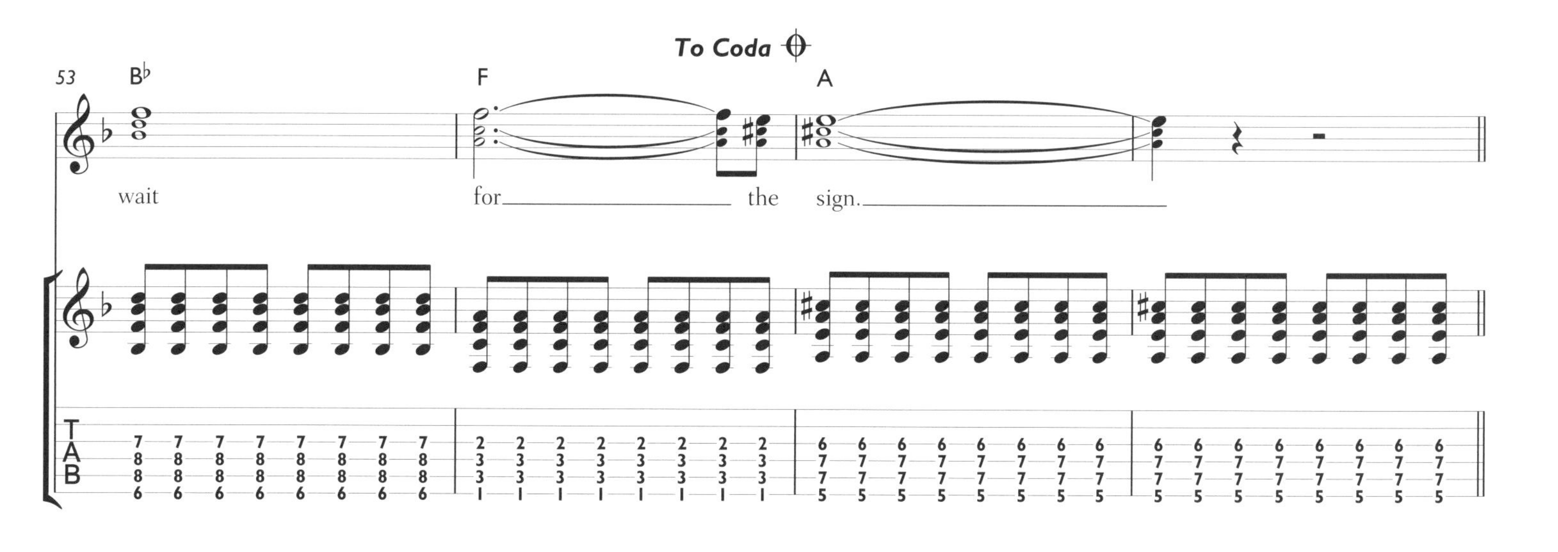
To Coda
B♭
F
A
wait
for
the
sign.

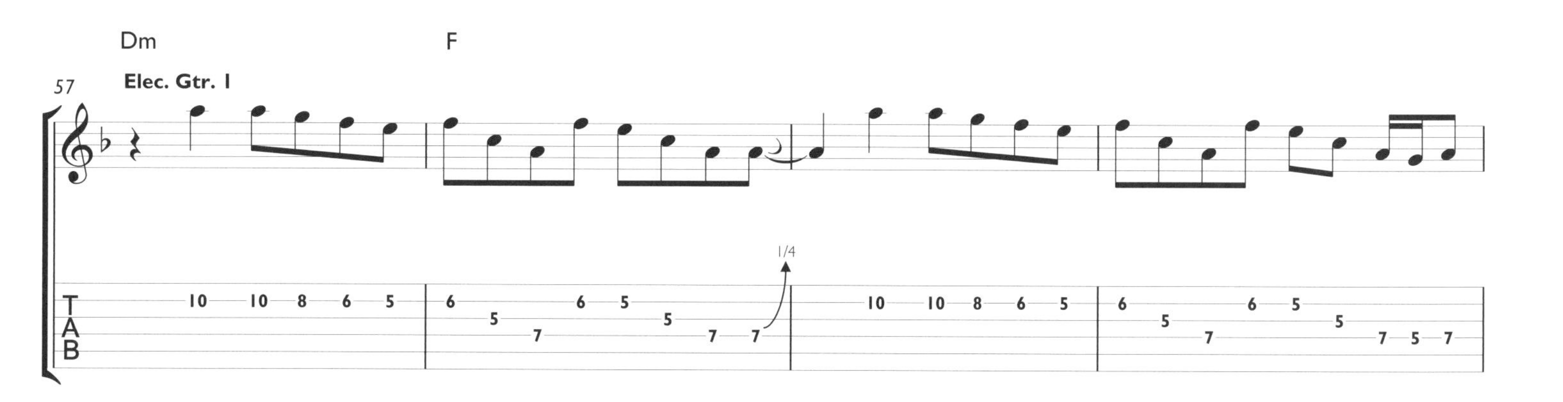
Dm
F
Elec. Gtr. 1

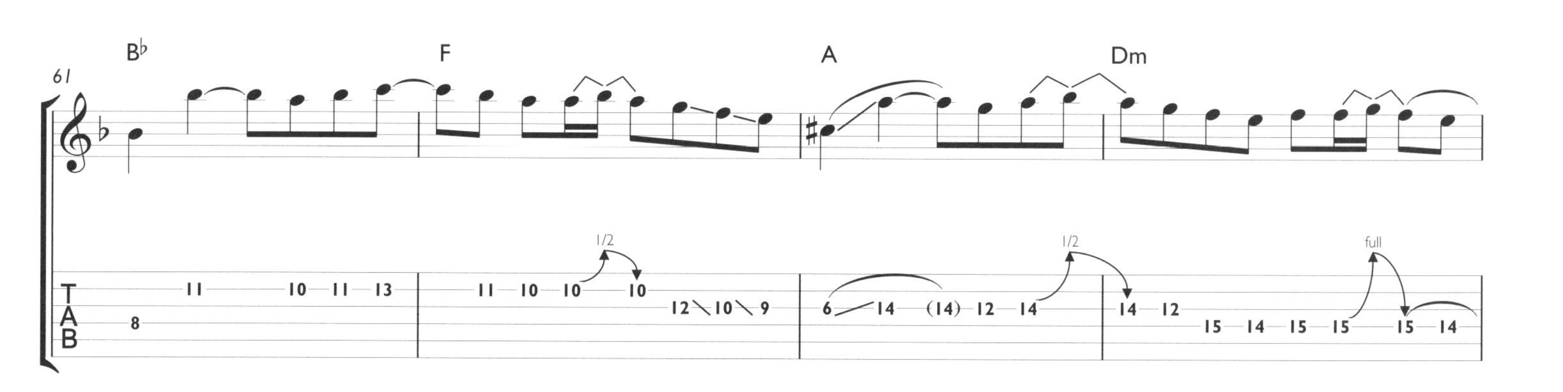
B♭
F
A
Dm

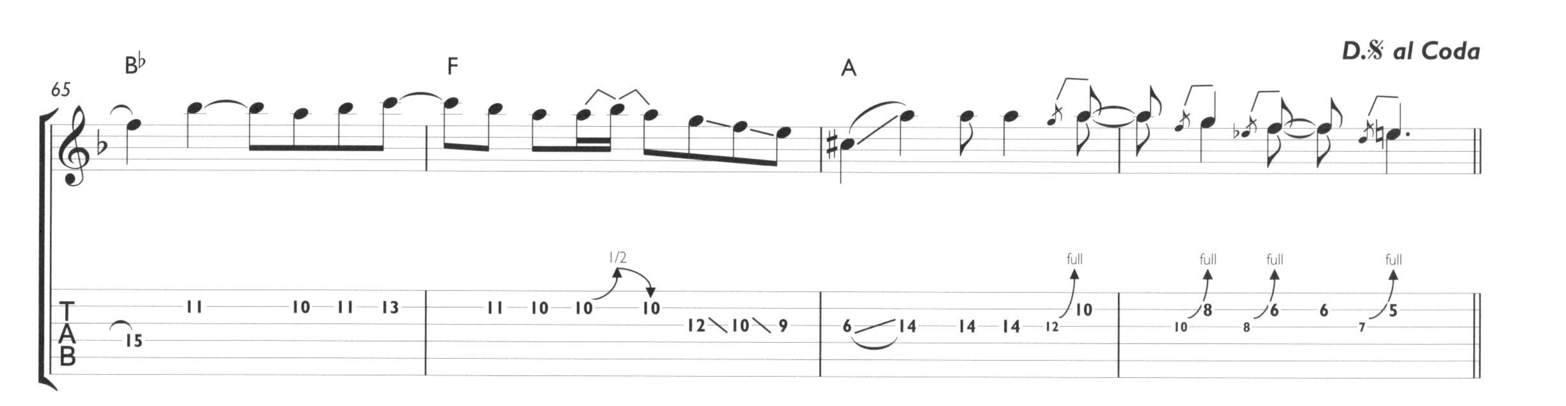
D.% al Coda
B♭
F
A

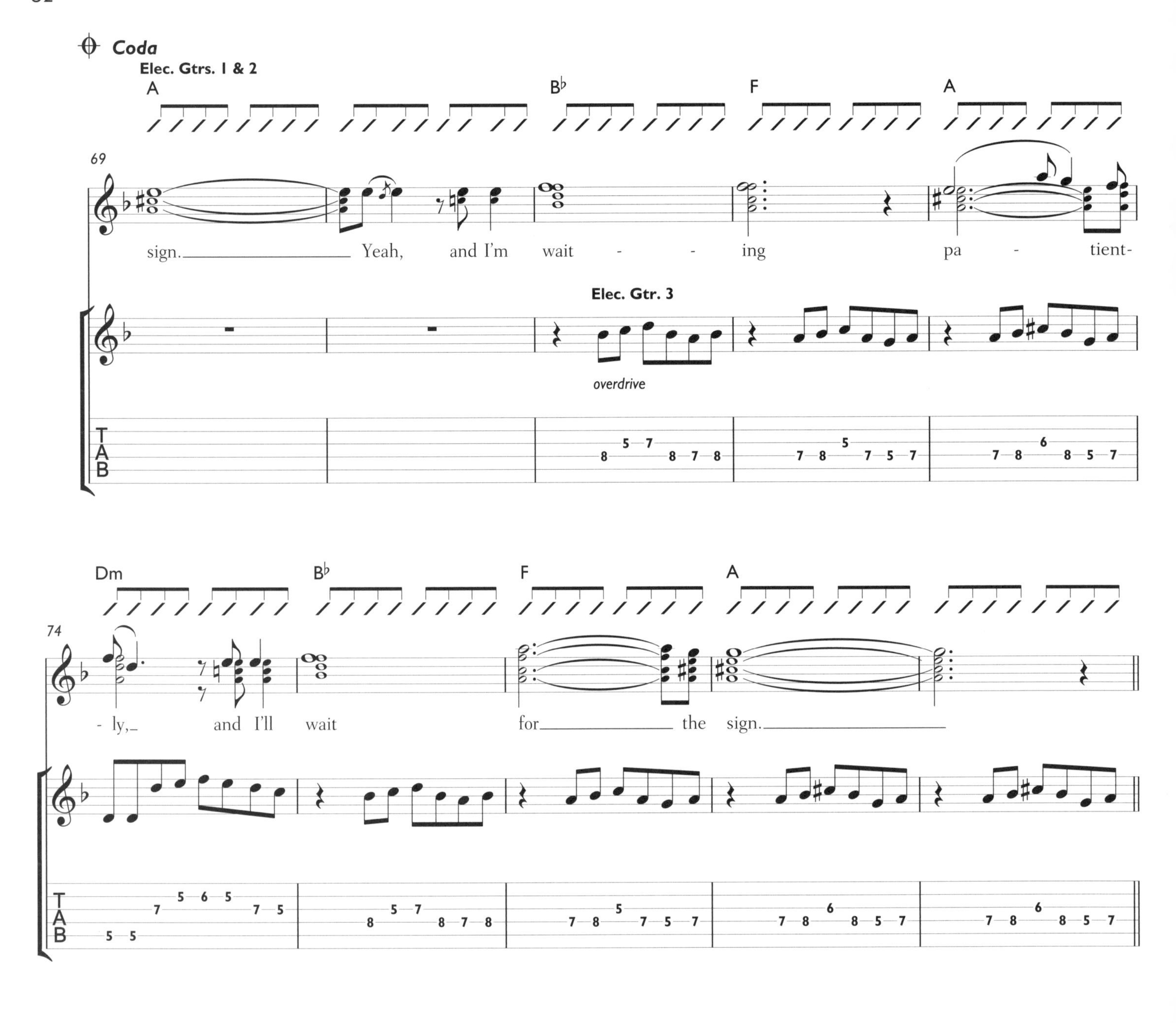
Coda
Elec. Gtrs. 1 & 2
A
B♭
F
A
69
sign. Yeah, and I'm wait - - ing pa - tient-
Elec. Gtr. 3
overdrive
Dm
B♭
F
A
74
- ly, and I'll wait for the sign.

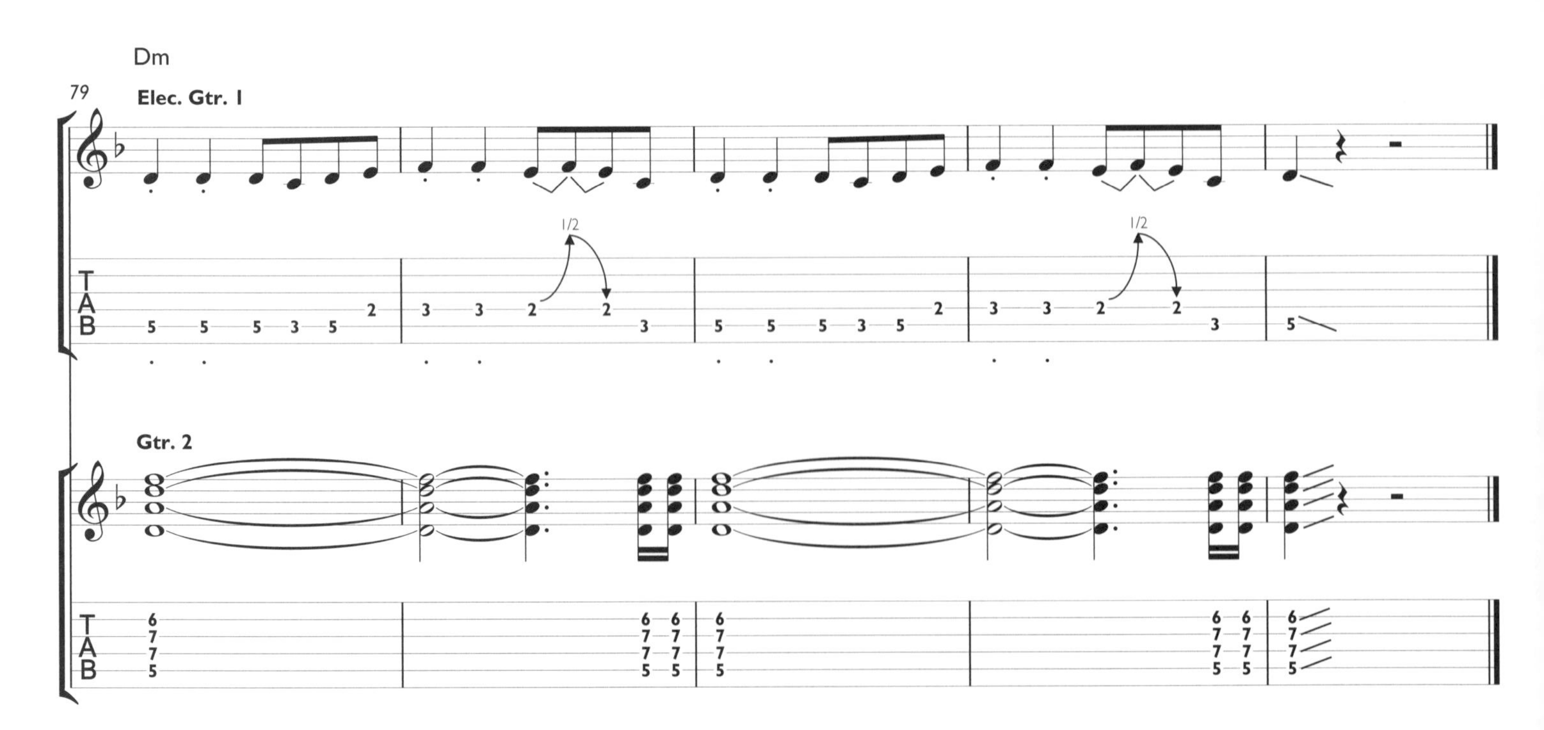
Dm
79
Elec. Gtr. 1
1/2
1/2
Gtr. 2

FALLING AWAY WITH YOU

Words and Music by Matthew Bellamy

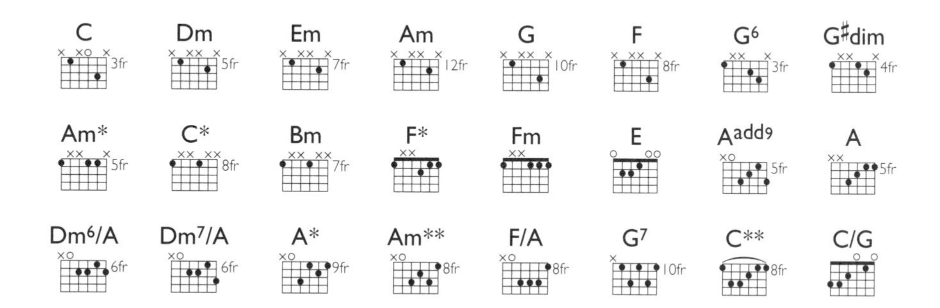

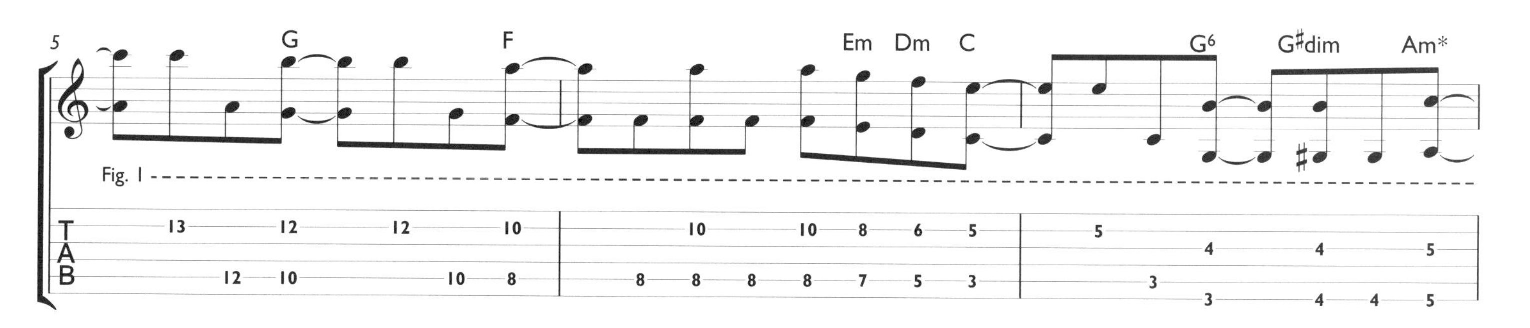

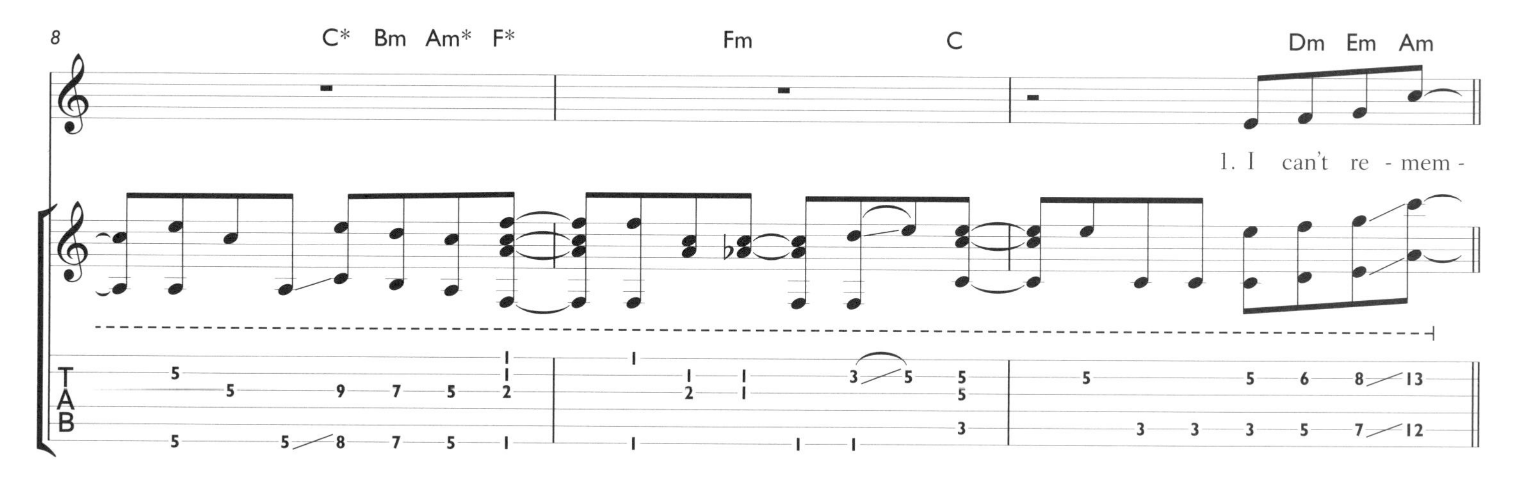

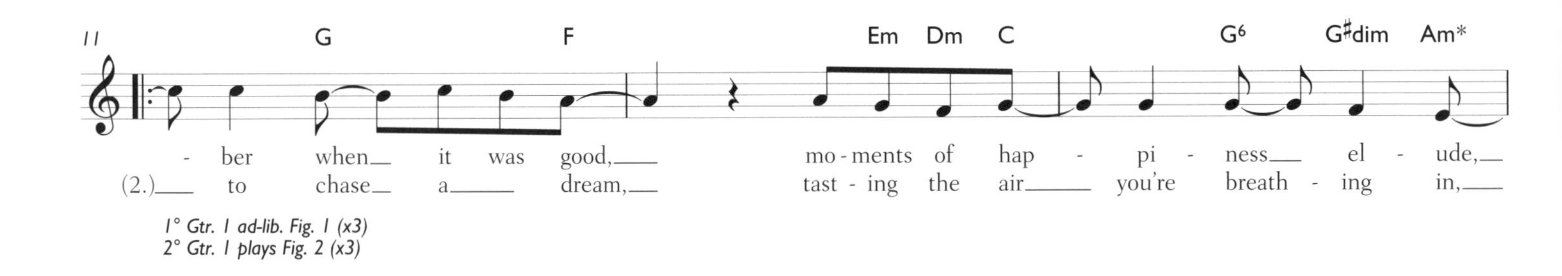
11
G F Em Dm C G6 G♯dim Am*
- ber when it was good, mo - ments of hap - pi - ness el - ude,
(2.) to chase a dream, tast - ing the air you're breath - ing in,
1° Gtr. 1 ad-lib. Fig. 1 (x3)
2° Gtr. 1 plays Fig. 2 (x3)

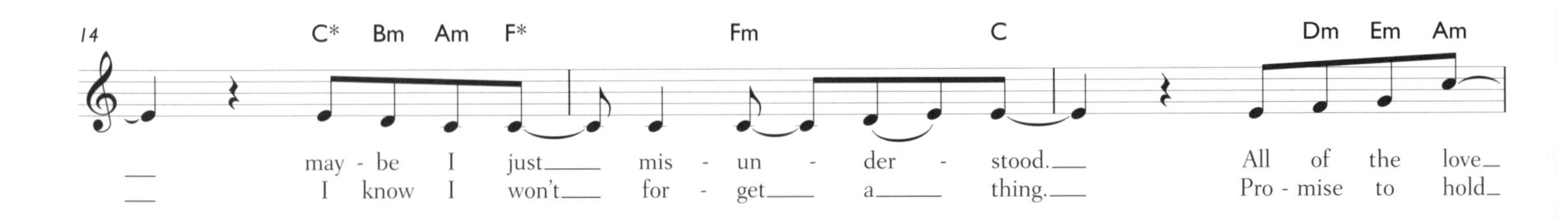
14
C* Bm Am F* Fm C Dm Em Am
may - be I just mis - un - der - stood. All of the love
I know I won't for - get a thing. Pro - mise to hold

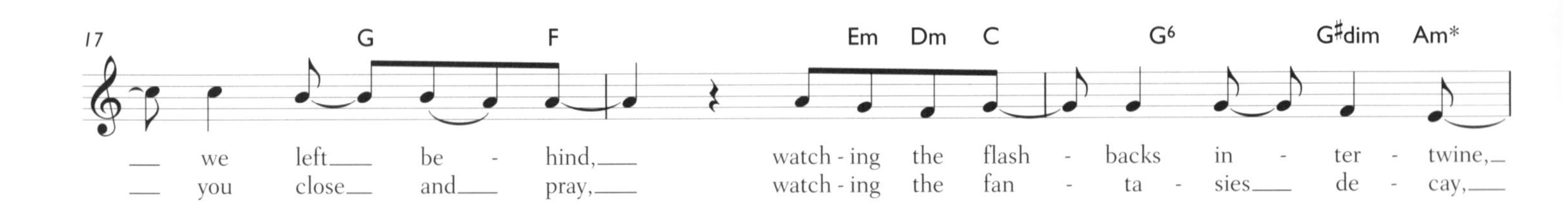
17
G F Em Dm C G6 G♯dim Am*
we left be - hind, watch - ing the flash - backs in - ter - twine,
you close and pray, watch - ing the fan - ta - sies de - cay,

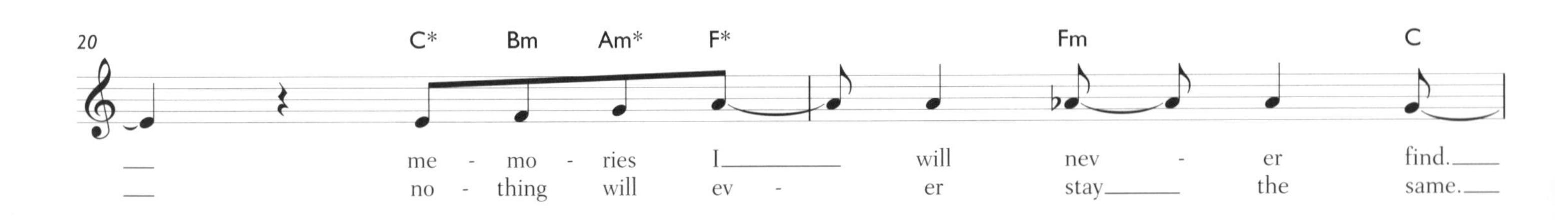
20
C* Bm Am* F* Fm C
me - mo - ries I will nev - er find.
no - thing will ev - er stay the same.

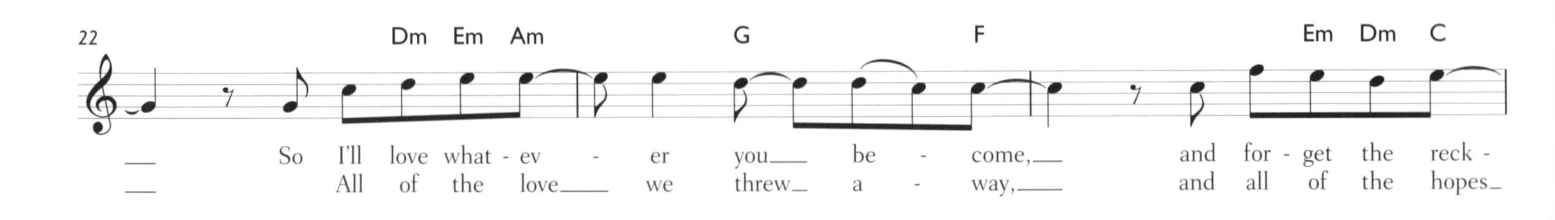
22
Dm Em Am G F Em Dm C
So I'll love what - ev - er you be - come, and for - get the reck -
All of the love we threw a - way, and all of the hopes

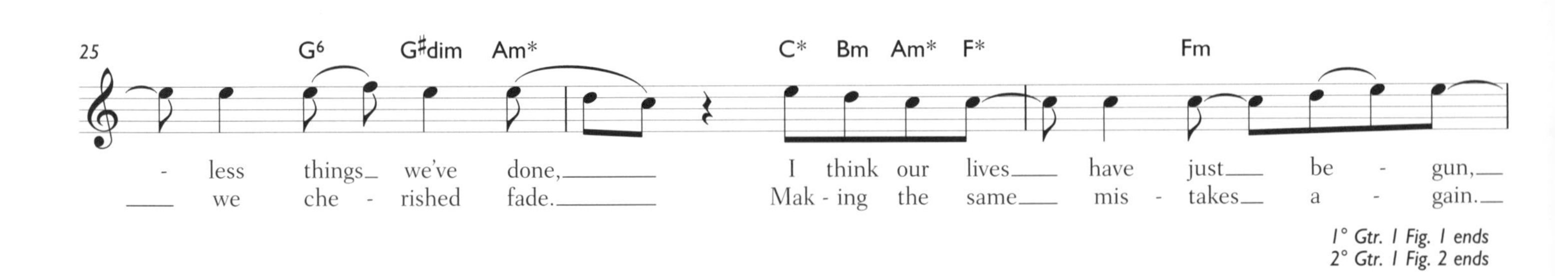
25
G6 G♯dim Am* C* Bm Am* F* Fm
- less things we've done, I think our lives have just be - gun,
we che - rished fade. Mak - ing the same mis - takes a - gain.
1° Gtr. 1 Fig. 1 ends
2° Gtr. 1 Fig. 2 ends

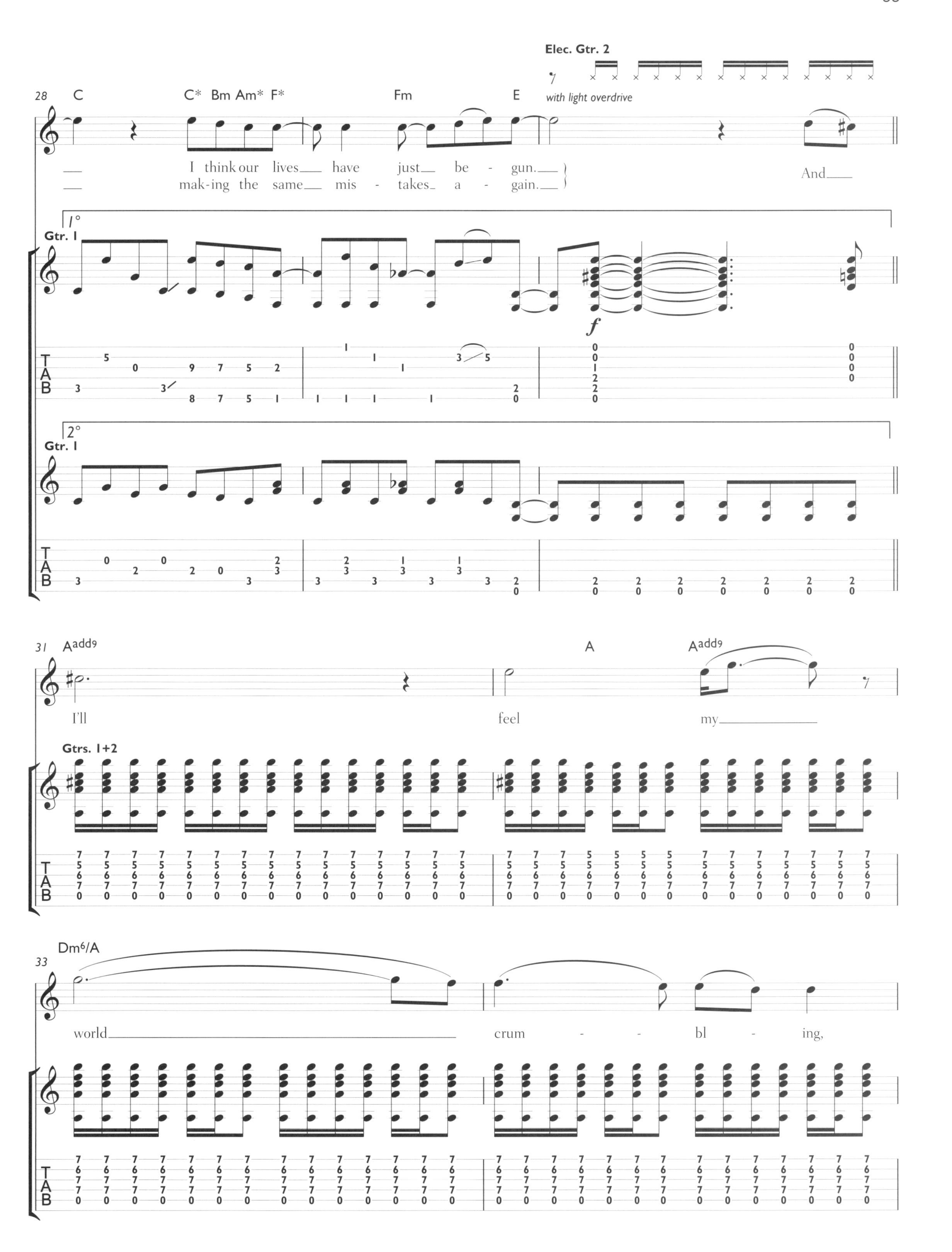
Elec. Gtr. 2
with light overdrive
28
C
C* Bm Am* F*
Fm
E
I think our lives have just be - gun.
mak-ing the same mis - takes a - gain.
And
1°
Gtr. 1
2°
Gtr. 1
31
Aadd9
A
Aadd9
I'll
feel
my
Gtrs. 1+2
33
Dm6/A
world
crum - - bl - ing,

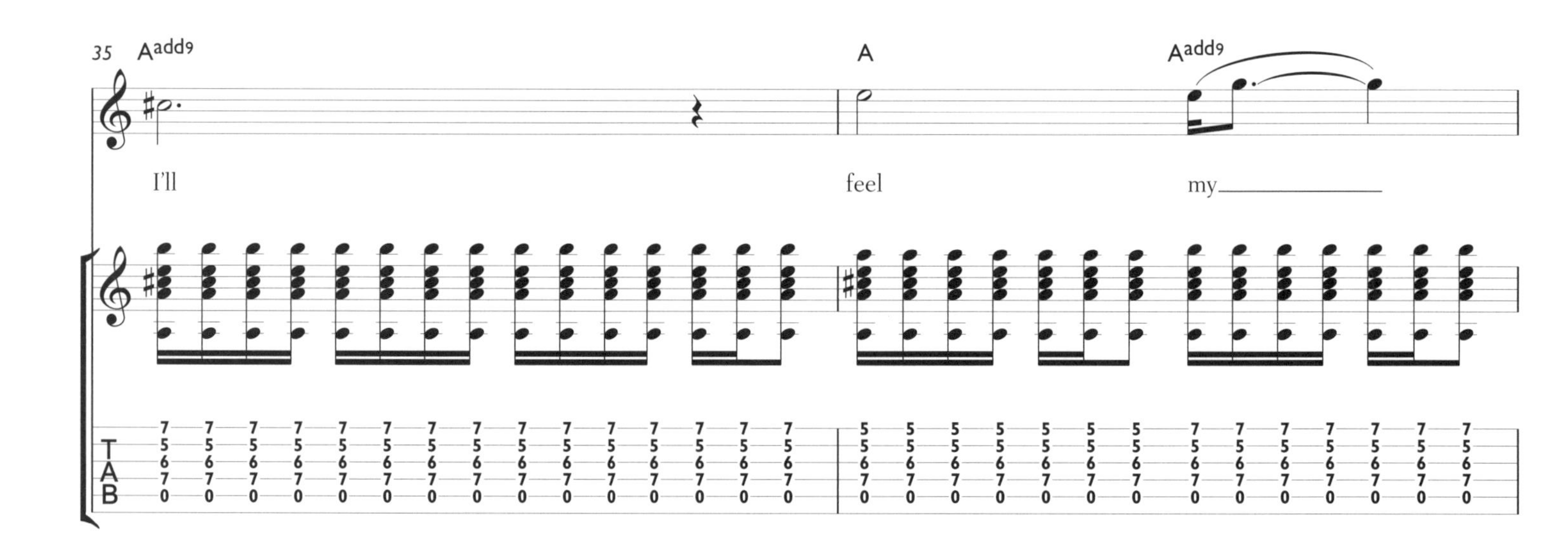
35
Aadd9
A
Aadd9
I'll
feel
my
T
A
B

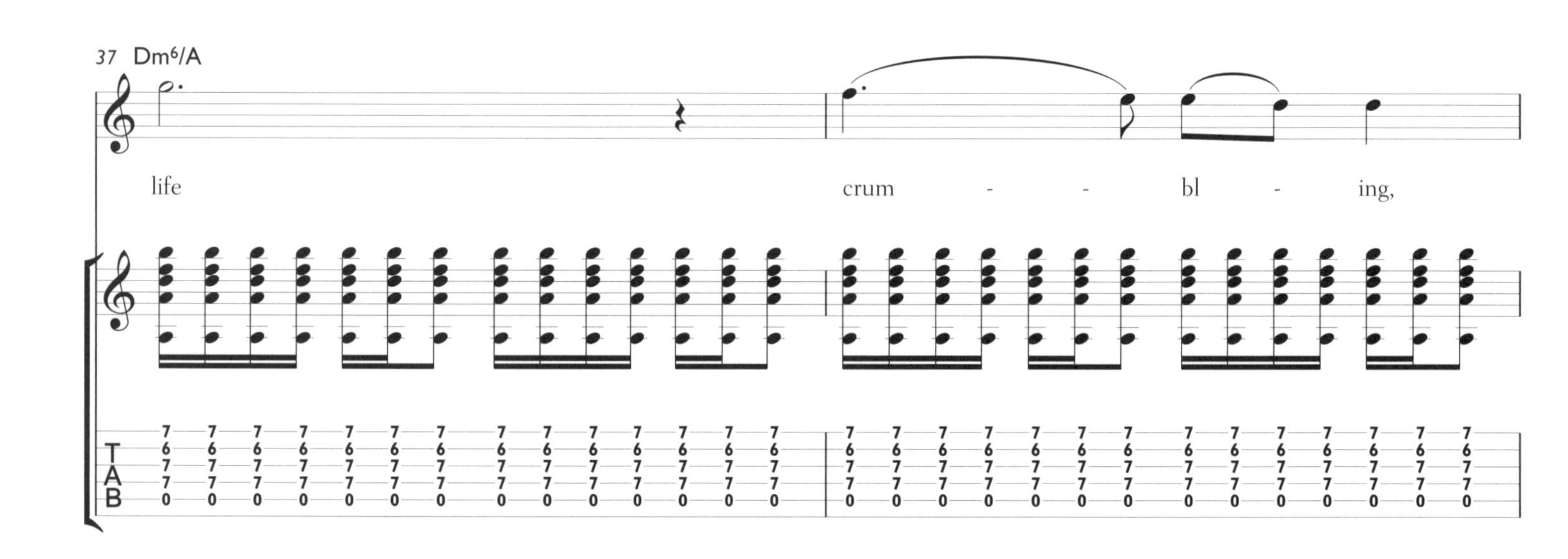
37
Dm6/A
life
crum - - bl - ing,
T
A
B

39
A
Aadd9
I'll
feel
my
T
A
B

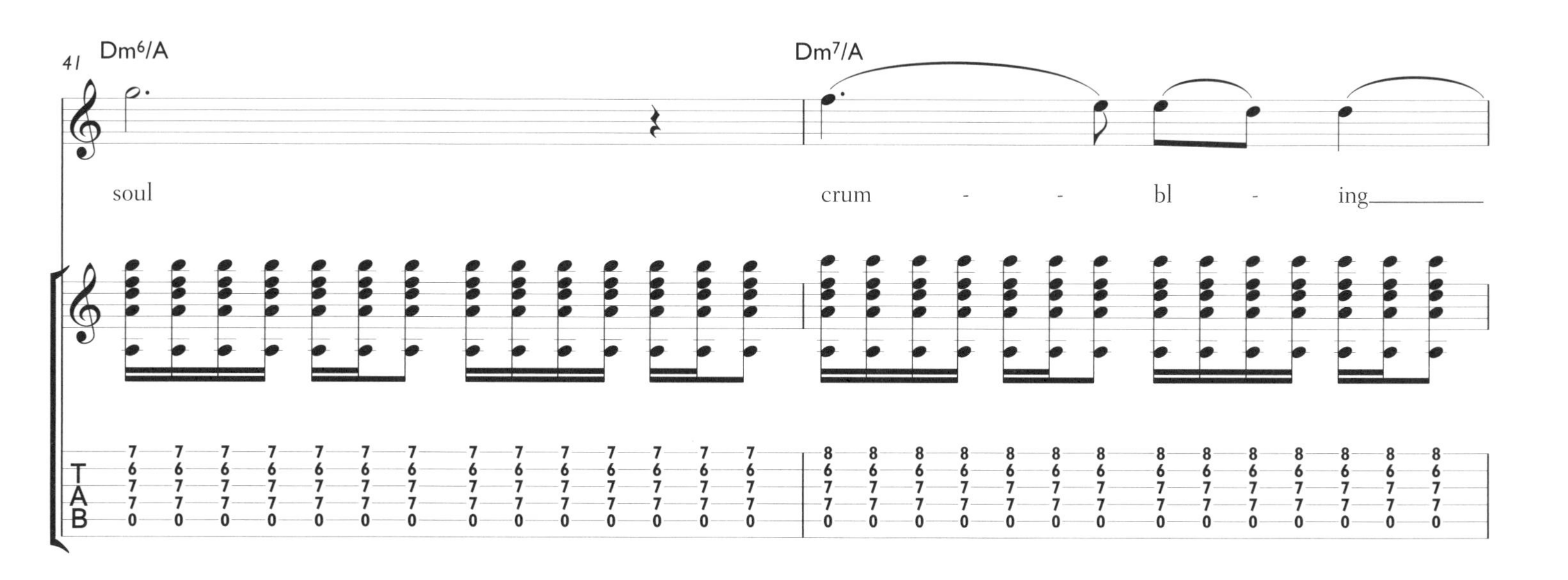
41
Dm6/A
Dm7/A
soul
crum - - bl - ing
TAB

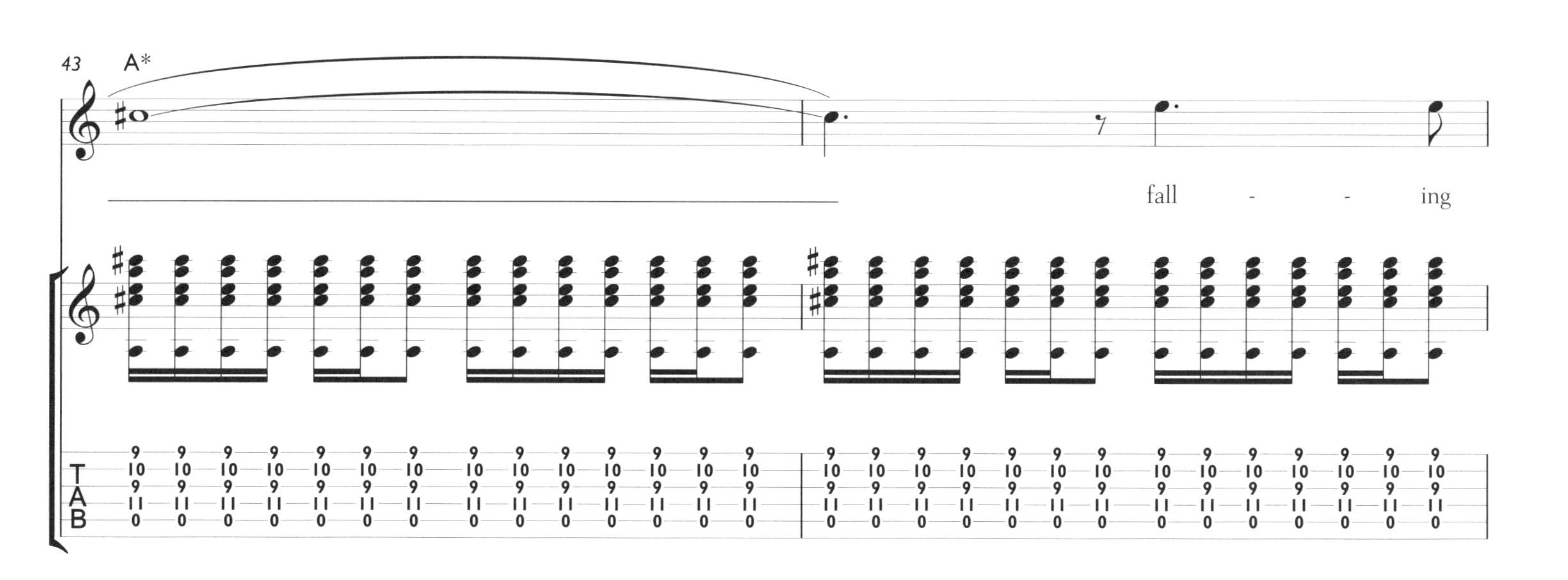
43
A*
fall - - ing
TAB

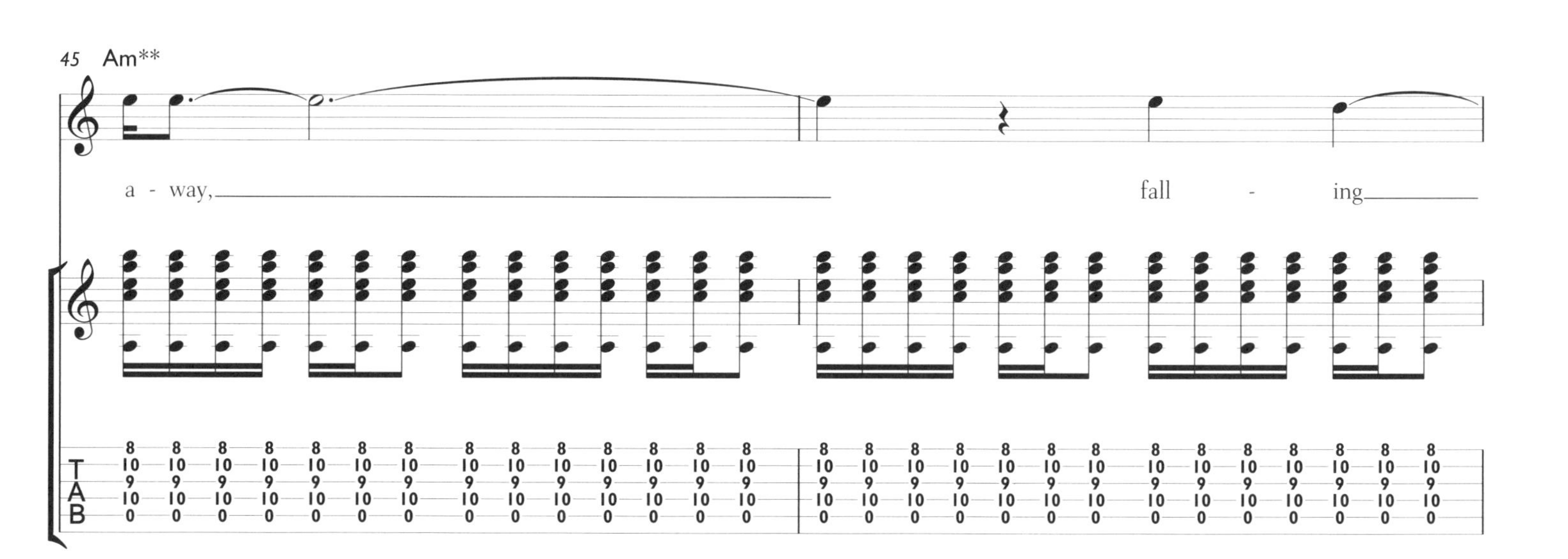
45
Am**
a - way,
fall - ing
TAB

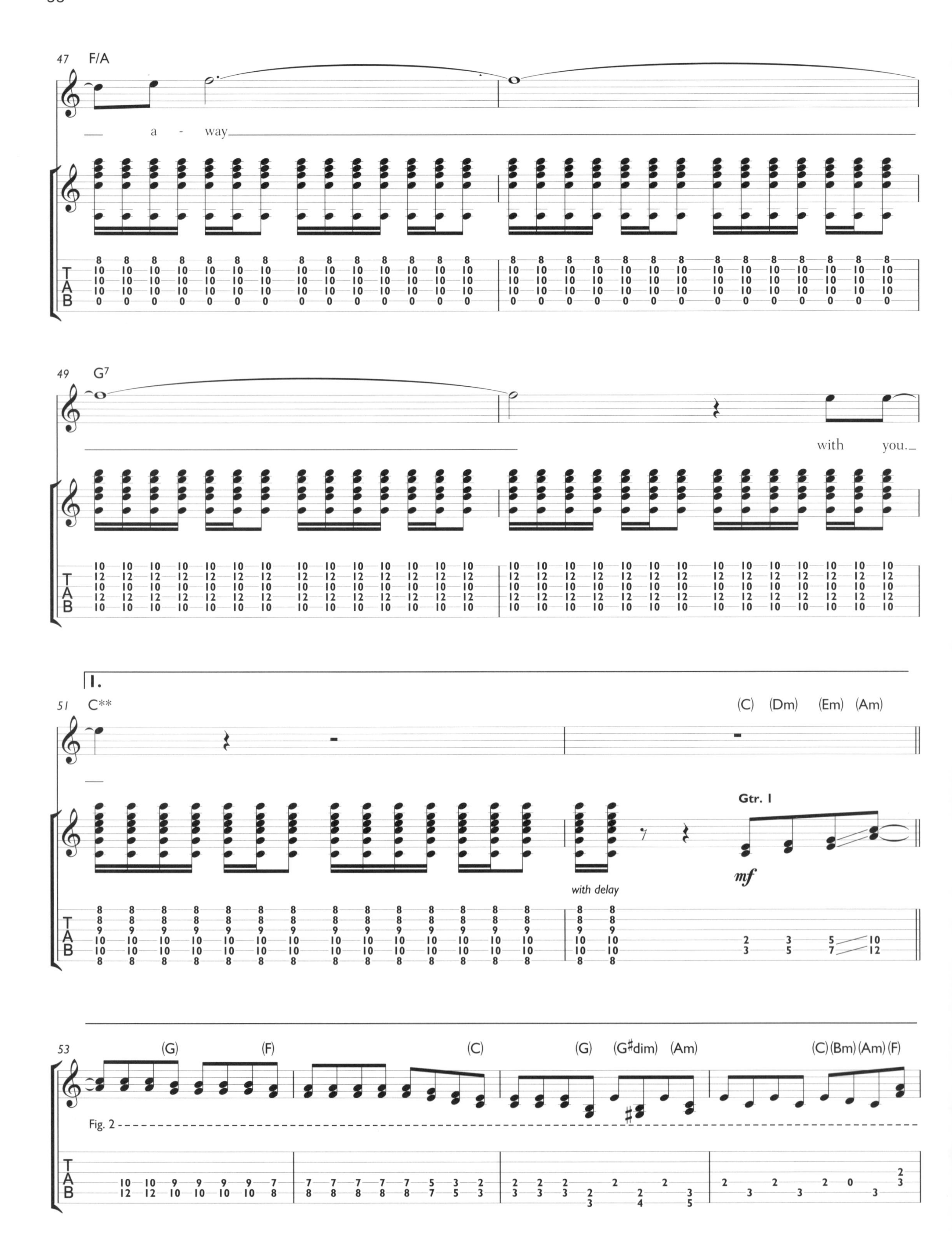

47
F/A
a - way
49
G7
with you.
1.
51
C**
(C) (Dm) (Em) (Am)
Gtr. 1
mf
with delay
53
(G) (F)
(C)
(G) (G#dim) (Am)
(C) (Bm) (Am) (F)
Fig. 2

57
(Fm)
(C)
2.
C**
2. Stay-ing a - wake
Fig. 2
TAB
60
C Dm Em Am
All of the love
Gtr. I
with delay
mp
63
G F Em Dm C G* G♯dim Am* C* Bm Am* F*
we've left be - hind, watch-ing the flash - backs in - ter - twine, me-mo-ries I
67
Fm C C* Bm Am* F* Fm C/G
rit.
will nev - er find, me - mo - ries I will nev - er find.

FALLING DOWN

Words and Music by Matthew Bellamy

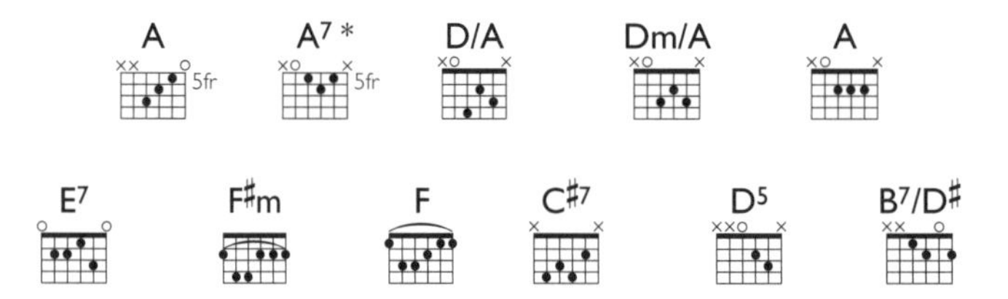

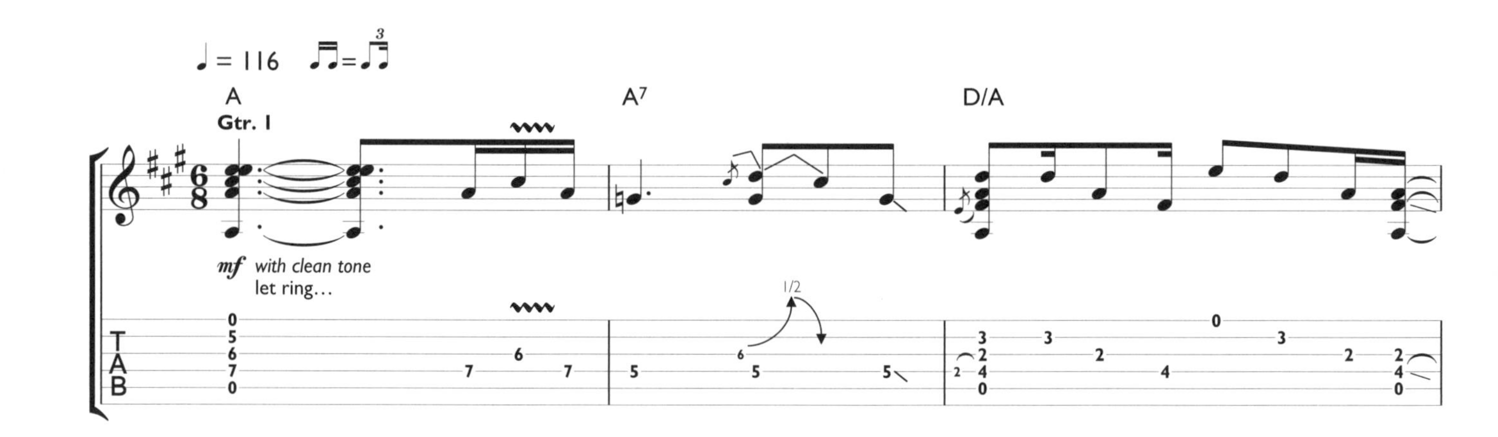

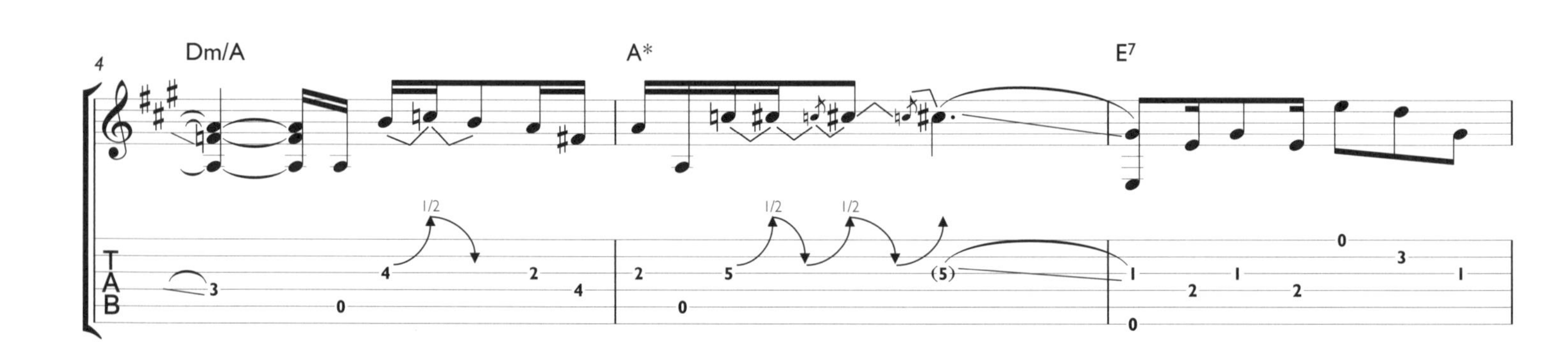

D/A
Dm/A
A*
down, and fif - teen thou-sand peo-ple scream,
your name but you would nev - er hear me sing
E7
D/A
A*
they were all beg-ging for your dream.
you would-n't let me be - gin.
A
A7
D/A
I'm fall - ing down,
So I'm crawl - ing a - way
Dm/A
A*
E7
five thou - sand hous-es burn-ing down yeah, no-one is gon-na save this
'cause you broke my heart in two yeah, no I will not for - get
TAB
1/2

D/A
A*
F♯m
town.
you.
Too late, I al - rea - dy
Too late, I al - rea - dy
F
C♯7
found what I was look - ing for.
found what I was look - ing for.
You know it was -
You know it was -
D5
B7/D♯
E7
1.
- n't here, no it was - n't here.
- n't you, no
2.
it was - n't you, no.
T
A
B

A A7 D/A
3. Fall - - - ing a - way
Dm/A A*
you would nev - er see me through
E7 D/A A*
no I could not for - get you.
A A7 D/A Dm/A
Fall - - ing down, five thou - sand hous-es

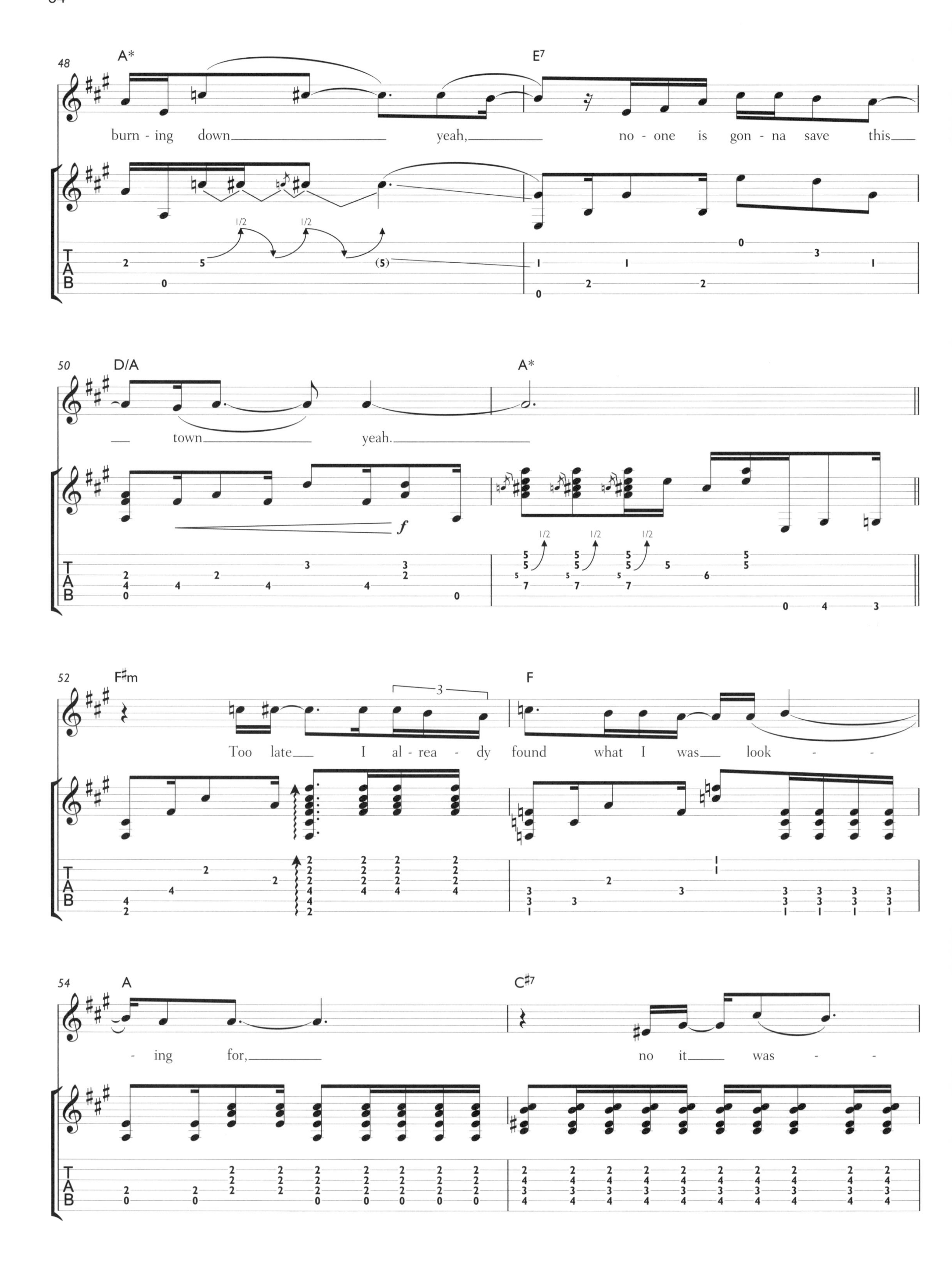
48
A*
E7
burn - ing down yeah, no - one is gon - na save this
1/2
50
D/A
A*
town yeah.
f
52
F♯m
F
Too late I al - rea - dy found what I was look - -
54
A
C♯7
- ing for, no it was - -

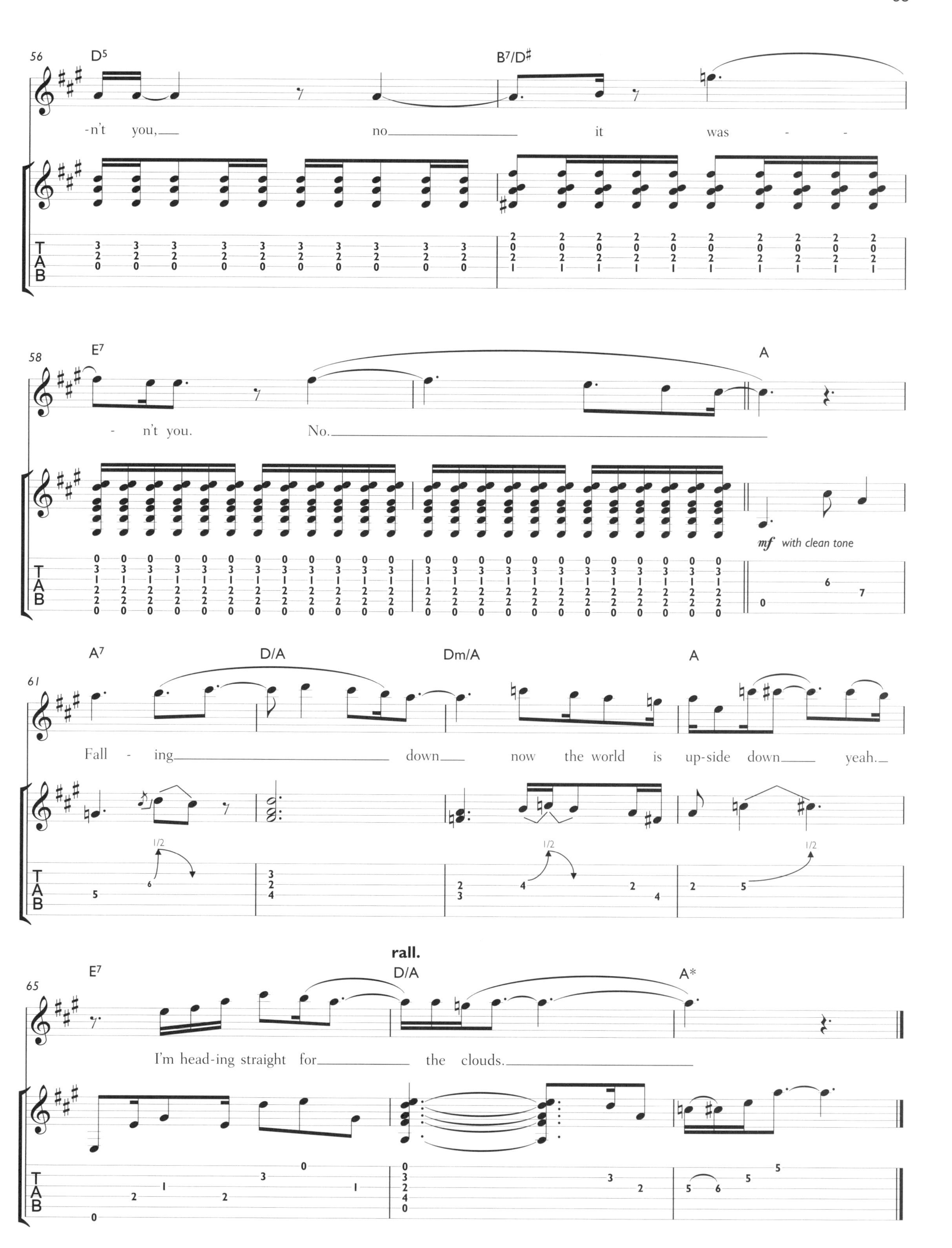
D5
B7/D♯
-n't you, no it was -
E7
A
- n't you. No.
mf with clean tone
A7
D/A
Dm/A
A
Fall - ing down now the world is up-side down yeah.
rall.
E7
D/A
A*
I'm head-ing straight for the clouds.

GUIDING LIGHT

Words and Music by Matthew Bellamy

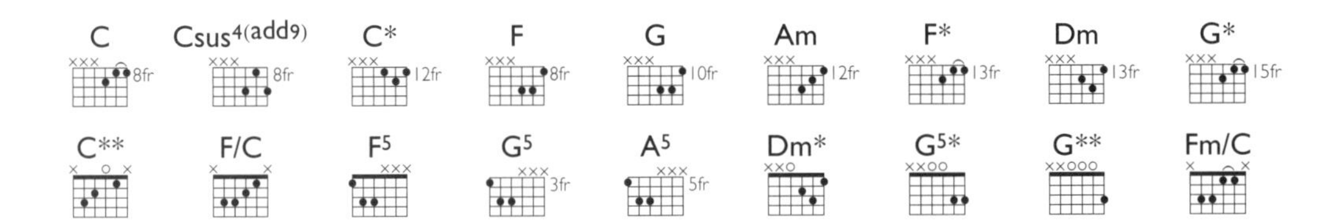

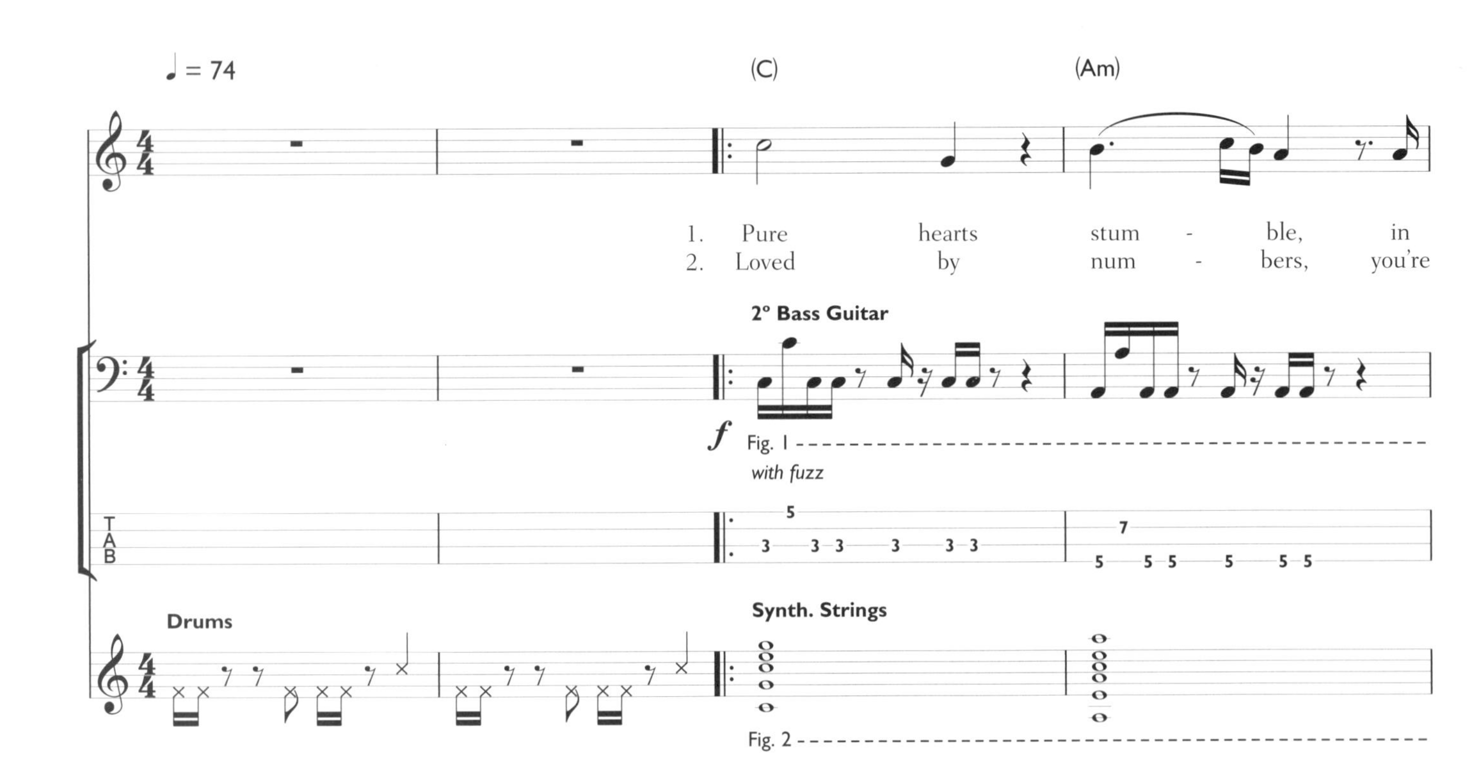

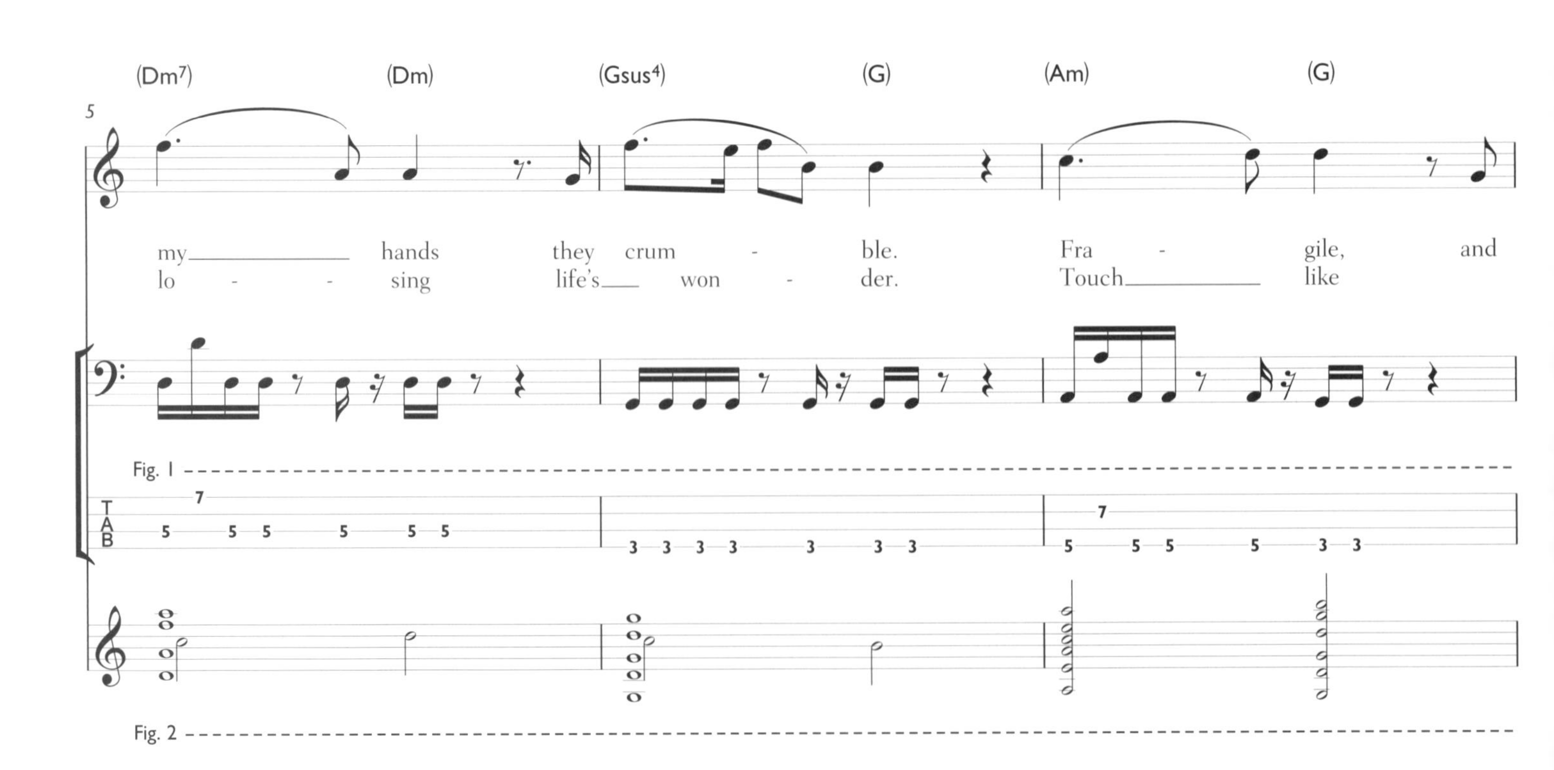

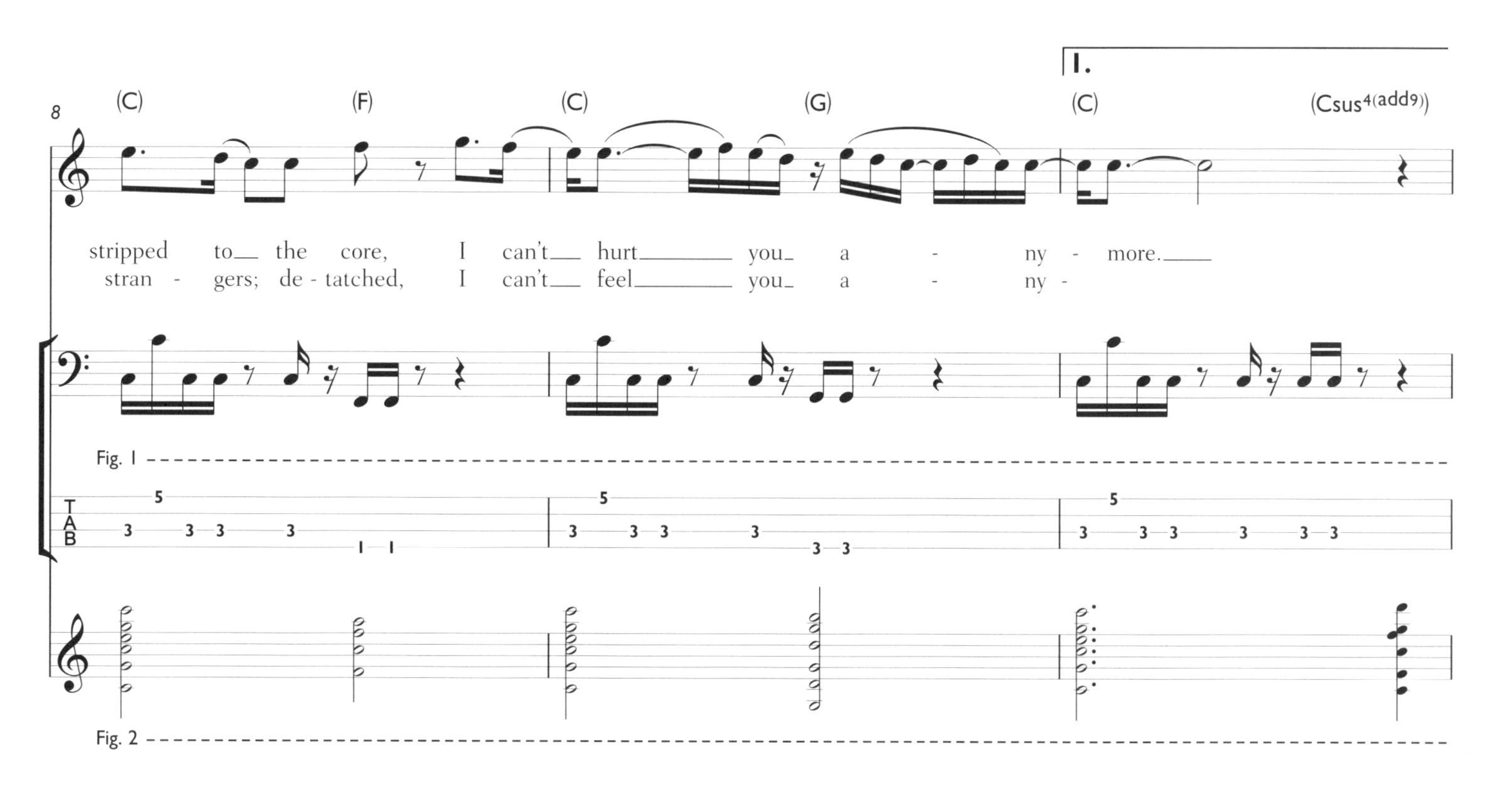

1.
(C)
(F)
(C)
(G)
(C)
(Csus4(add9))
stripped to the core, I can't hurt you a - ny - more.
stran - gers; de - tatched, I can't feel you a - ny -
Fig. 1
Fig. 2

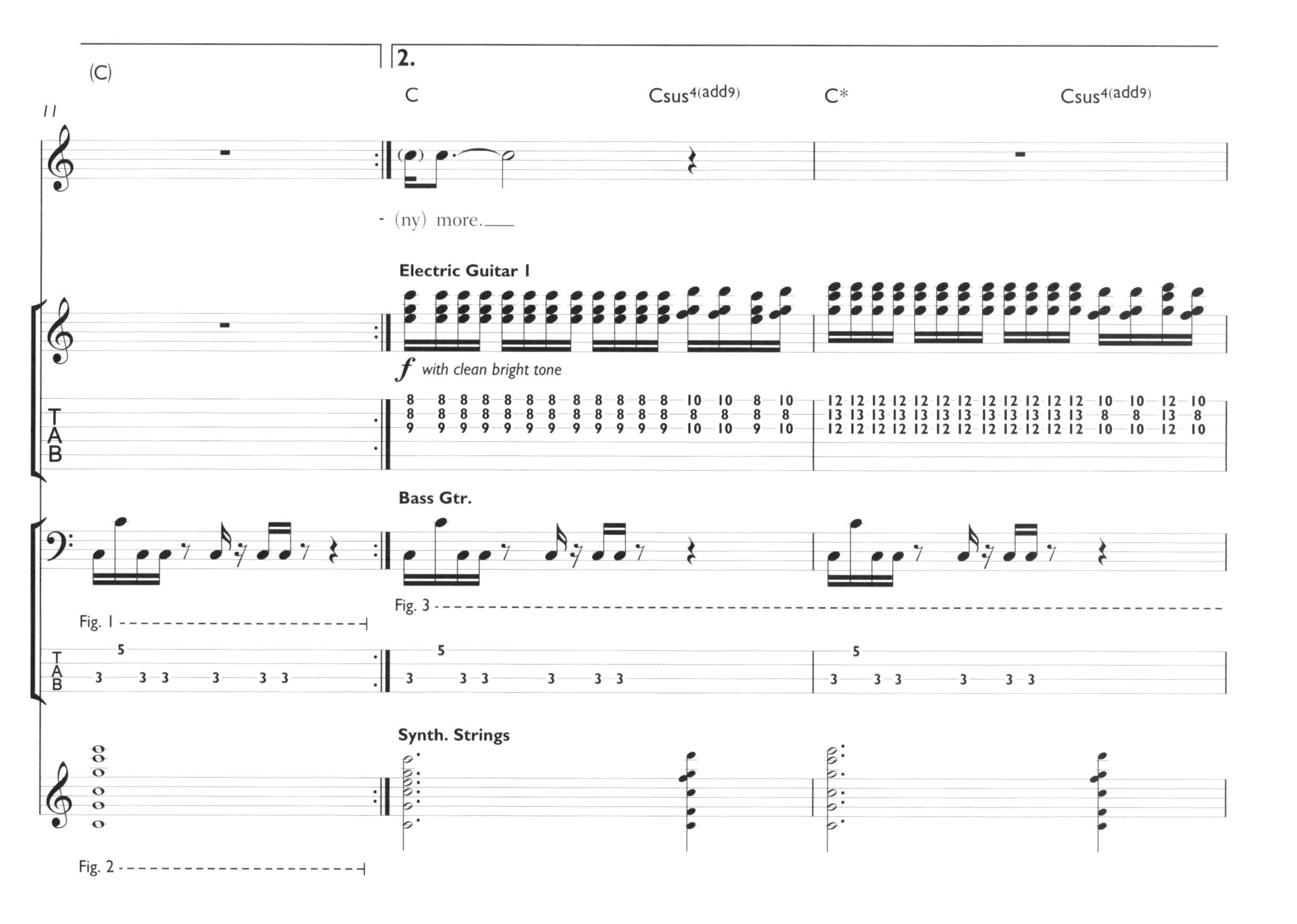

(C)
2.
C
Csus4(add9)
C*
Csus4(add9)
- (ny) more.
Electric Guitar 1
f with clean bright tone
Bass Gtr.
Fig. 3
Fig. 1
Synth. Strings
Fig. 2

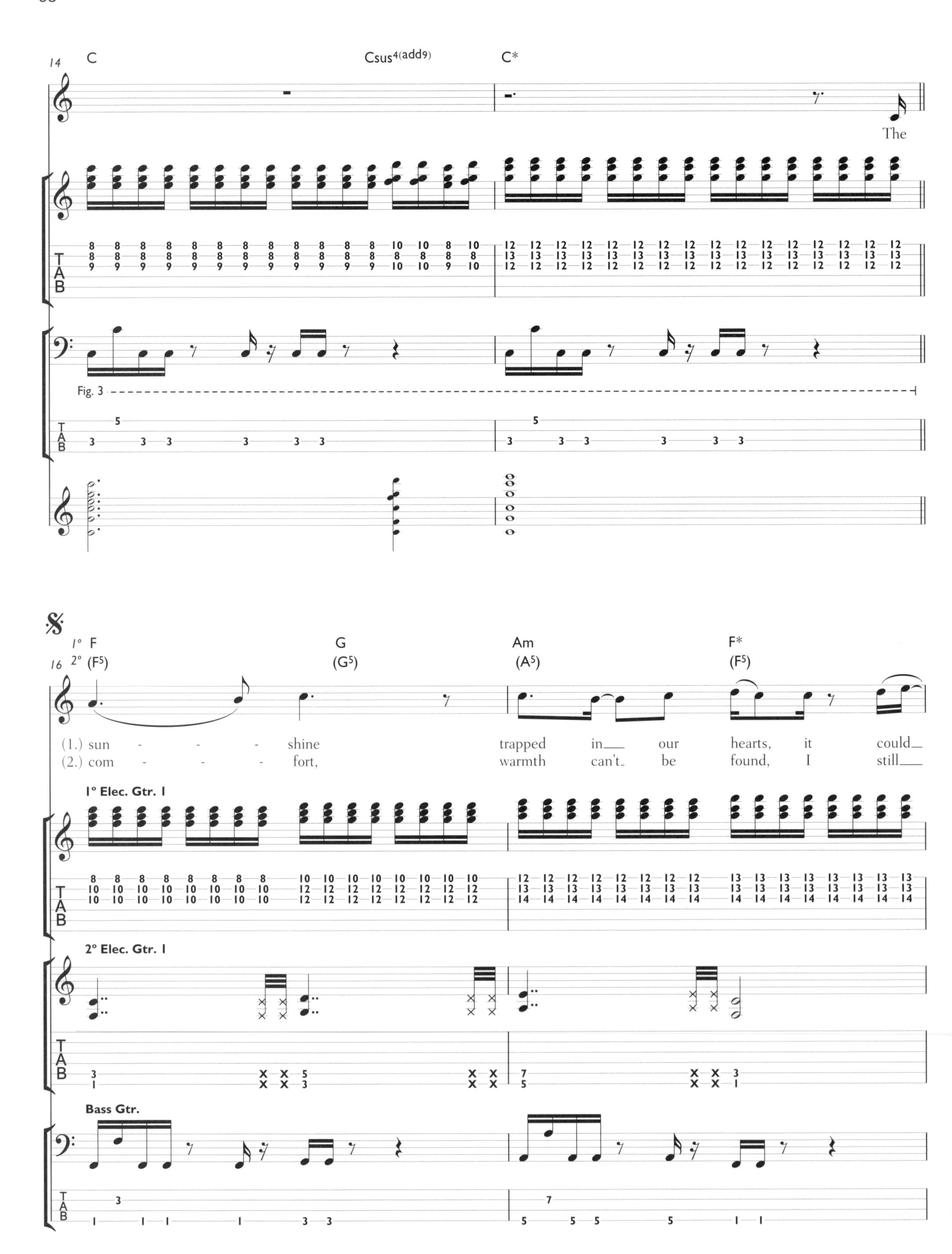
14
C
Csus4(add9)
C*
The
Fig. 3
16
1° F
2° (F5)
G
(G5)
Am
(A5)
F*
(F5)
(1.) sun - - - - shine trapped in our hearts, it could
(2.) com - - - - fort, warmth can't be found, I still
1° Elec. Gtr. 1
2° Elec. Gtr. 1
Bass Gtr.

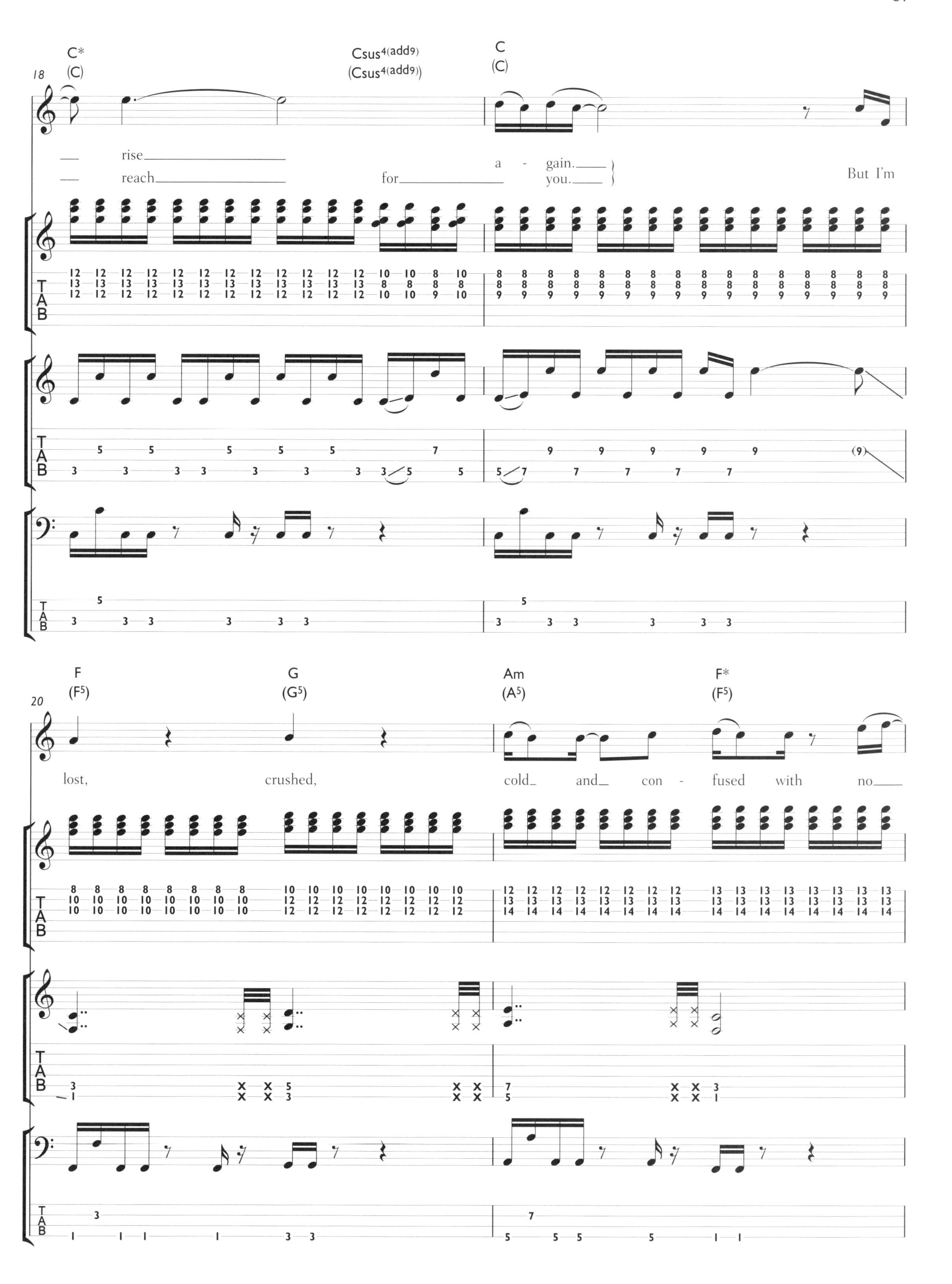
C*
(C)
Csus4(add9)
(Csus4(add9))
C
(C)
— rise
— reach
for
a - gain.
you.
But I'm
F
(F5)
G
(G5)
Am
(A5)
F*
(F5)
lost, crushed, cold and con - fused with no

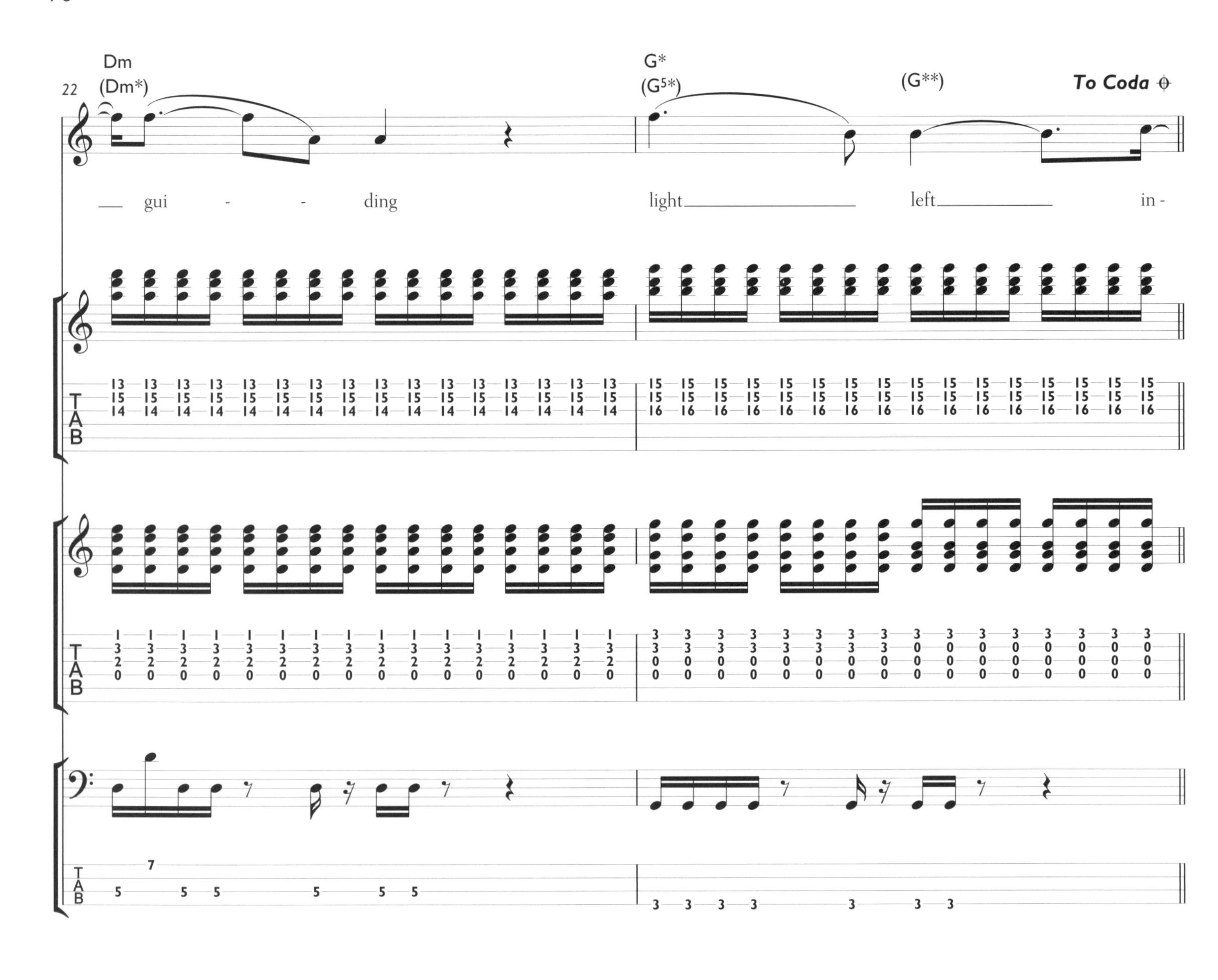
Dm
(Dm*)
22
guiding
G*
(G5*)
light
(G**)
left
in-
To Coda

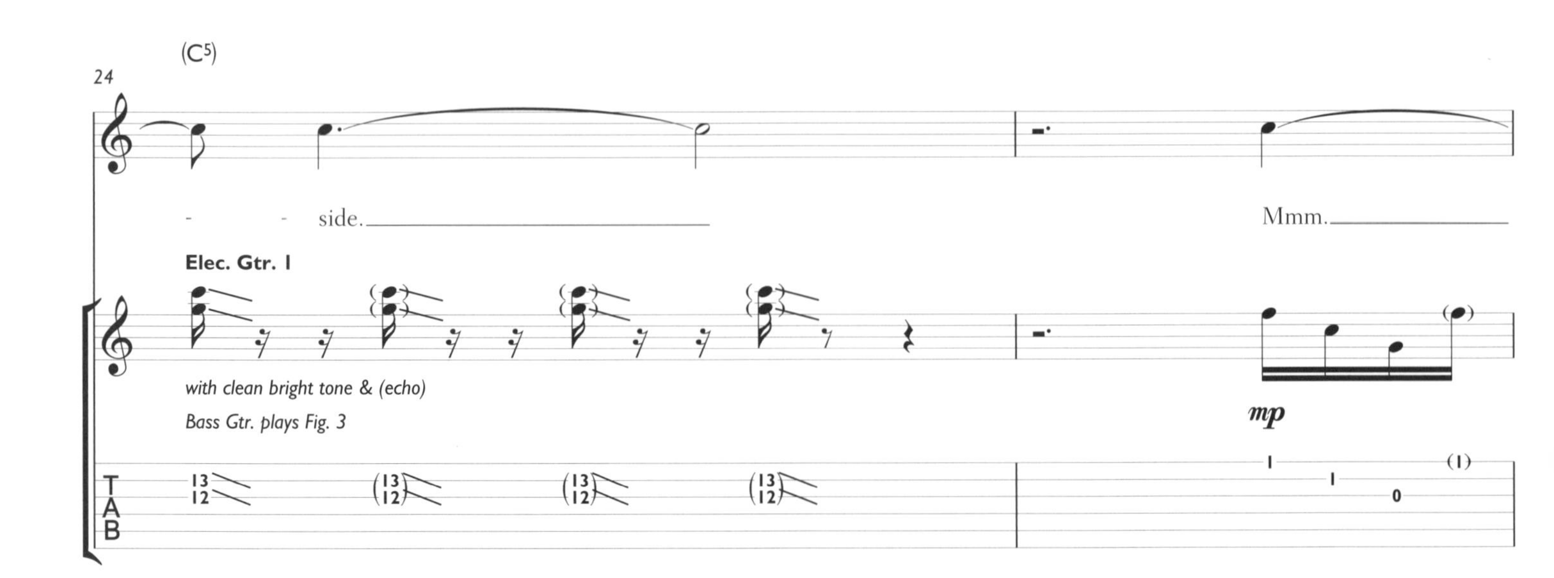
(C5)
24
side.
Mmm.
Elec. Gtr. 1
with clean bright tone & (echo)
Bass Gtr. plays Fig. 3
mp

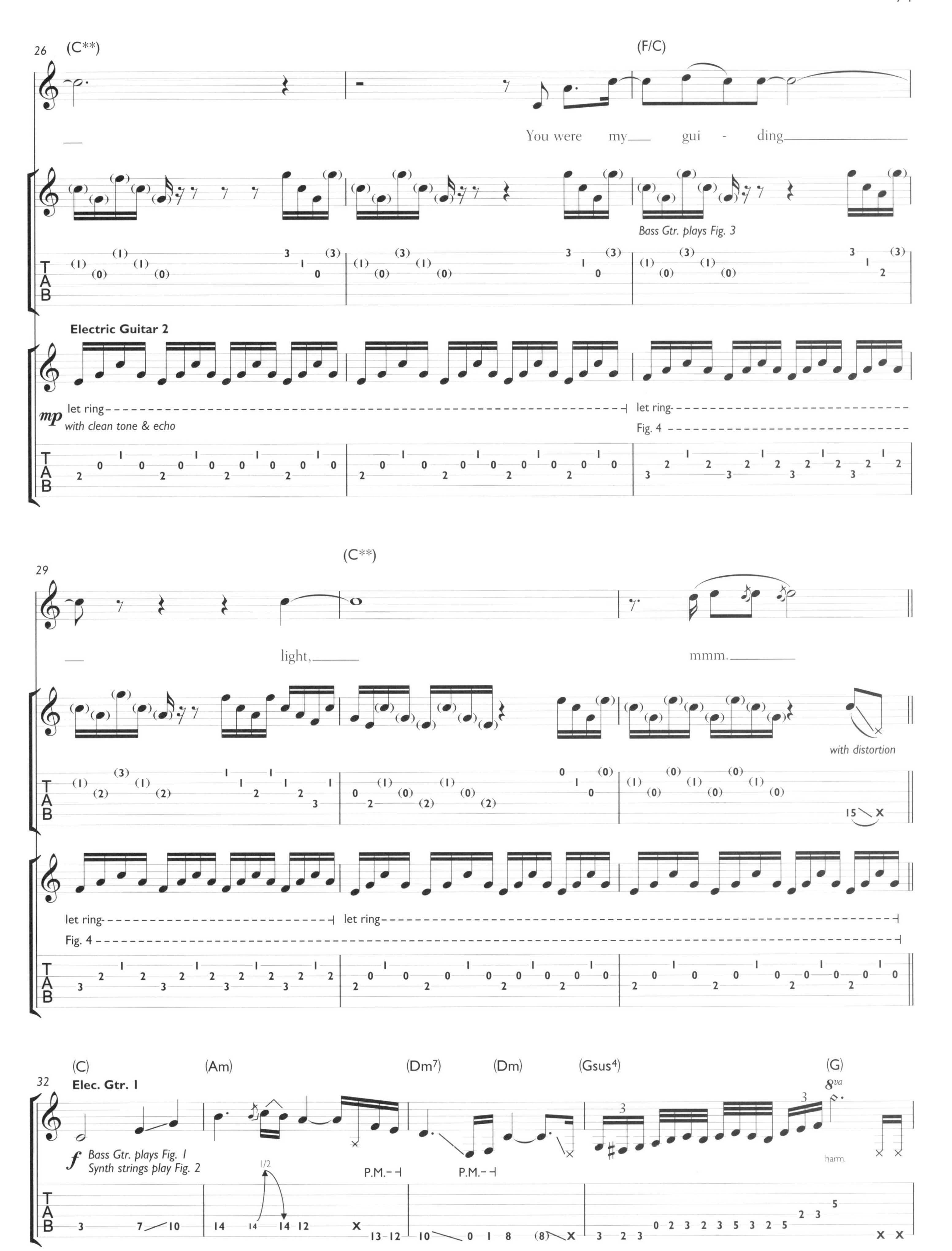
26
(C**)
(F/C)
You were my guiding
Bass Gtr. plays Fig. 3
Electric Guitar 2
let ring
mp
with clean tone & echo
Fig. 4
29
(C**)
light,
mmm.
with distortion
let ring
Fig. 4
(C)
(Am)
(Dm7)
(Dm)
(Gsus4)
(G)
32
Elec. Gtr. 1
f
Bass Gtr. plays Fig. 1
Synth strings play Fig. 2
P.M.
harm.
8va

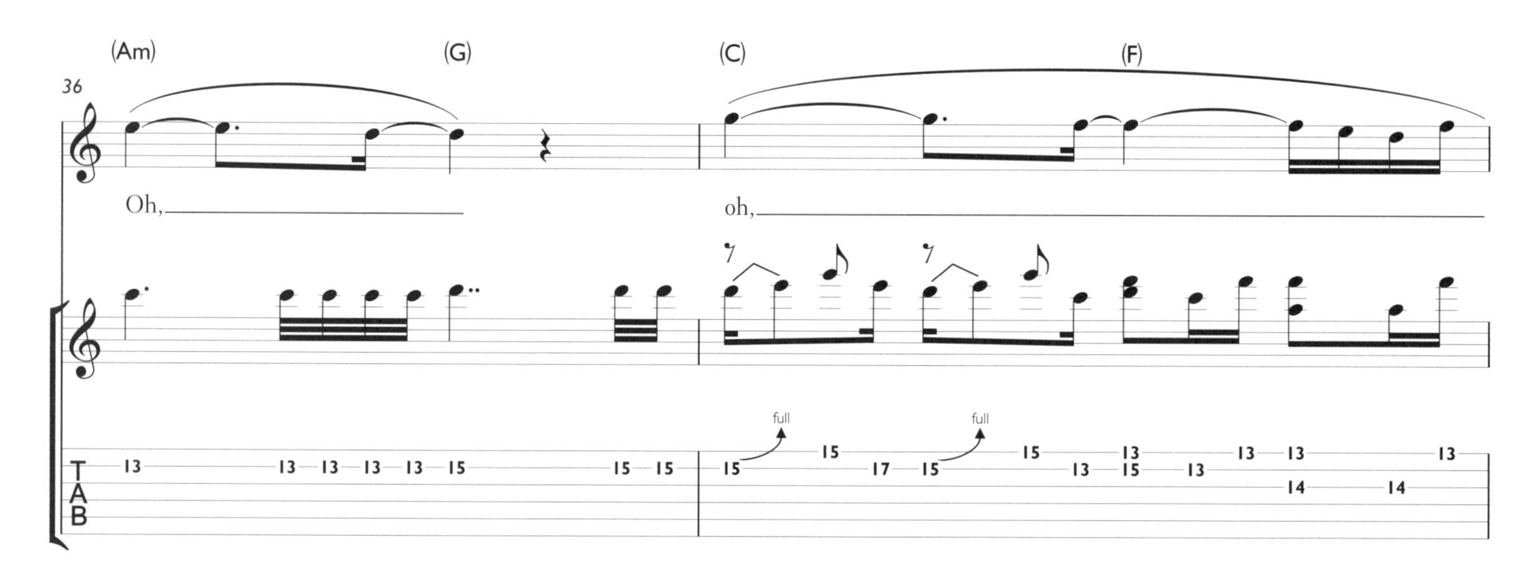
(Am)
(G)
(C)
(F)
36
Oh,
oh,
full
full

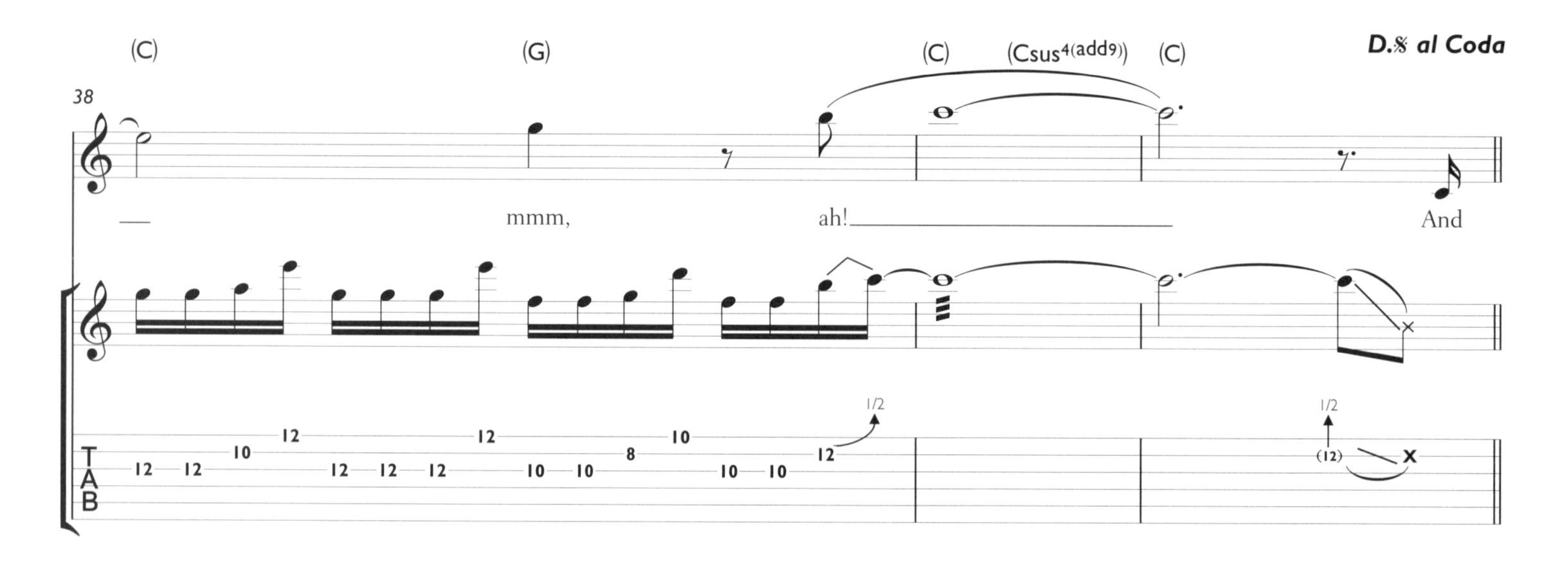
(C)
(G)
(C)
(Csus4(add9))
(C)
D.𝄋 al Coda
38
mmm,
ah!
And
1/2
1/2

Coda

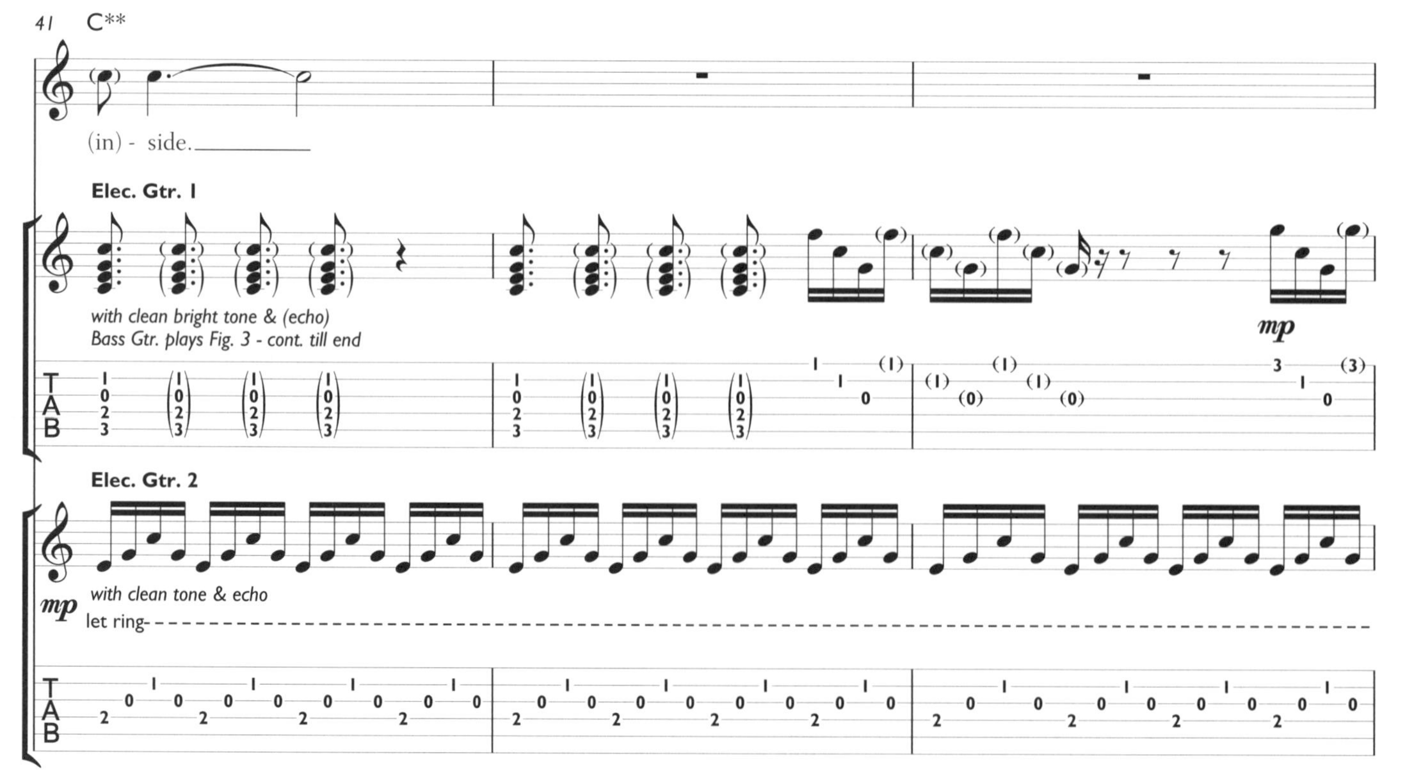
41
C**
(in) - side.
Elec. Gtr. 1
with clean bright tone & (echo)
Bass Gtr. plays Fig. 3 - cont. till end
mp
Elec. Gtr. 2
mp
with clean tone & echo
let ring

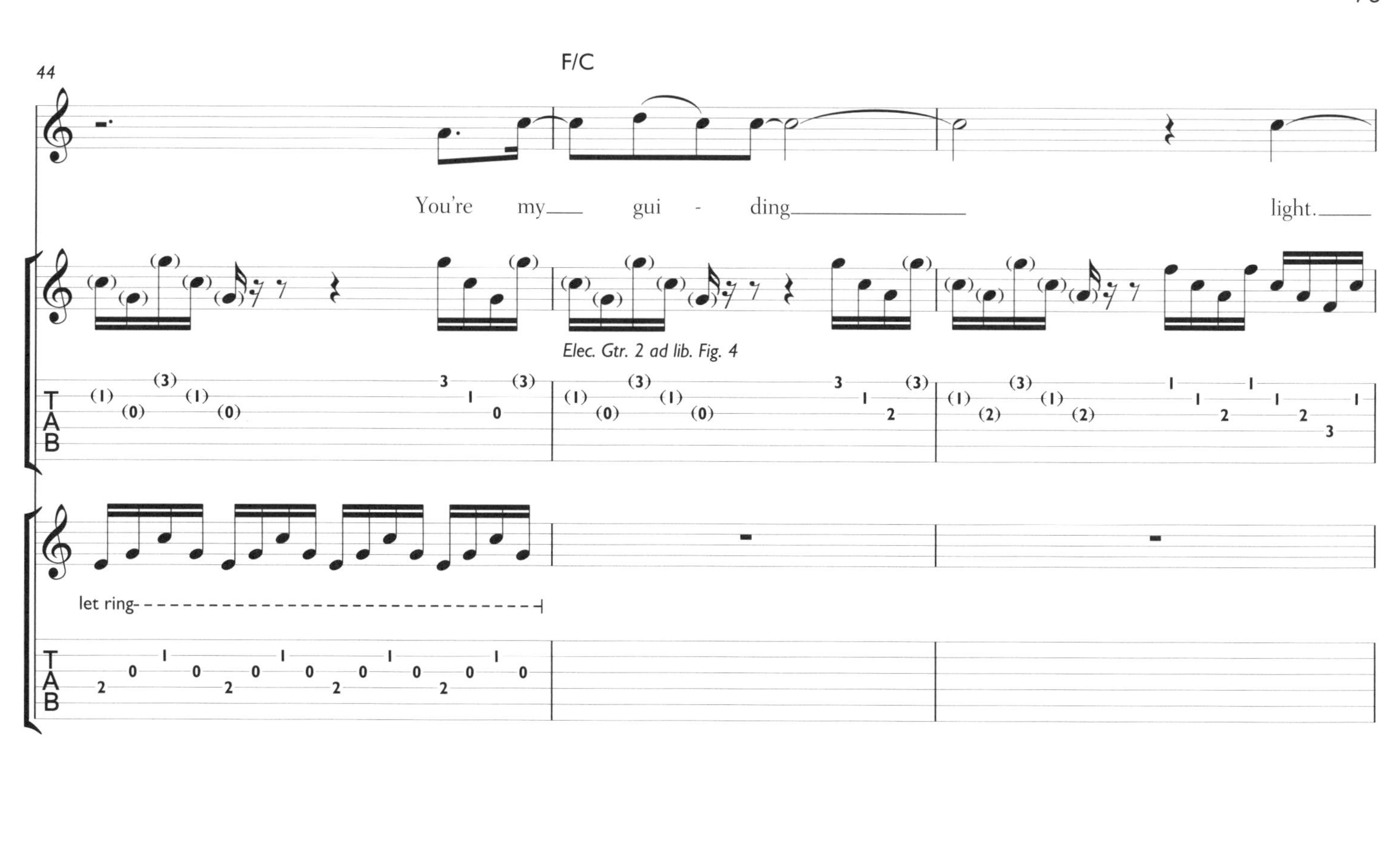
44
F/C
You're my guiding light.
Elec. Gtr. 2 ad lib. Fig. 4
let ring

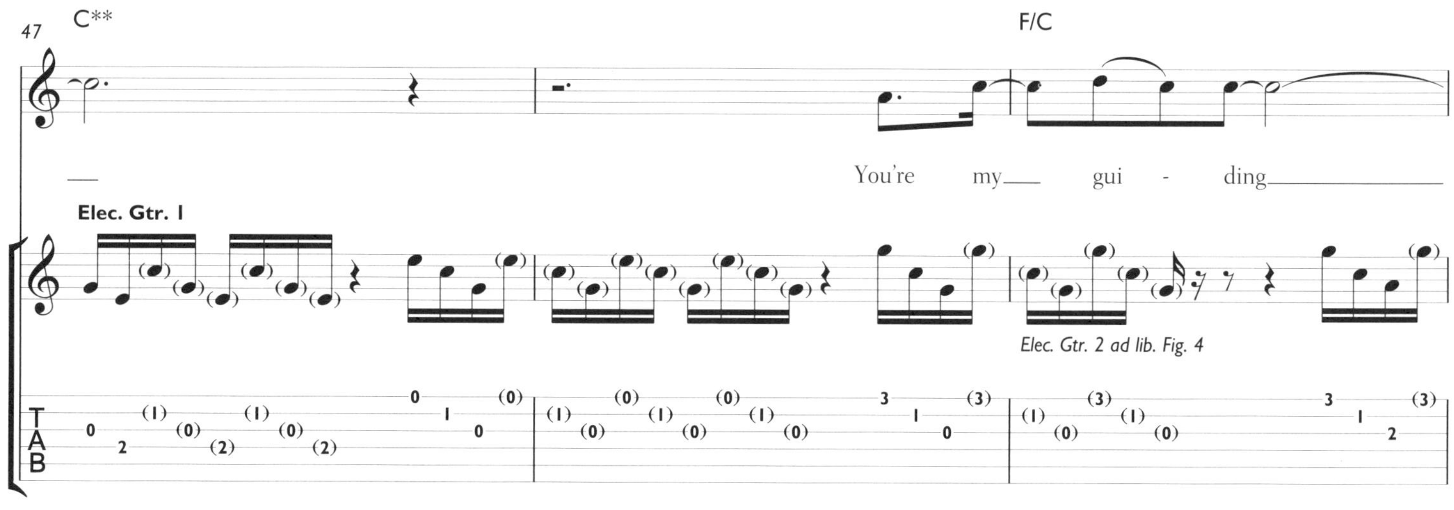
47
C**
F/C
You're my guiding
Elec. Gtr. 1
Elec. Gtr. 2 ad lib. Fig. 4

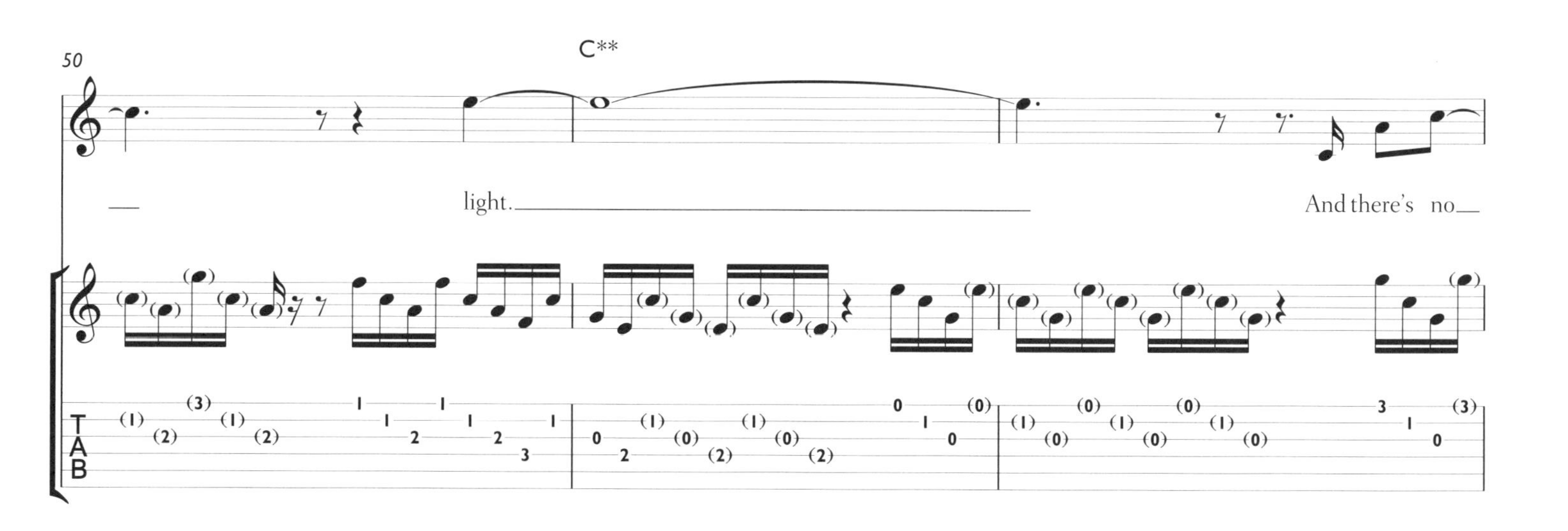
50
C**
light.
And there's no

F/C
Fm/C
C**
53
guiding
light left in - side.
Elec. Gtr. 1
Elec. Gtr. 2
let ring
Fig. 5
56
F/C
And there's no guiding
Elec. Gtr. 2 ad lib. Fig. 5
58
Fm/C
C**
light in our lives.
Elec. Gtr. 1

HYPER MUSIC

Words and Music by Matthew Bellamy

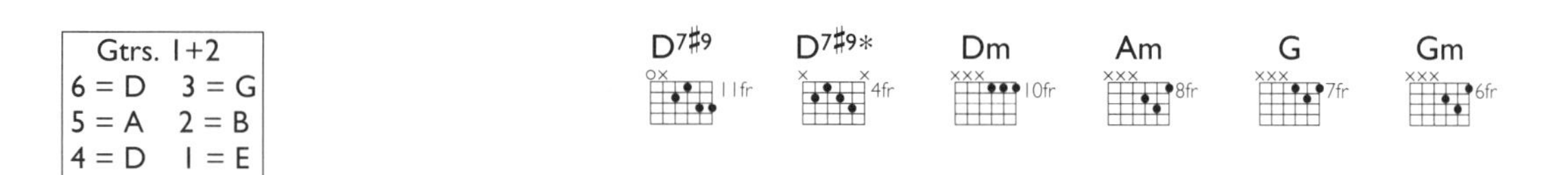

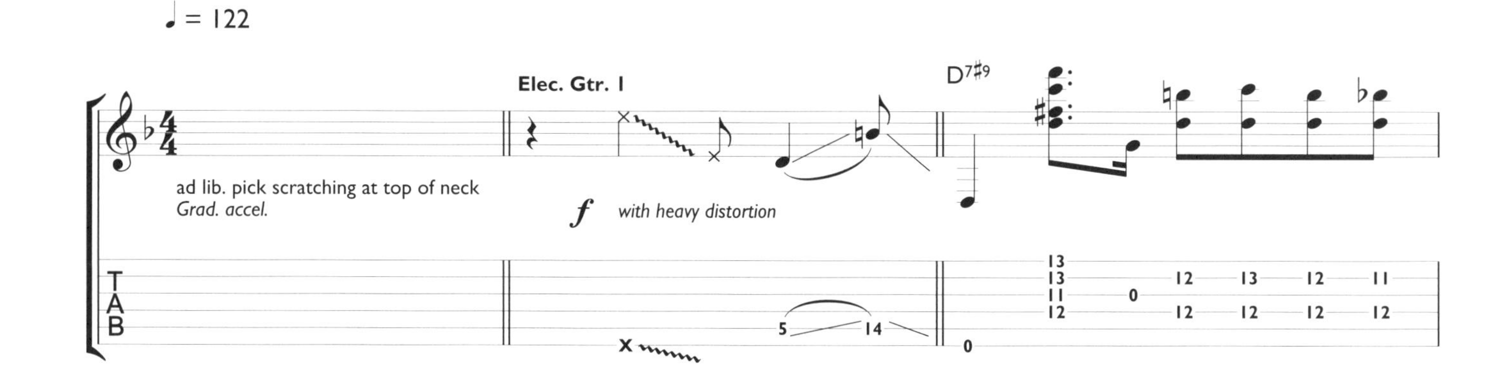

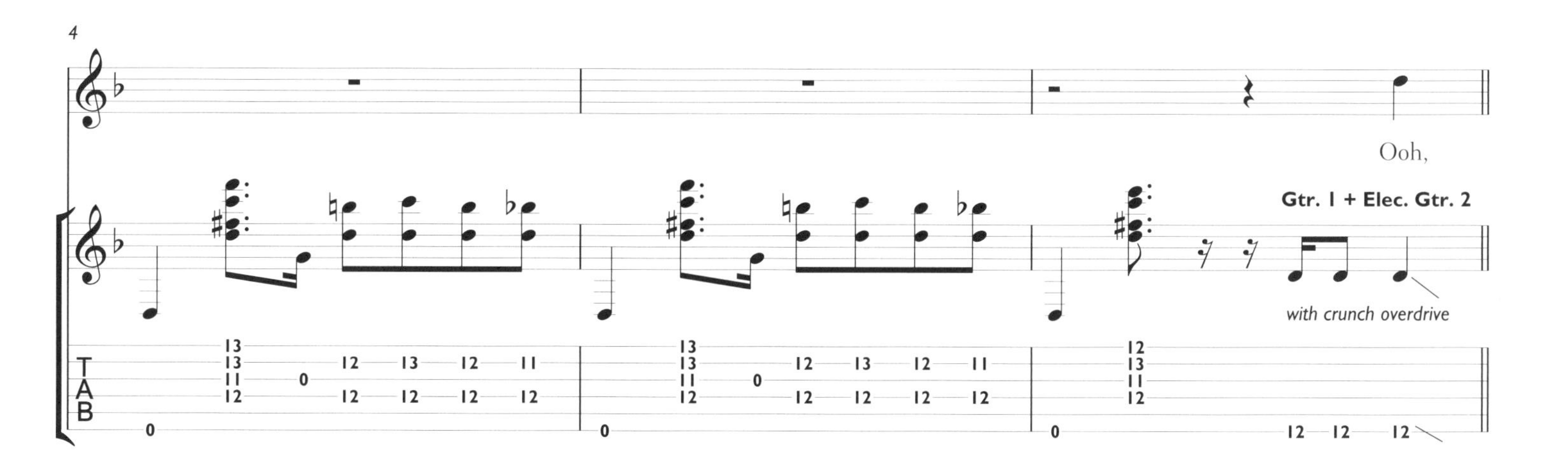

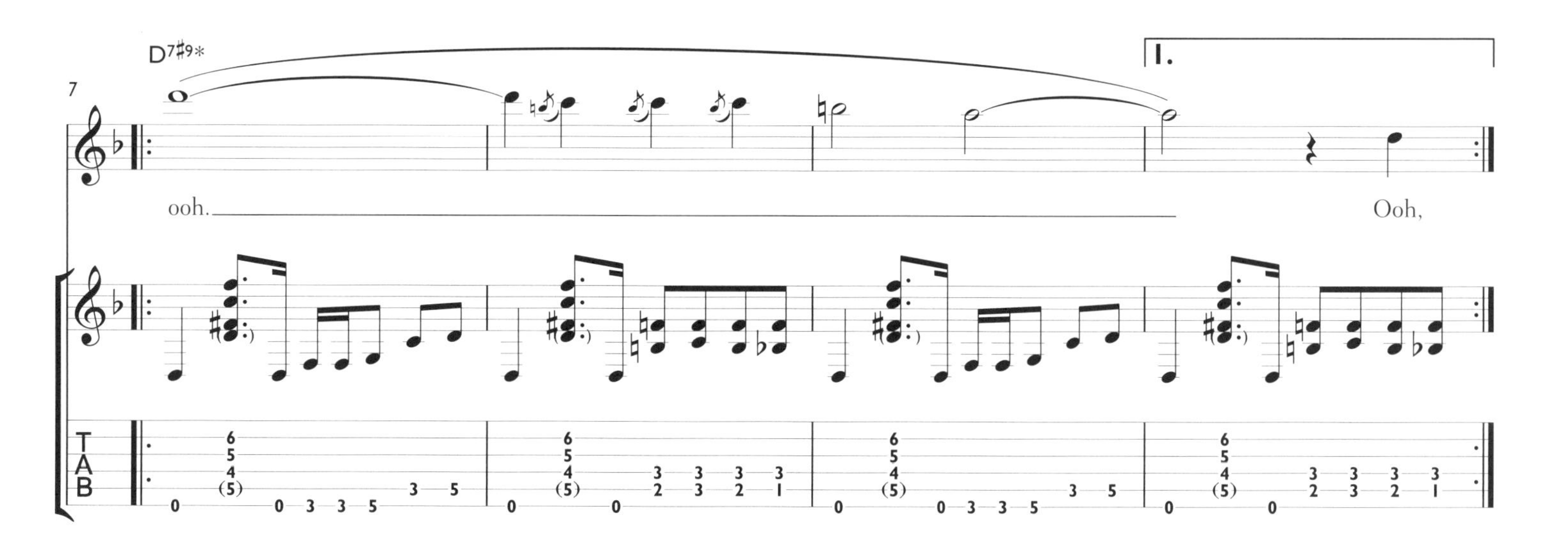

2.
Dm
Gtr. 2
etc.
Mm.
Gtr. 1
Gtr. 2 cont. in slashes
Dm
cont. sim.
Am
G
(Vocal ad lib. on repeat)
Fuzz bass arr. for gtr.
1.
2.
Dm
cont. sim.
Gtr. 2
Gm
Gm
1. Your gol - den skies
(2.)
2° Gtr. 2 plays harmonics with selector switch + whammy pedal
Am
G
Gm
feed my role
than I was worth
in this for - got - ten space
and you think I was scared

Dm
Am
G
Gm
race
un - der my con - trol.
Who's
yeah,
and you need - ed
proof.
Who
Dm
Am
G
re - turned
from the dead?
real-ly cares
a - ny - more?
2° Gtr. 2
Gm
Dm
Am
G
Who
re - mains
Who
re - strains
TAB

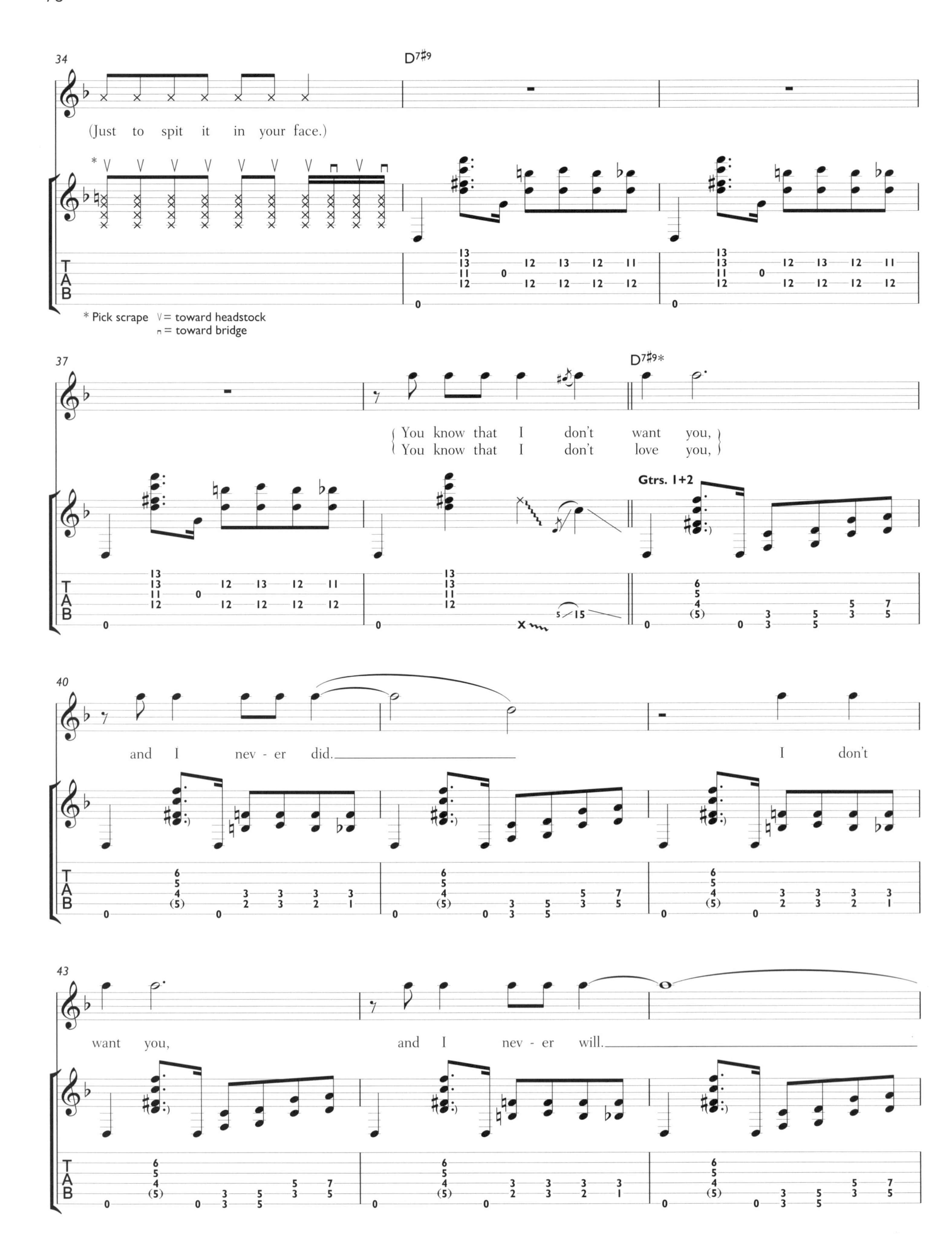

34
D7#9
(Just to spit it in your face.)
* Pick scrape V = toward headstock
⊓ = toward bridge
37
D7#9*
You know that I don't want you,
You know that I don't love you,
Gtrs. 1+2
40
and I nev - er did.
I don't
43
want you,
and I nev - er will.

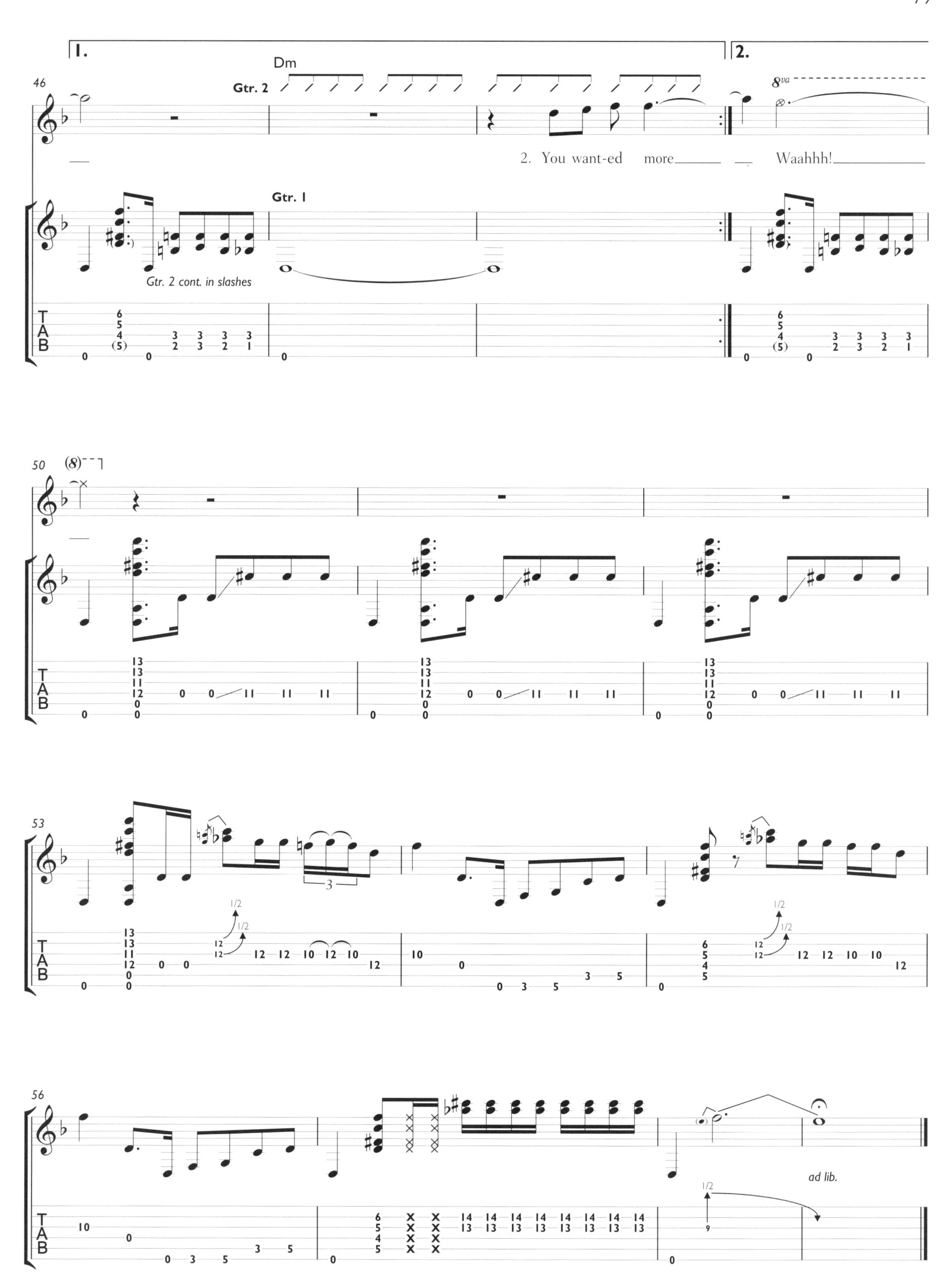
1.
2.
Dm
Gtr. 2
8va
2. You want-ed more
Waahhh!
Gtr. 1
Gtr. 2 cont. in slashes
(8)
ad lib.

HYPER CHONDRIAC MUSIC

Words and Music by Matthew Bellamy

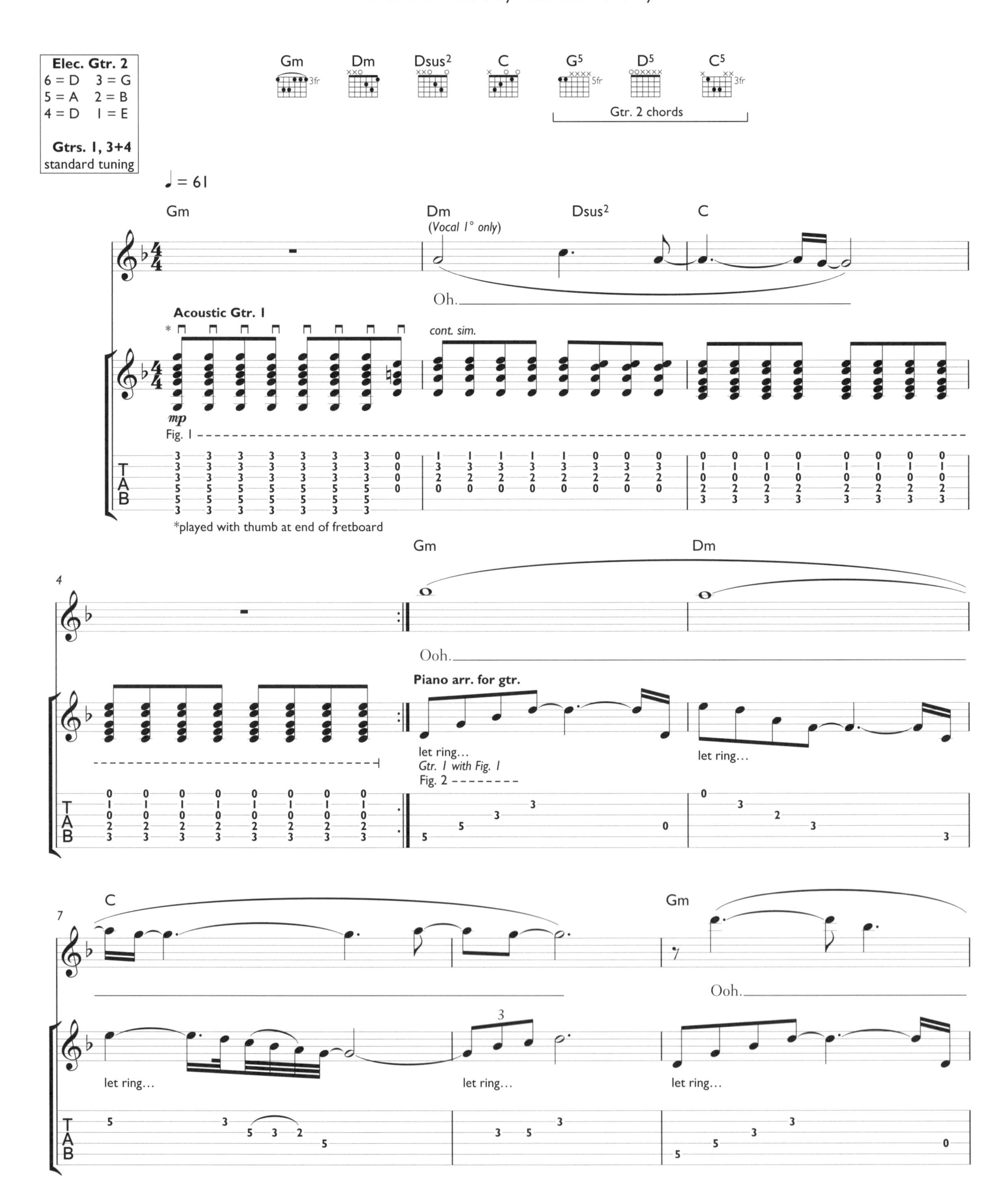

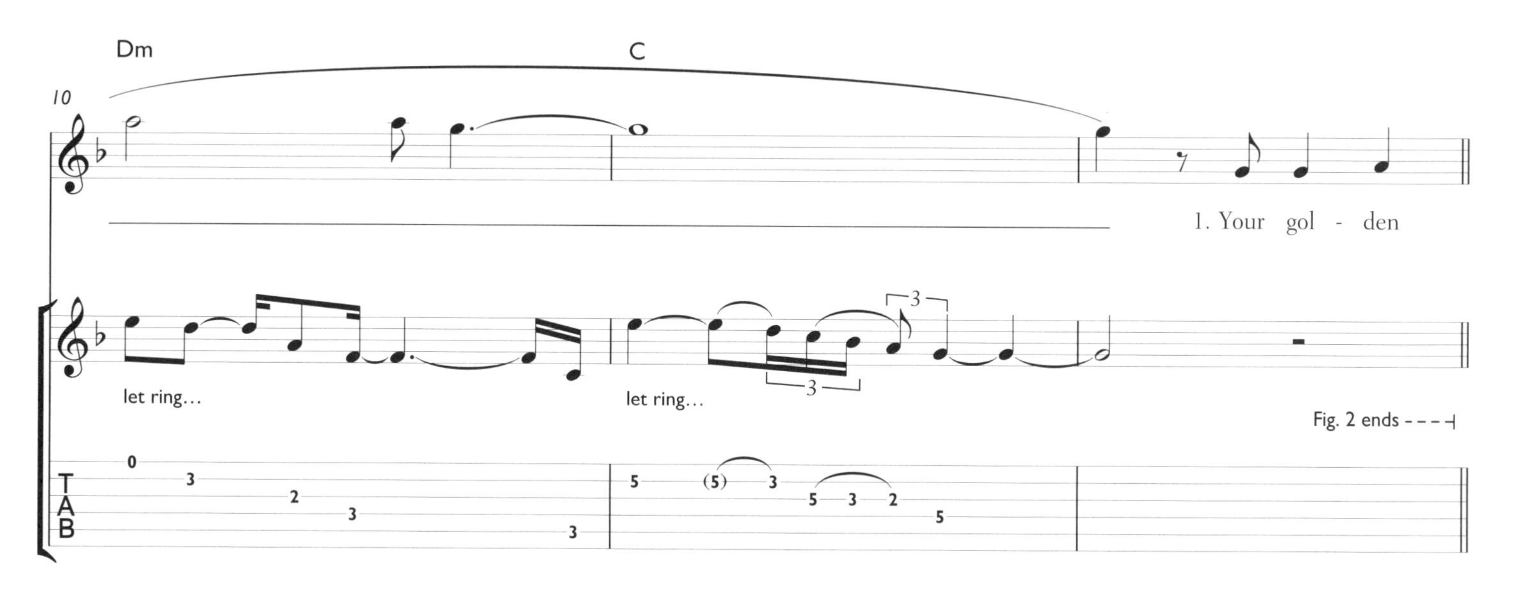
Dm
C
10
1. Your gol - den
let ring…
let ring…
Fig. 2 ends
T
A
B

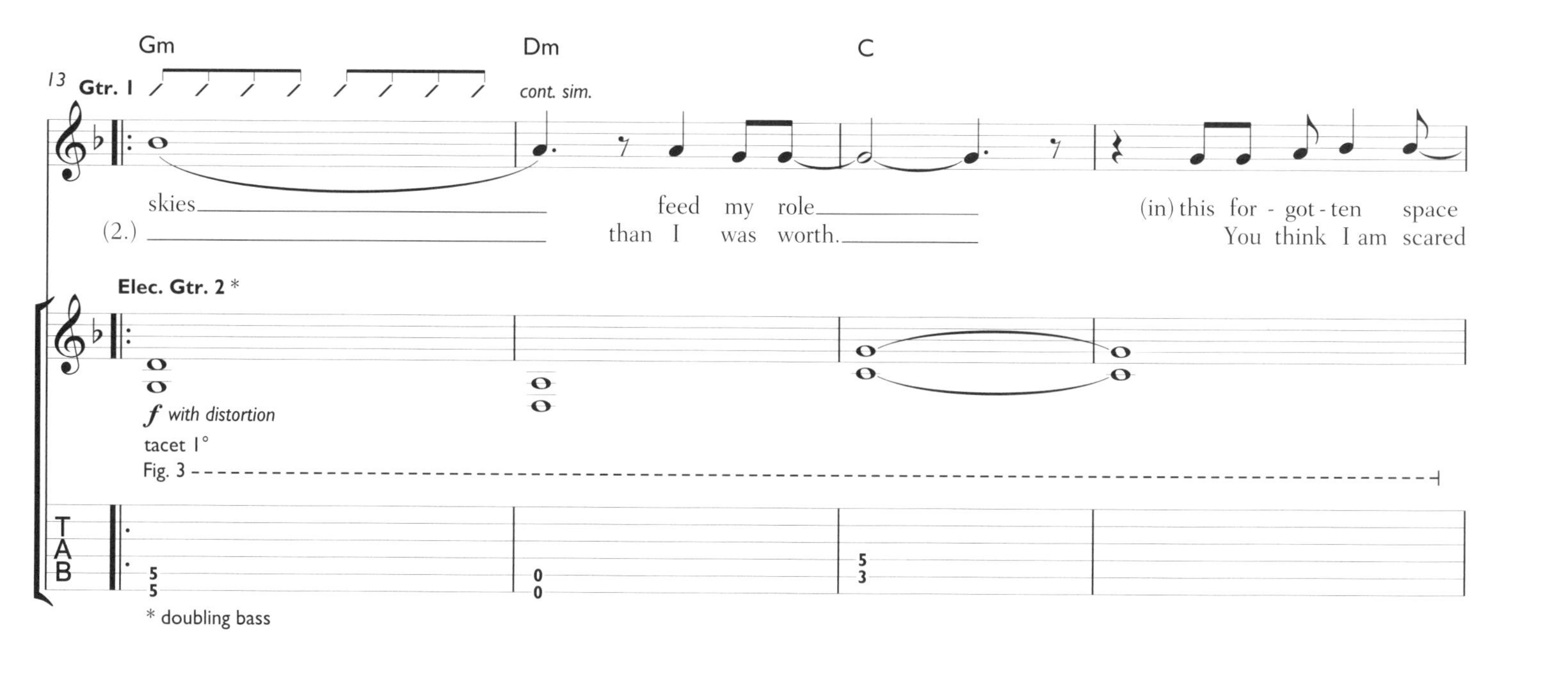
Gm
Dm
C
13
Gtr. 1
cont. sim.
skies feed my role (in) this for - got - ten space
(2.) than I was worth. You think I am scared
Elec. Gtr. 2 *
f with distortion
tacet 1°
Fig. 3
T
A
B
* doubling bass

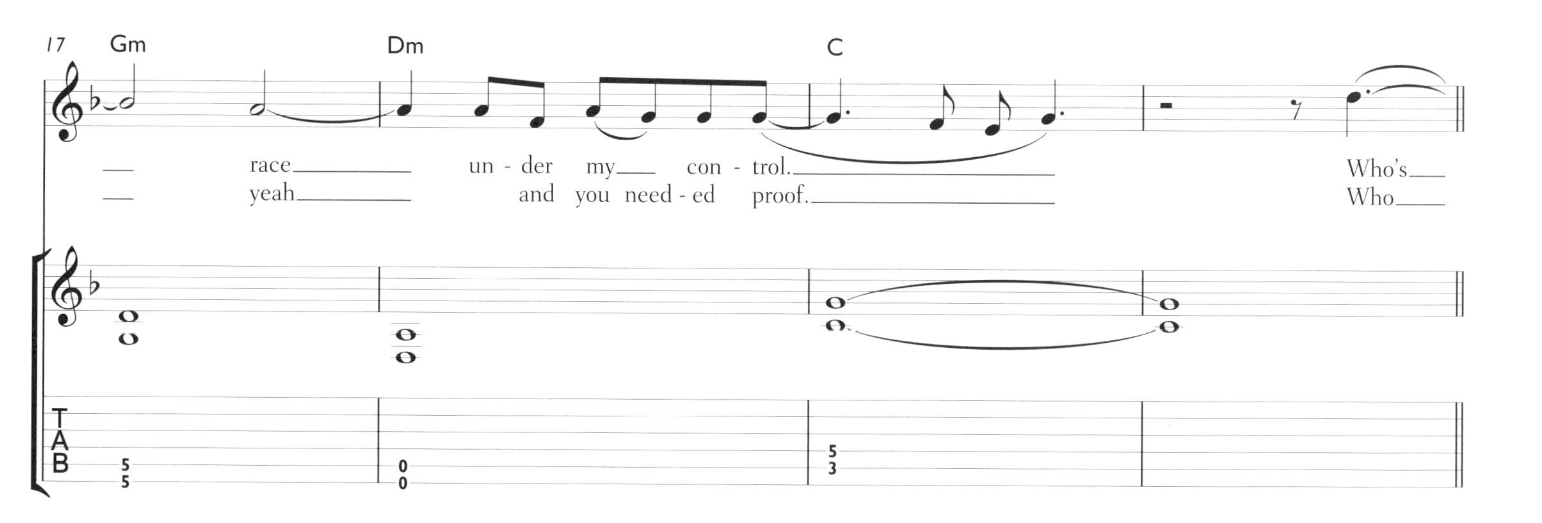
17
Gm
Dm
C
race un - der my con - trol. Who's
yeah and you need - ed proof. Who
T
A
B

Gm
Dm
C
re - turned from the dead?
real - ly cares a - ny - more?
Pno. with Fig. 2
Who re - mains?
Who re - mains?
1.
2.
2. You want - ed more
Elec. Gtr. 3
with distortion
Gtr. 1 with Fig. 1
Gtr. 2 with Fig. 3
1/2
with bar ad lib.
let ring...

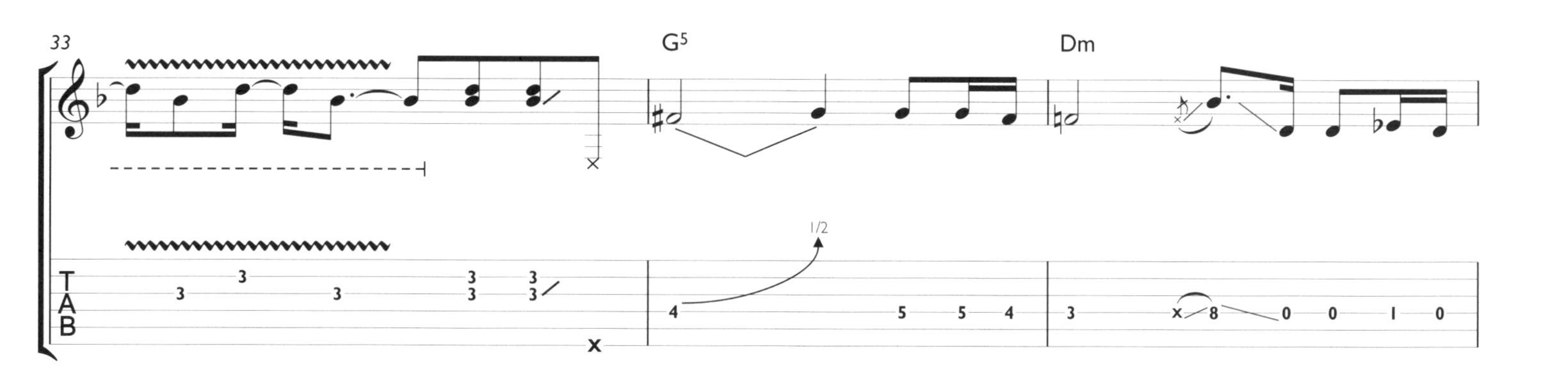
33
G5
Dm
1/2

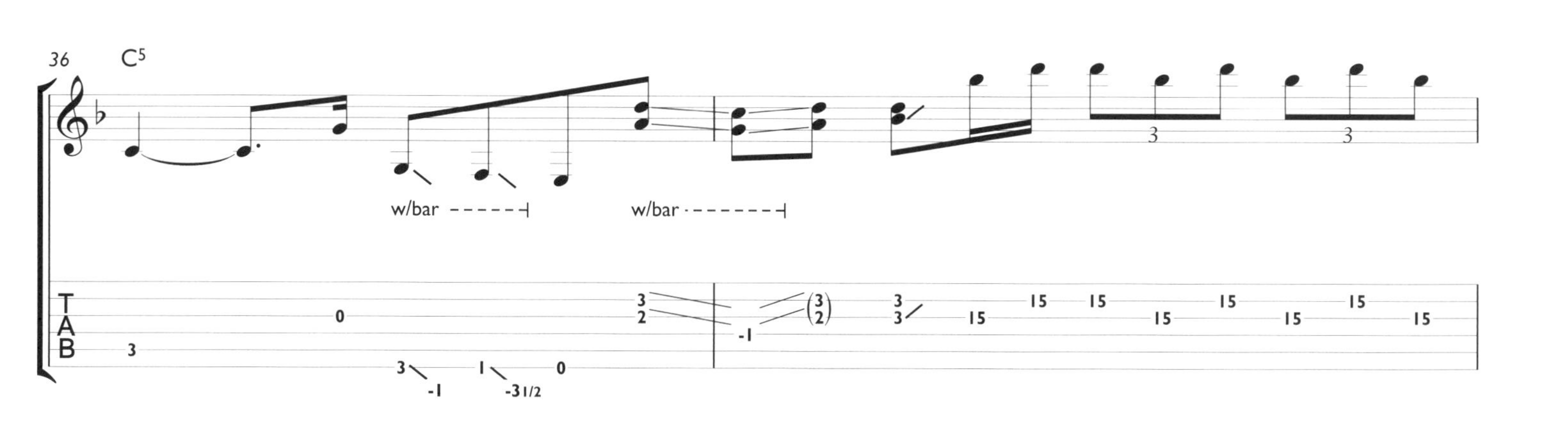
36
C5
w/bar
w/bar

38
G5

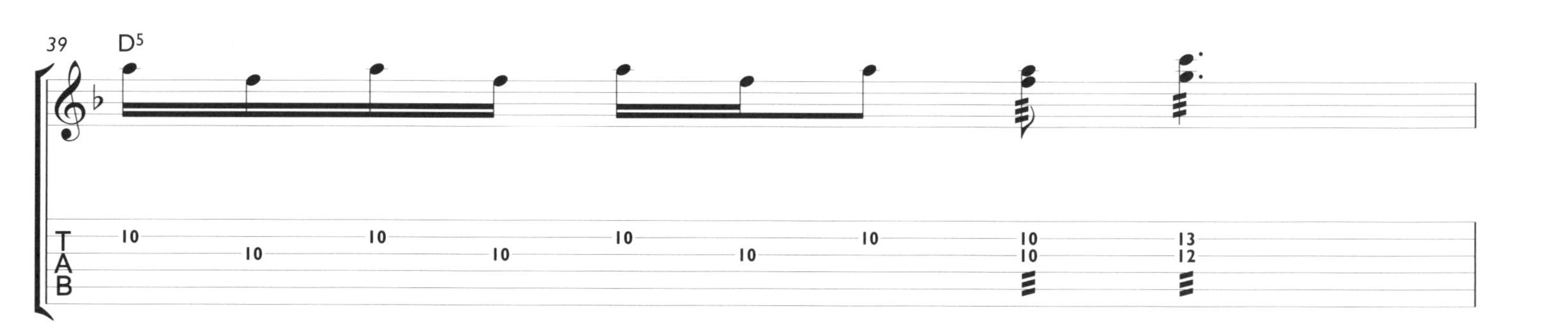
39
D5

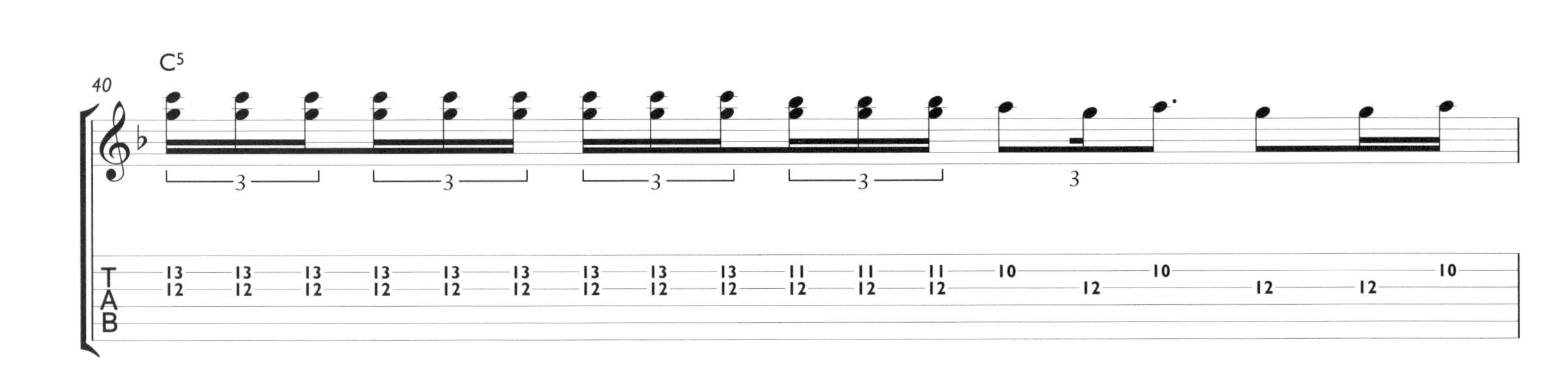
C5
40

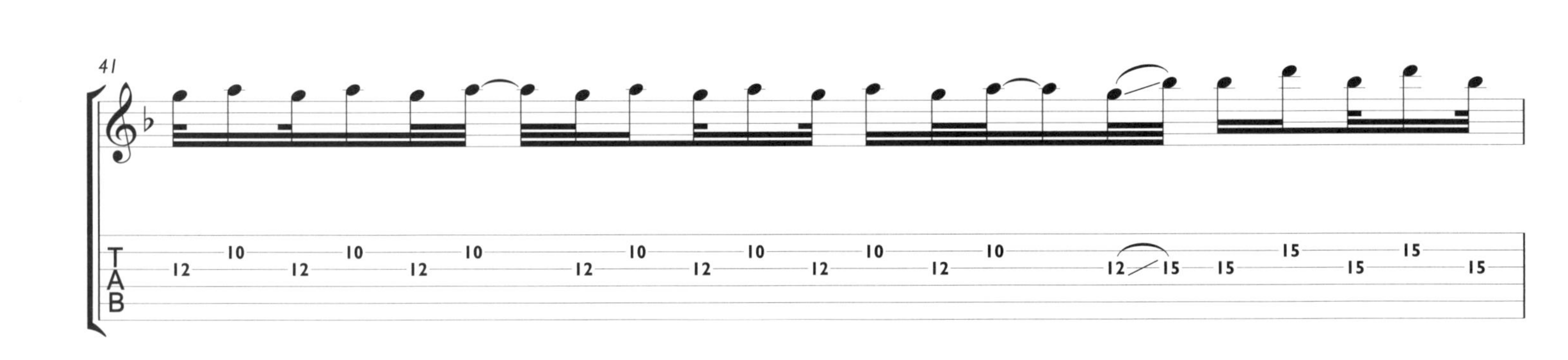
41

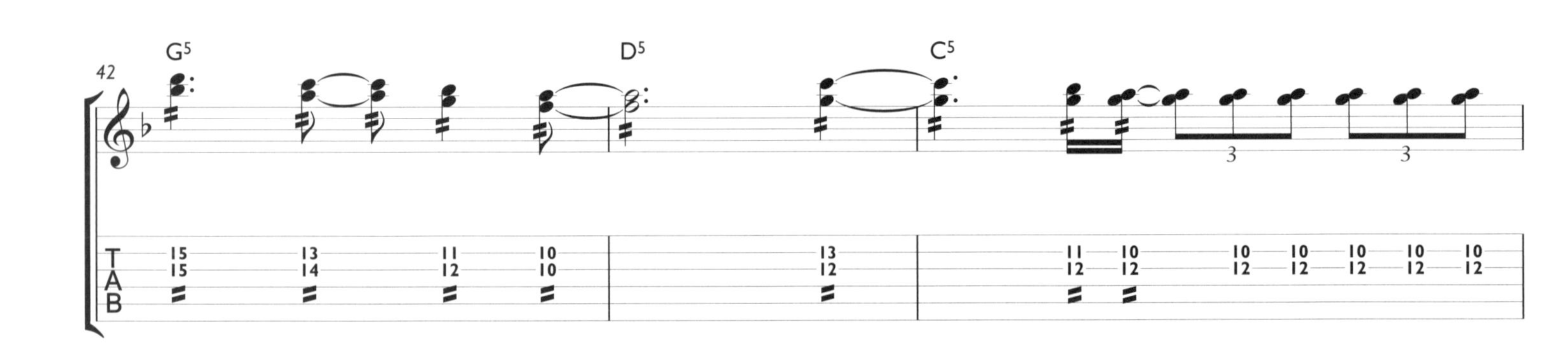
G5
42
D5
C5

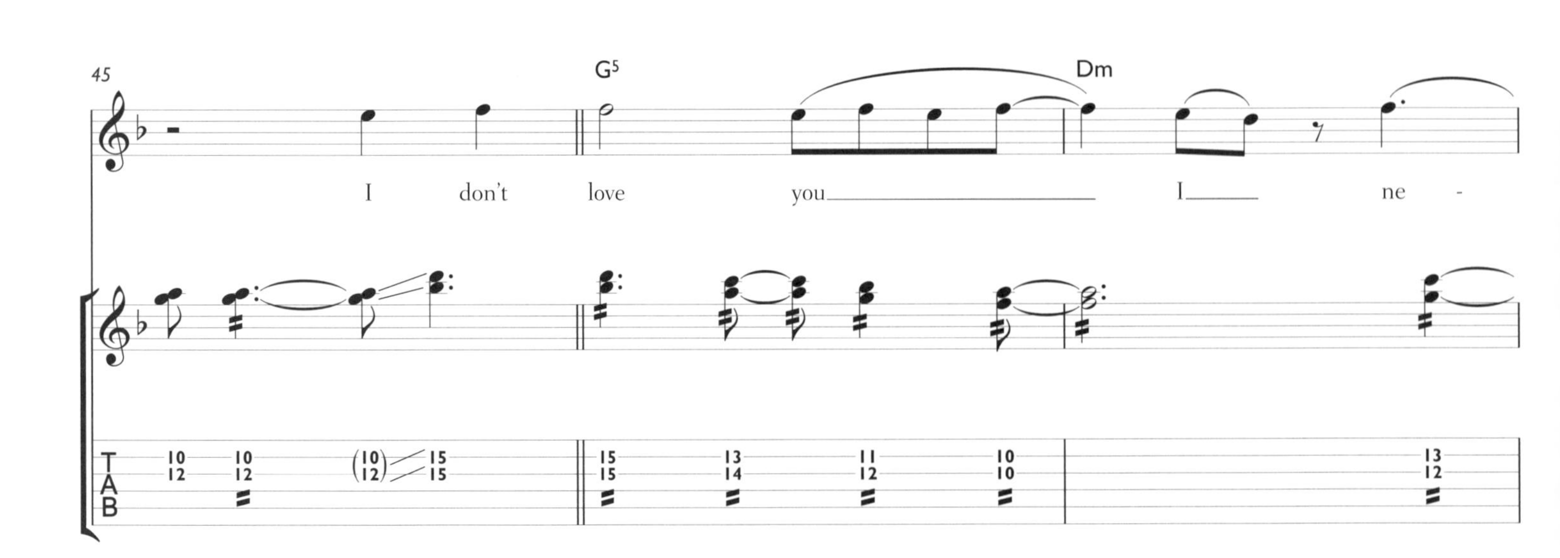
45
G5
Dm
I don't love you I ne -

48
C5
G5
- ver did.
I don't love you

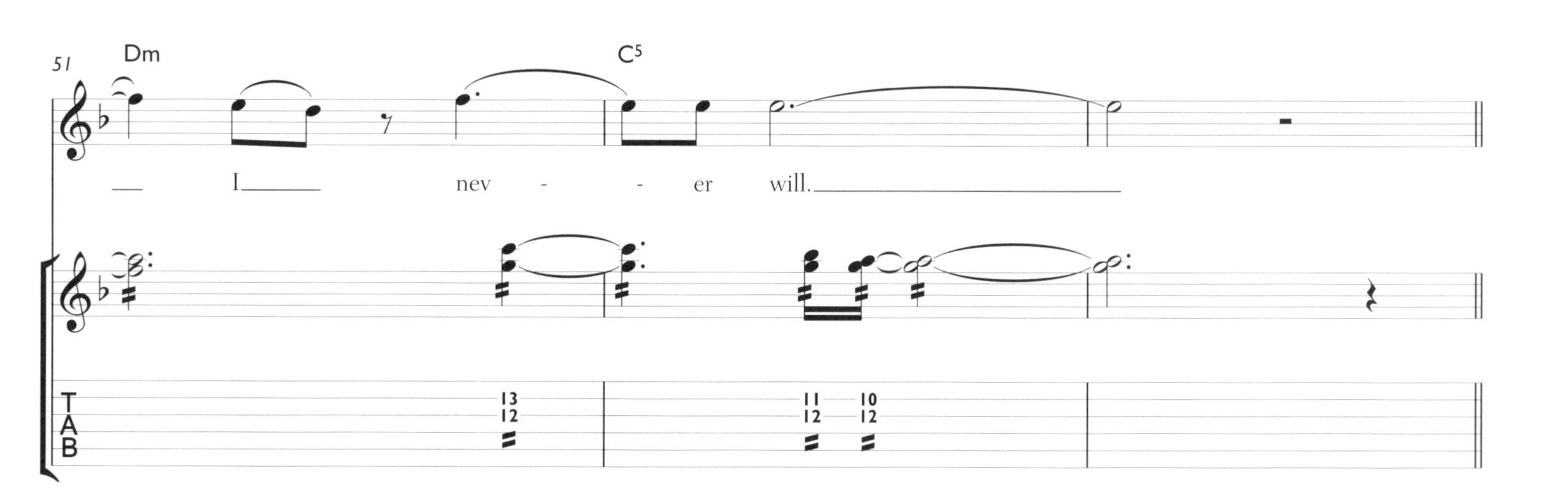
51
Dm
C5
I nev - - er will.

54
Gm
Gtr. 1
Dm
Dsus2
C
cont. sim.
mp
Gtr. 3 tacet

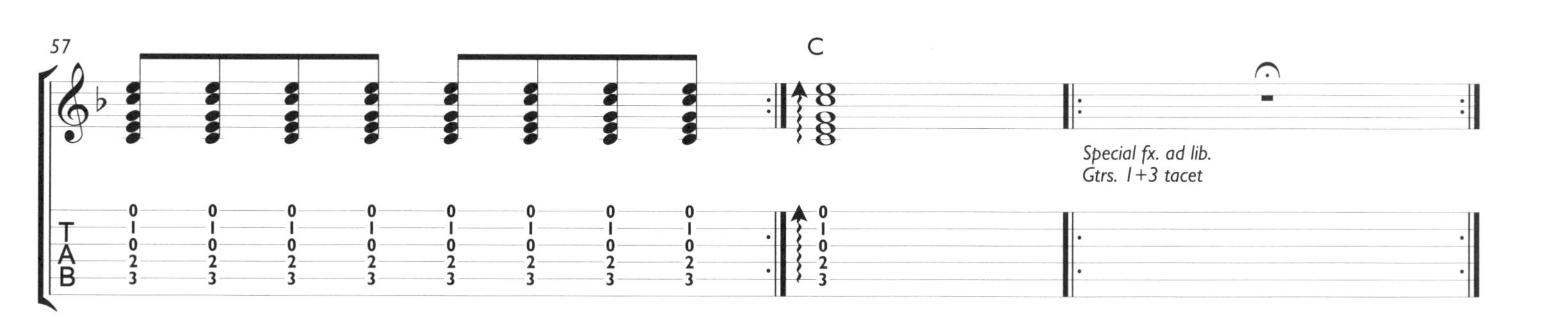
57
C
Special fx. ad lib.
Gtrs. 1+3 tacet

HYSTERIA

Words and Music by Matthew Bellamy

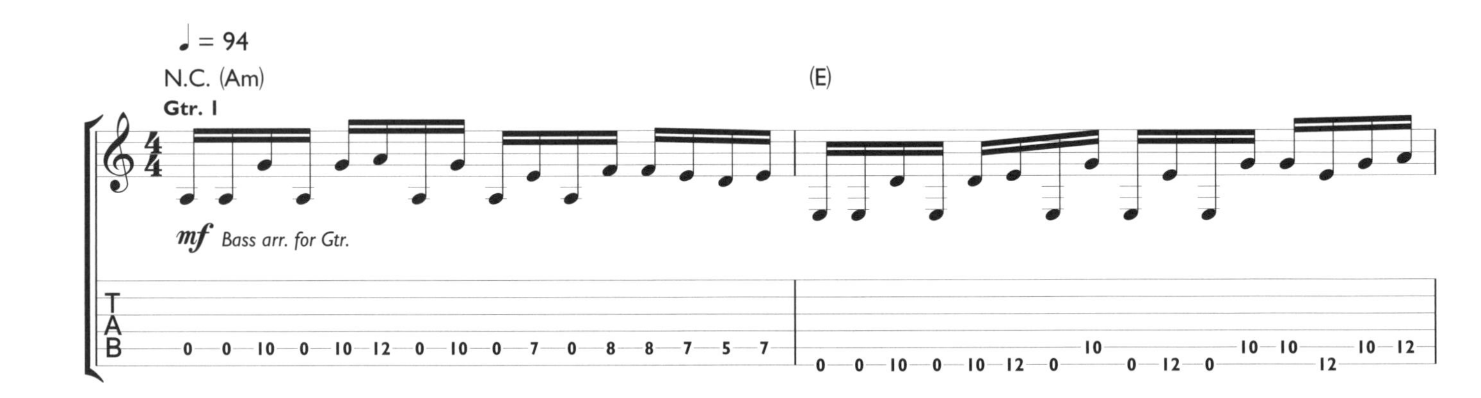

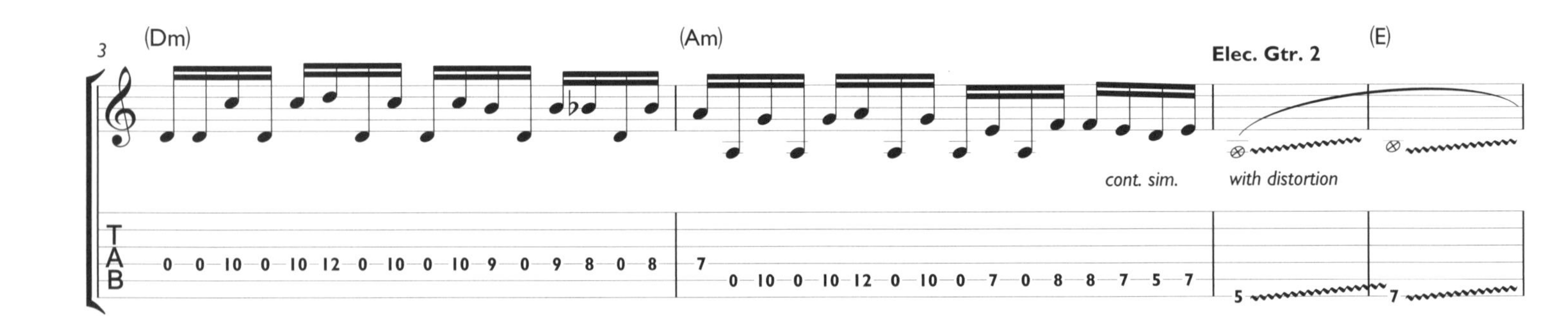

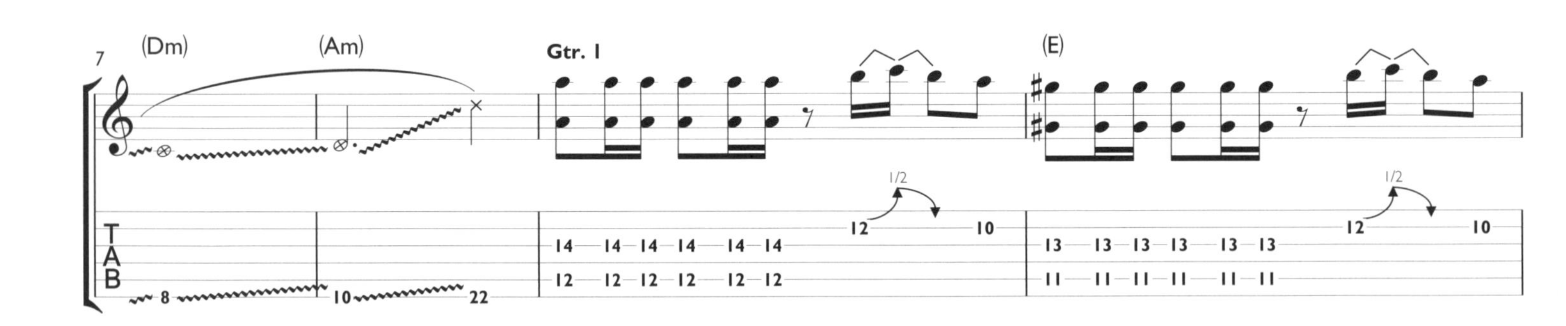

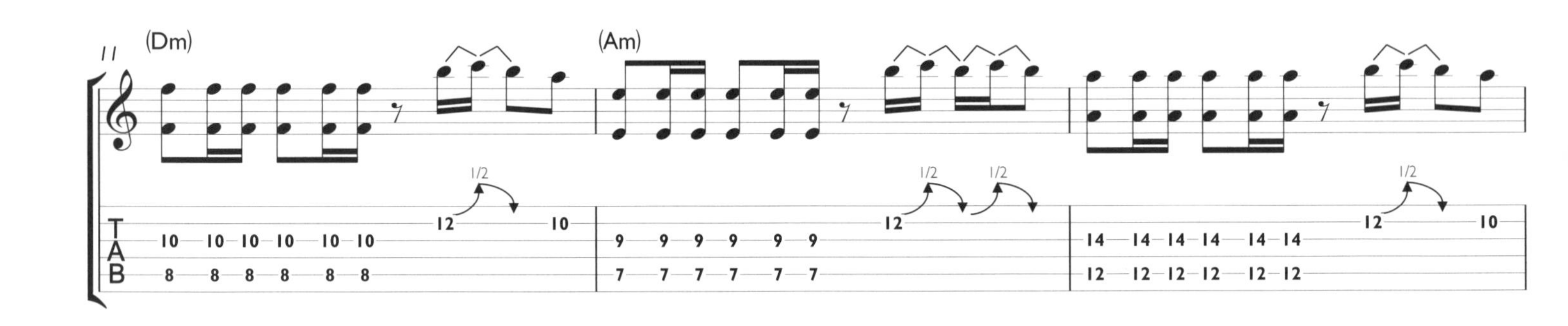

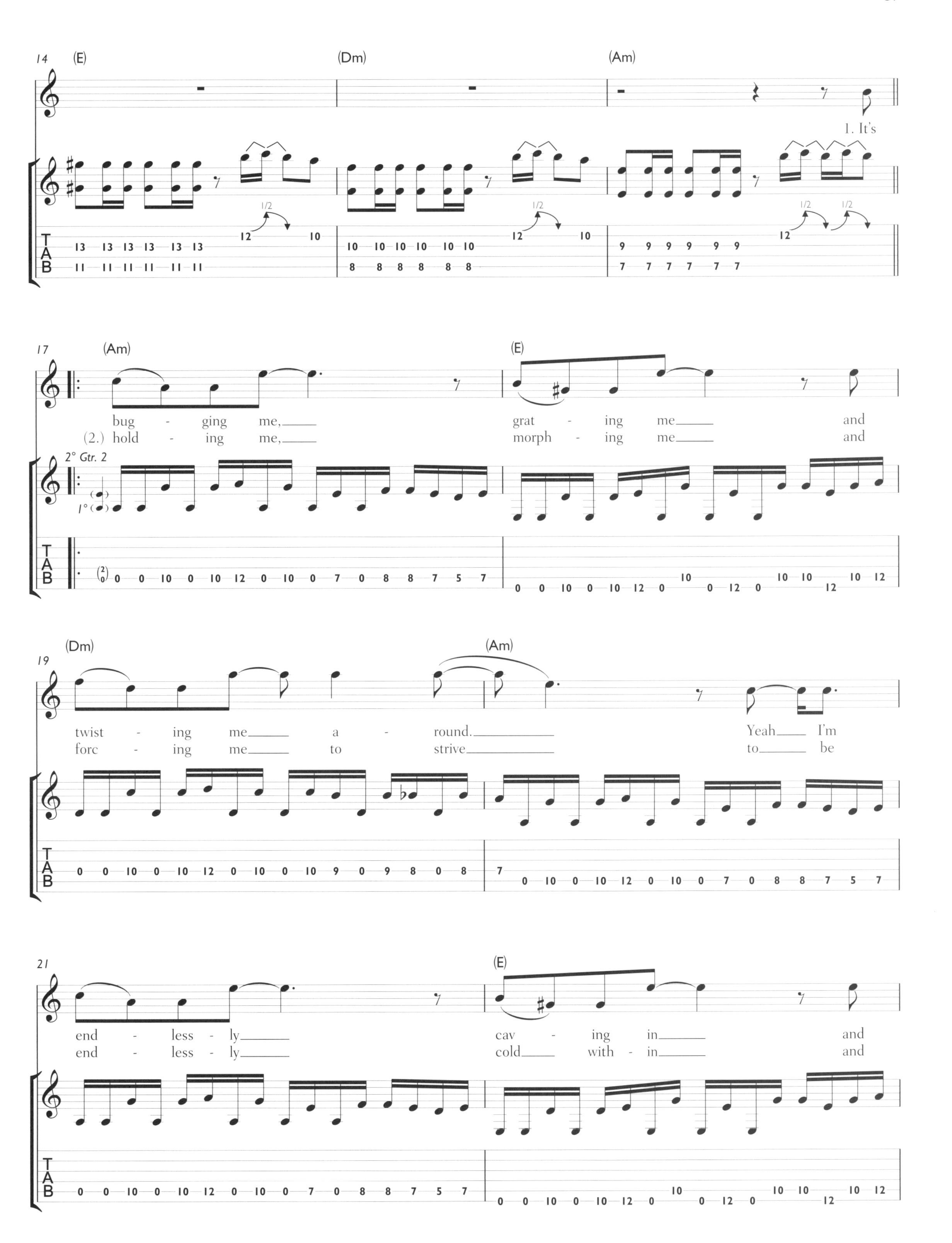
14
(E)
(Dm)
(Am)
1. It's
1/2
17
(Am)
(E)
bug - ging me, grat - ing me and
(2.) hold - ing me, morph - ing me and
2° Gtr. 2
1°
19
(Dm)
(Am)
twist - ing me a - round. Yeah I'm
forc - ing me to strive to be
21
(E)
end - less - ly cav - ing in and
end - less - ly cold with - in and
T
A
B

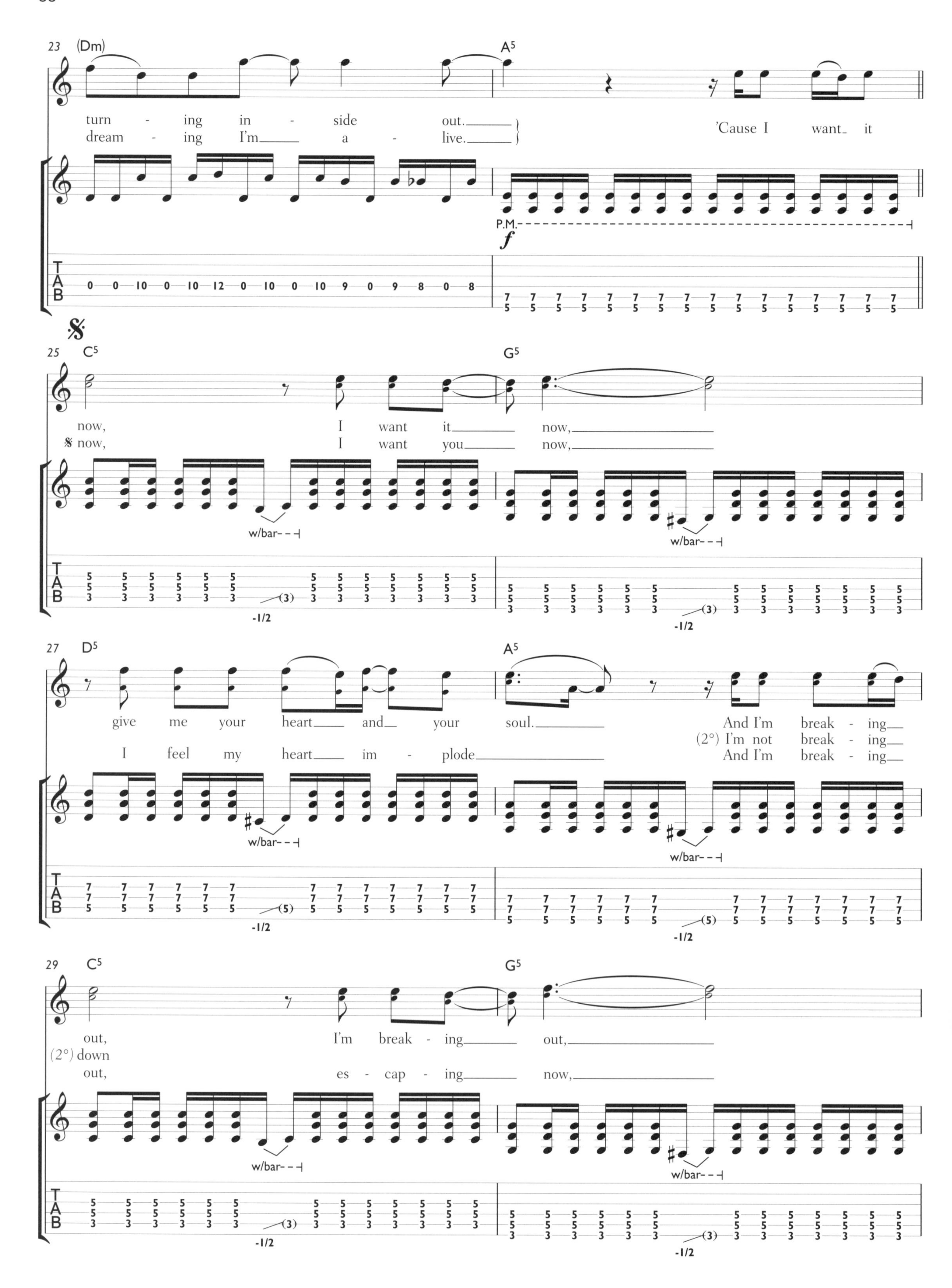
23 (Dm)
A5
turn - ing in - side out.
dream - ing I'm a - live.
'Cause I want it
P.M.
f
25 C5
G5
now, I want it now,
now, I want you now,
w/bar
-1/2
27 D5
A5
give me your heart and your soul.
I feel my heart im - plode
And I'm break - ing
(2°) I'm not break - ing
And I'm break - ing
29 C5
G5
out, I'm break - ing out,
(2°) down
out, es - cap - ing now,

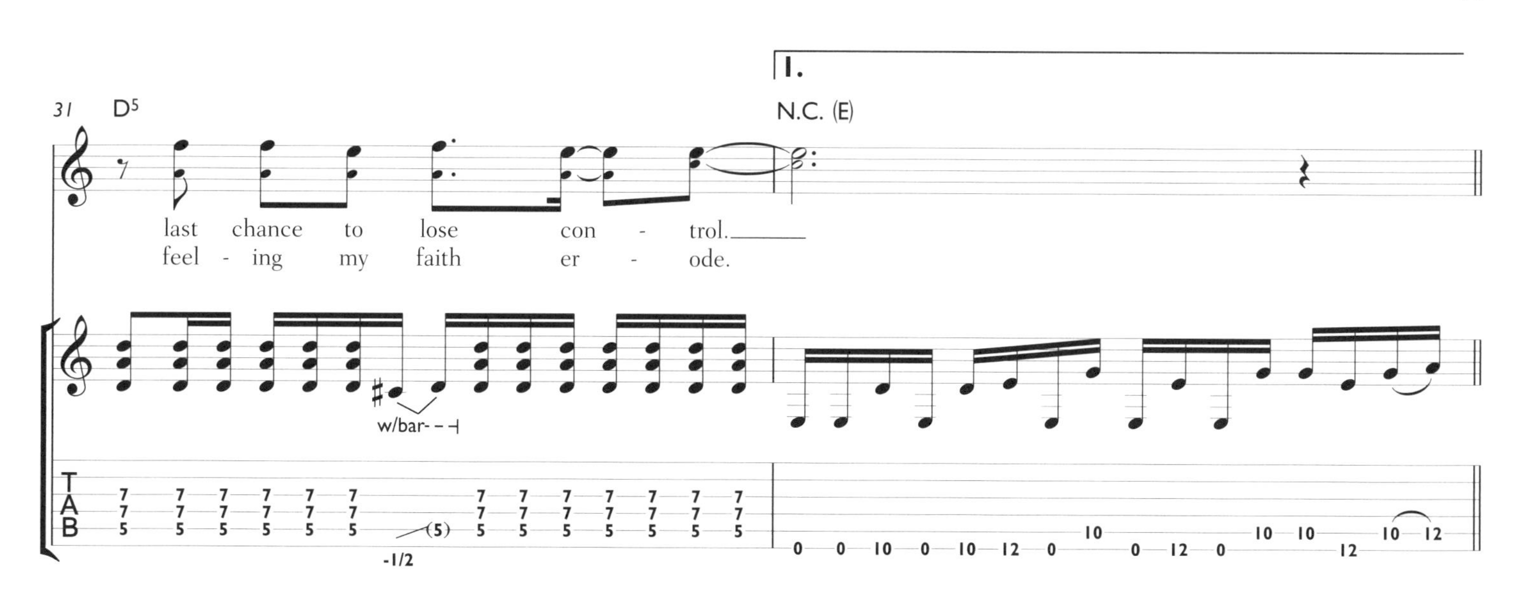
1.
31 D5
N.C. (E)
last chance to lose con - trol.
feel - ing my faith er - ode.
w/bar
-1/2

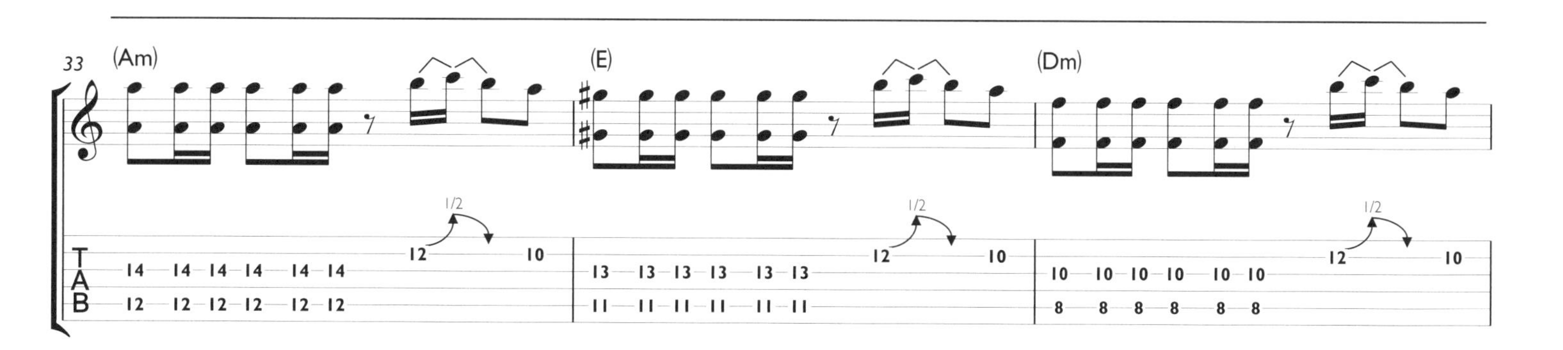
33 (Am)
(E)
(Dm)
1/2

2.3.
36 (Am)
A5
2. Yeah it's
1/2
P.M.

38 N.C. (E)

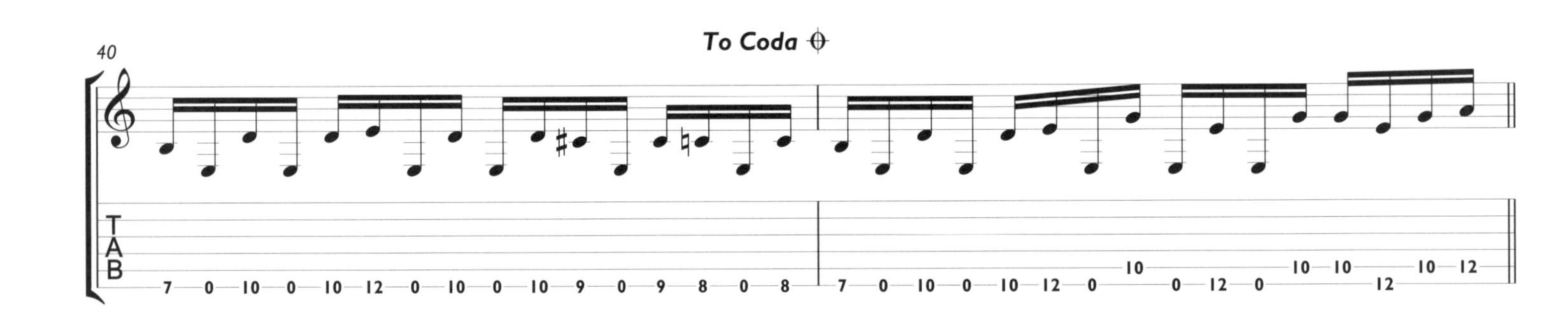
40
To Coda
TAB

N.C. (Am)
(E)
42
8va
TAB

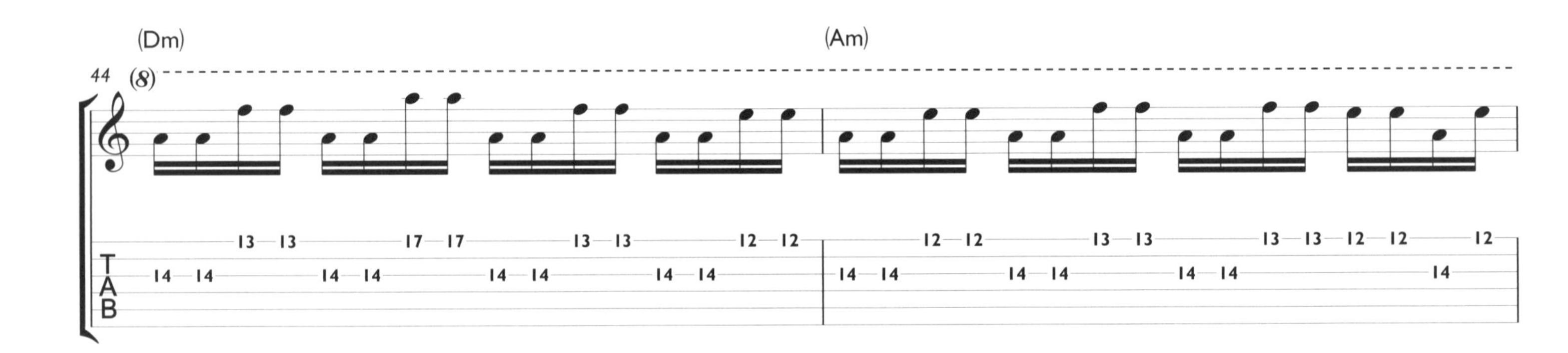
(Dm)
(Am)
44
(8)
TAB

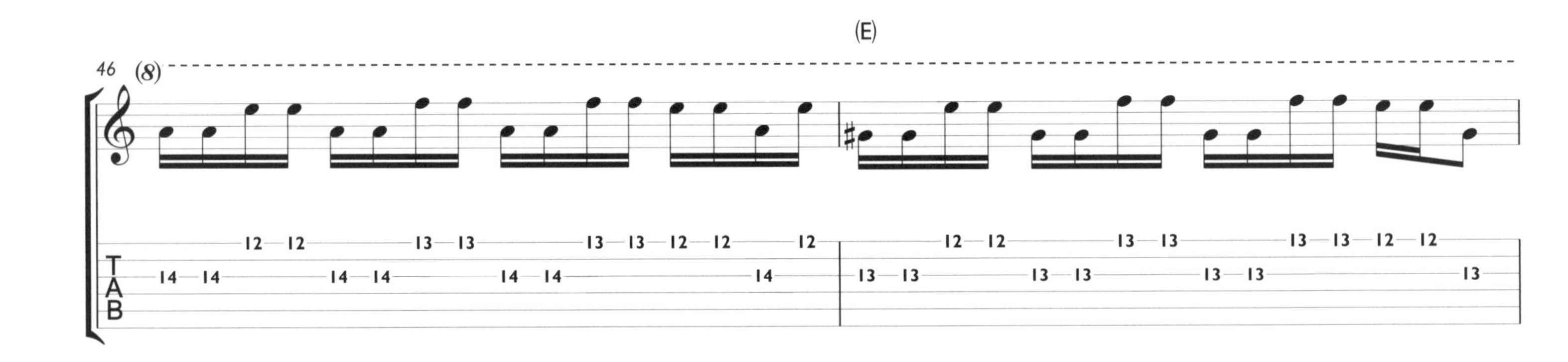
(E)
46
(8)
TAB

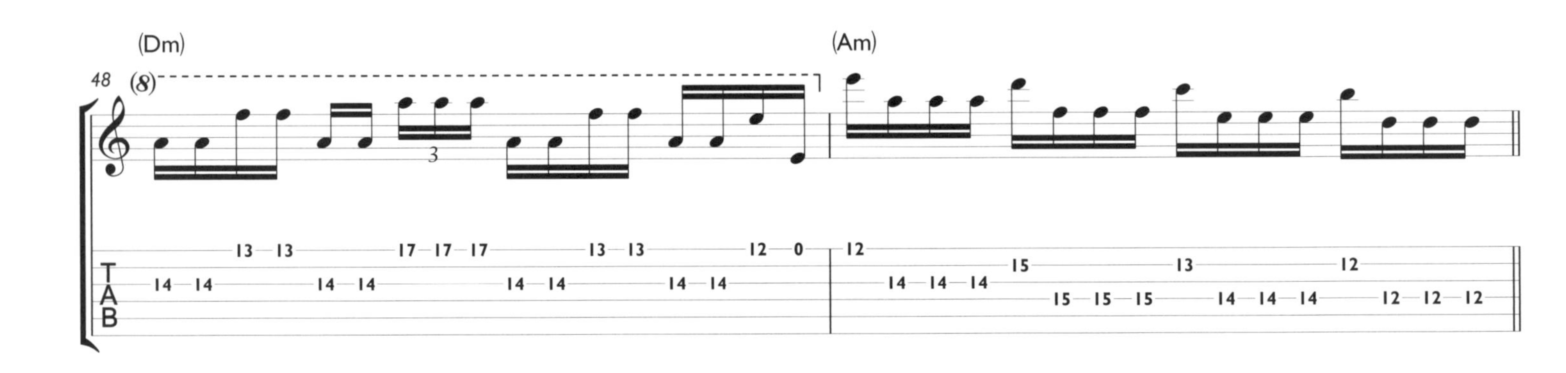
(Dm)
(Am)
48
(8)
TAB

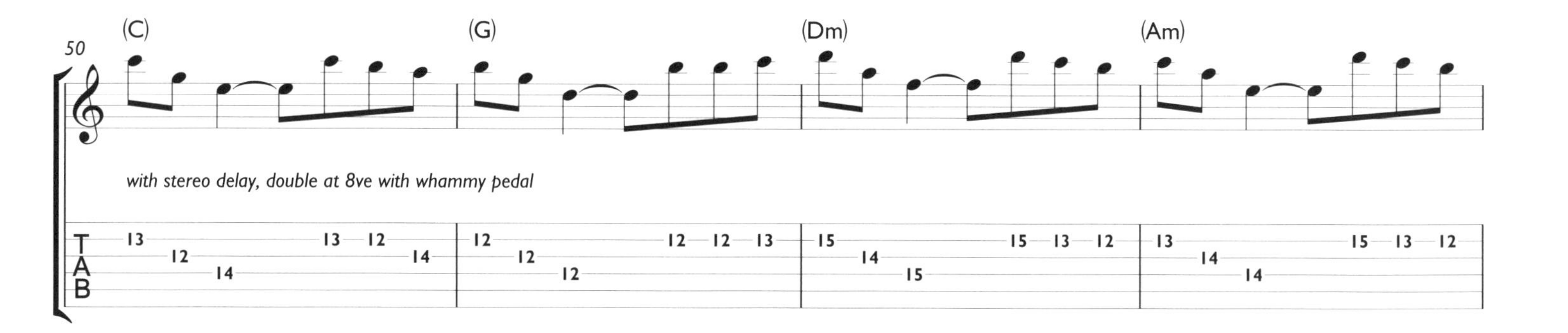
50
(C)
(G)
(Dm)
(Am)
with stereo delay, double at 8ve with whammy pedal

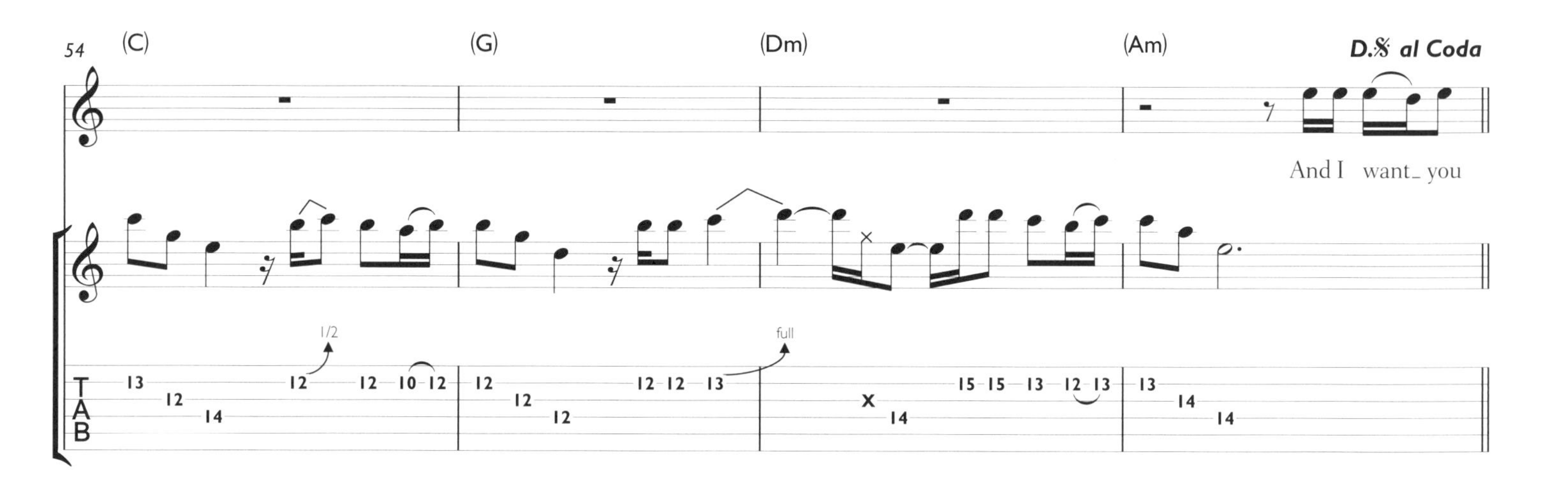
54
(C)
(G)
(Dm)
(Am)
D.𝄋 al Coda
And I want_ you
1/2
full

⊕ Coda

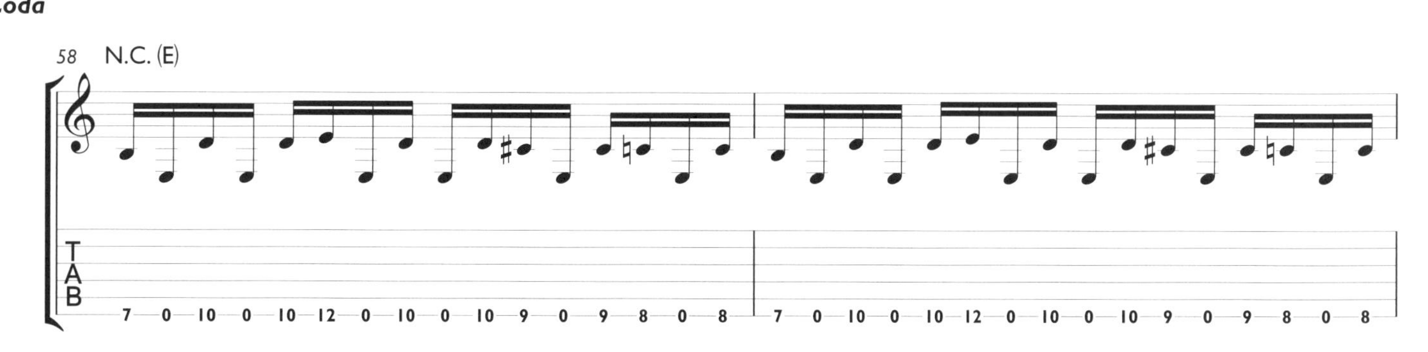
58
N.C. (E)

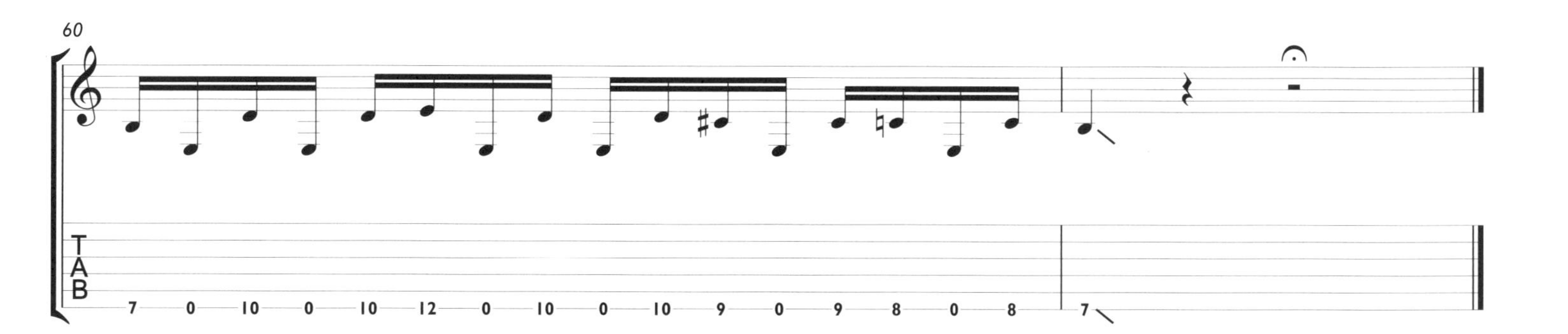
60

KNIGHTS OF CYDONIA

Words and Music by Matthew Bellamy

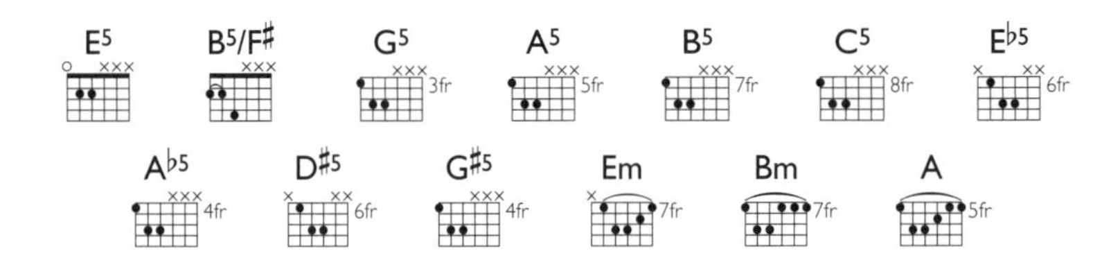

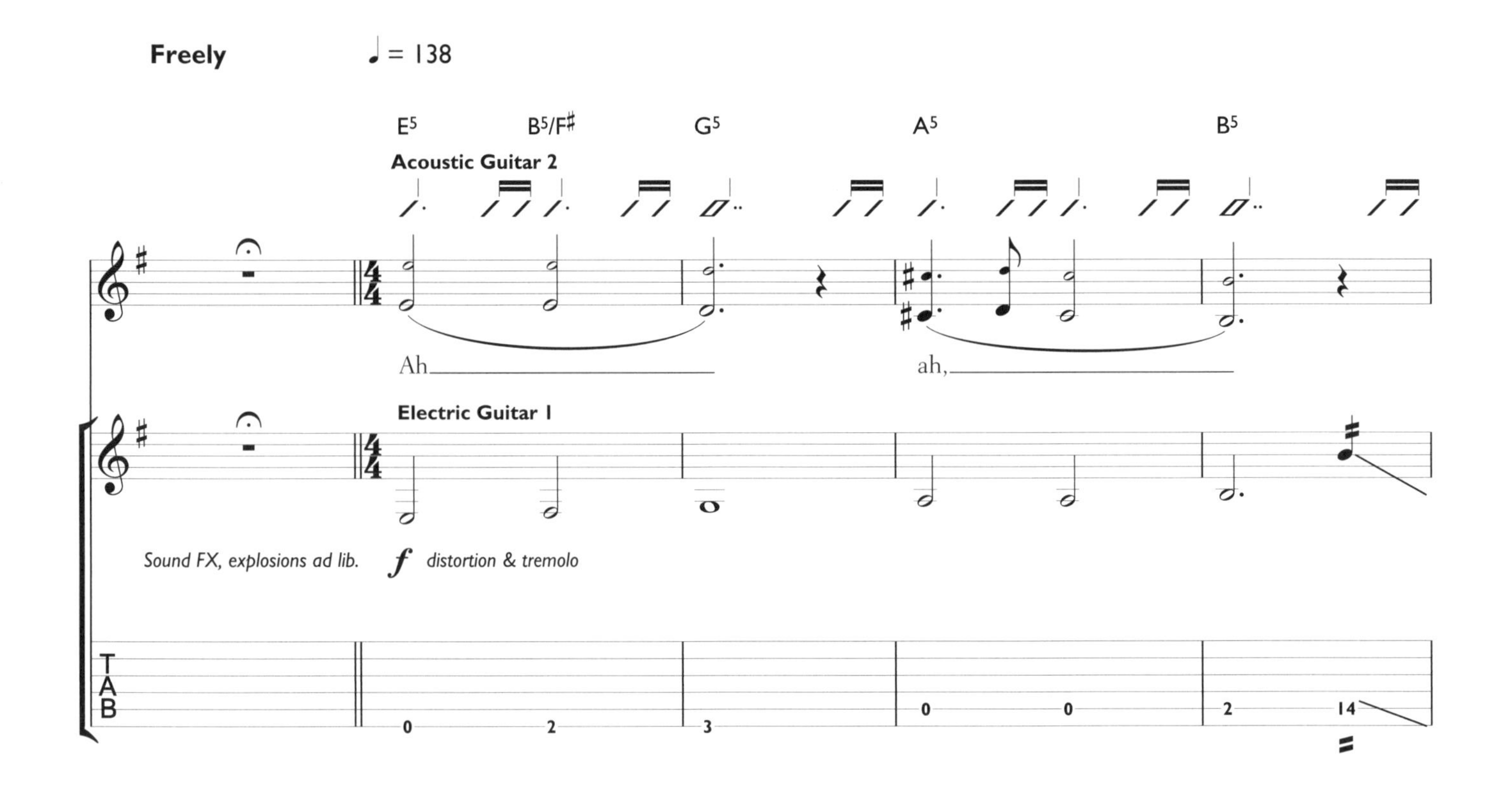

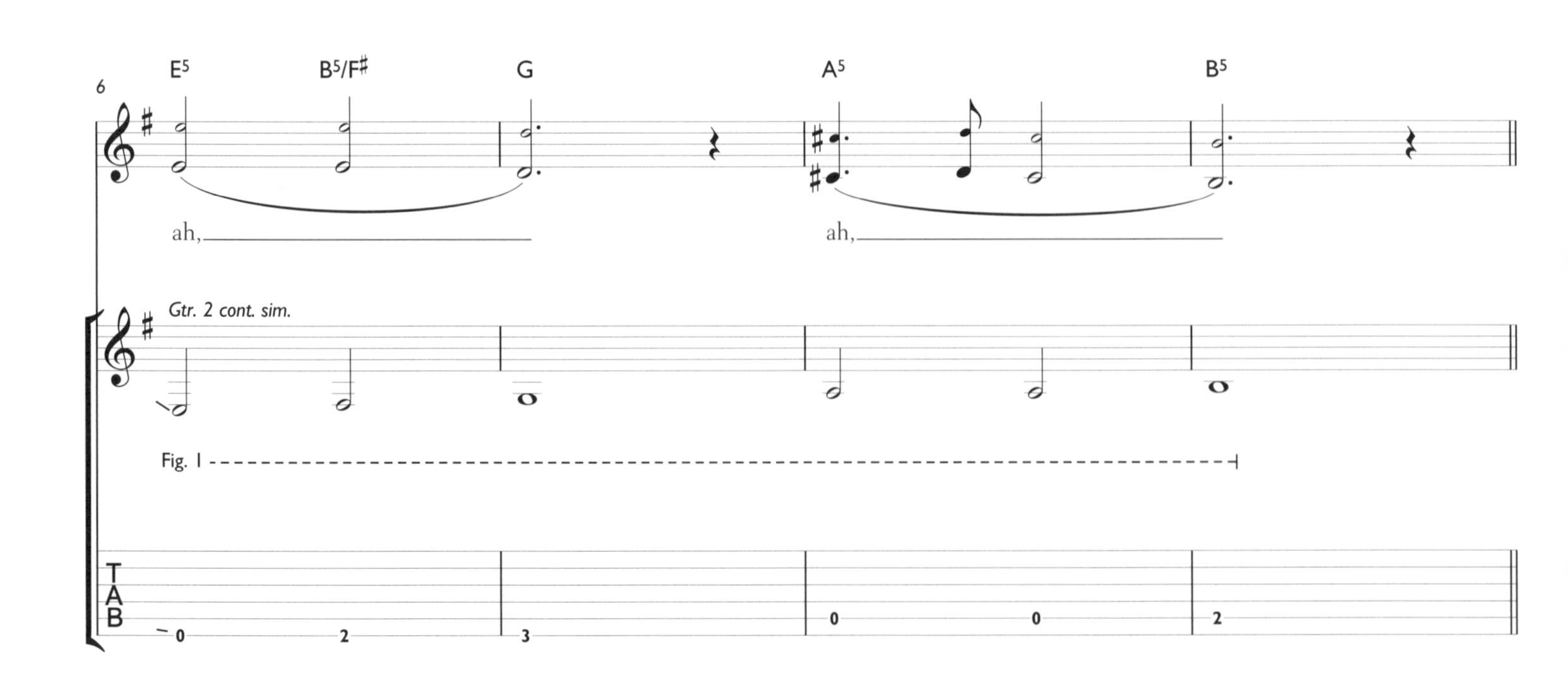

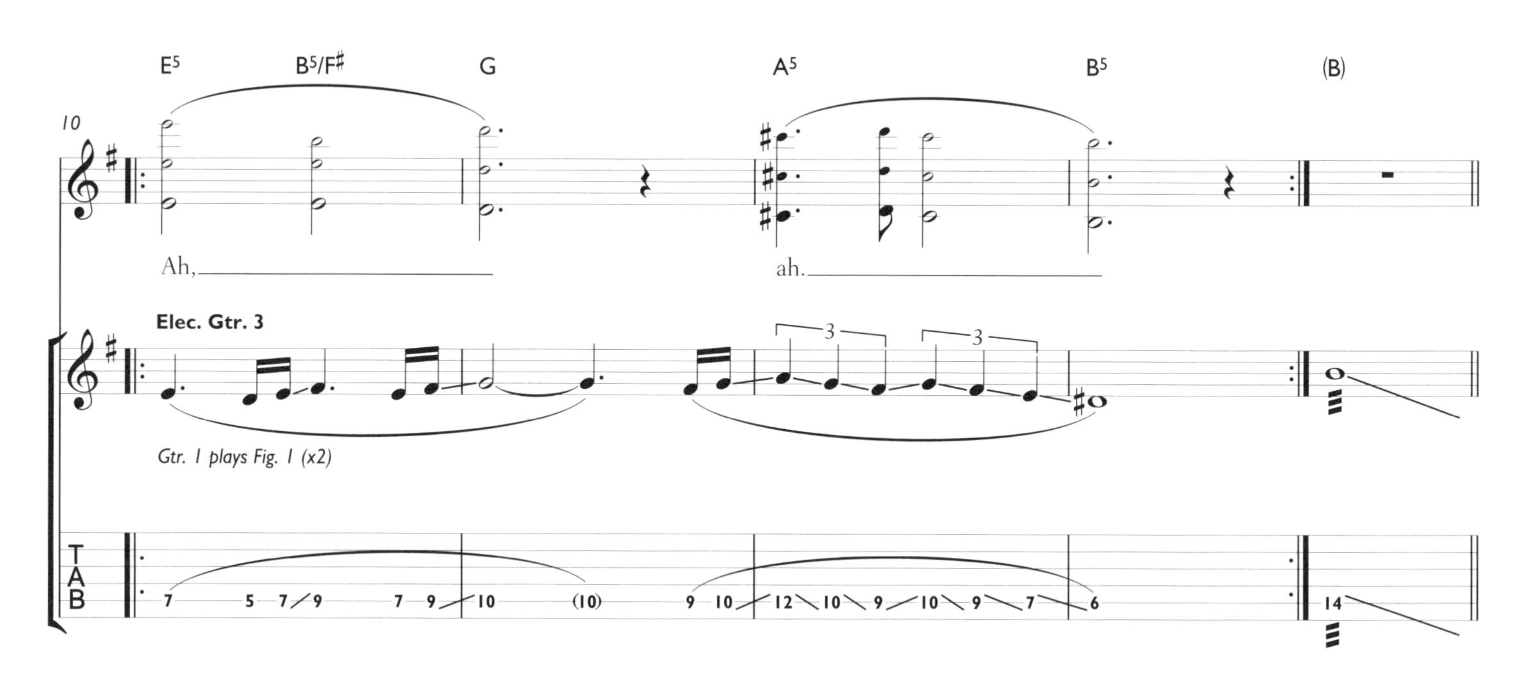
E5
B5/F#
G
A5
B5
(B)
10
Ah,
ah.
Elec. Gtr. 3
Gtr. 1 plays Fig. 1 (x2)
TAB

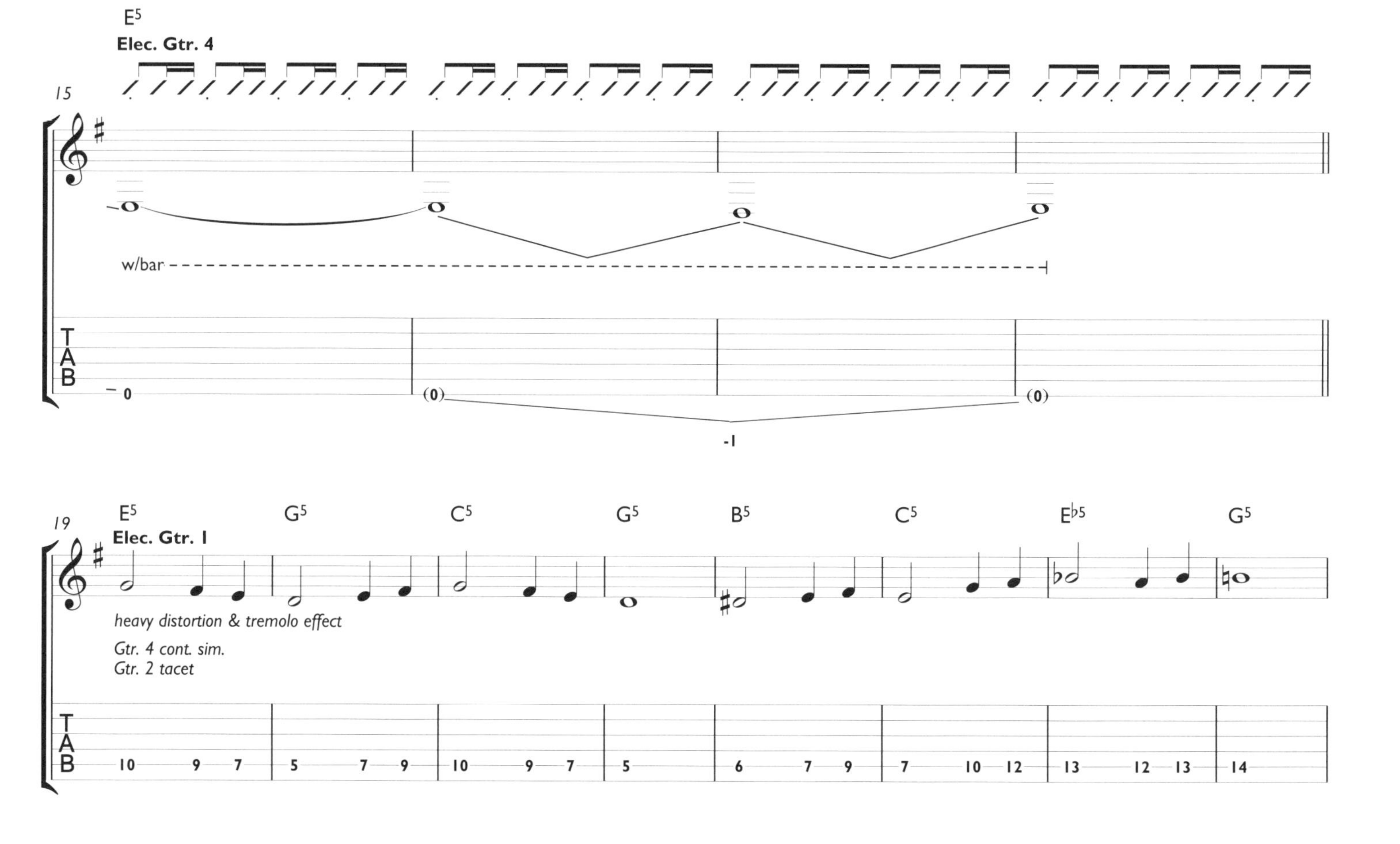
E5
Elec. Gtr. 4
15
w/bar
TAB
19
E5
G5
C5
G5
B5
C5
Eb5
G5
Elec. Gtr. 1
heavy distortion & tremolo effect
Gtr. 4 cont. sim.
Gtr. 2 tacet

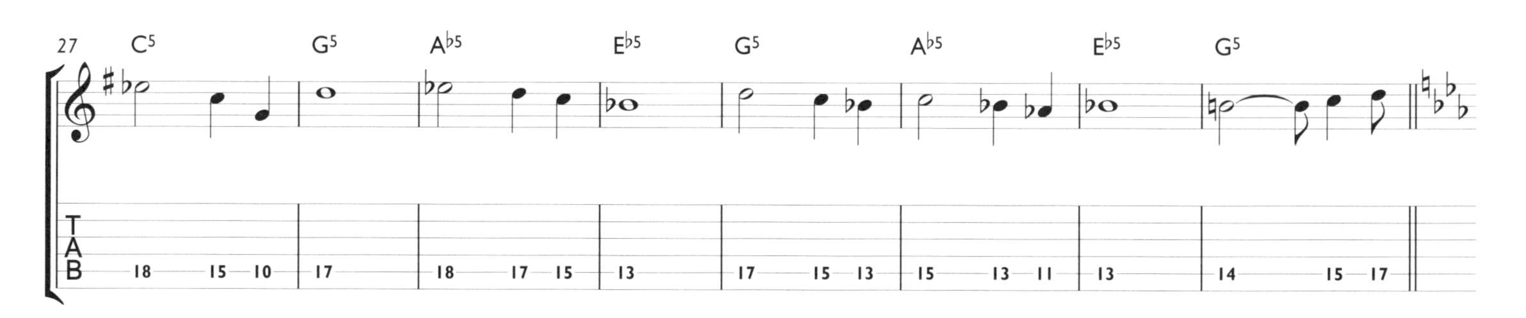
27
C5
G5
Ab5
Eb5
G5
Ab5
Eb5
G5
TAB

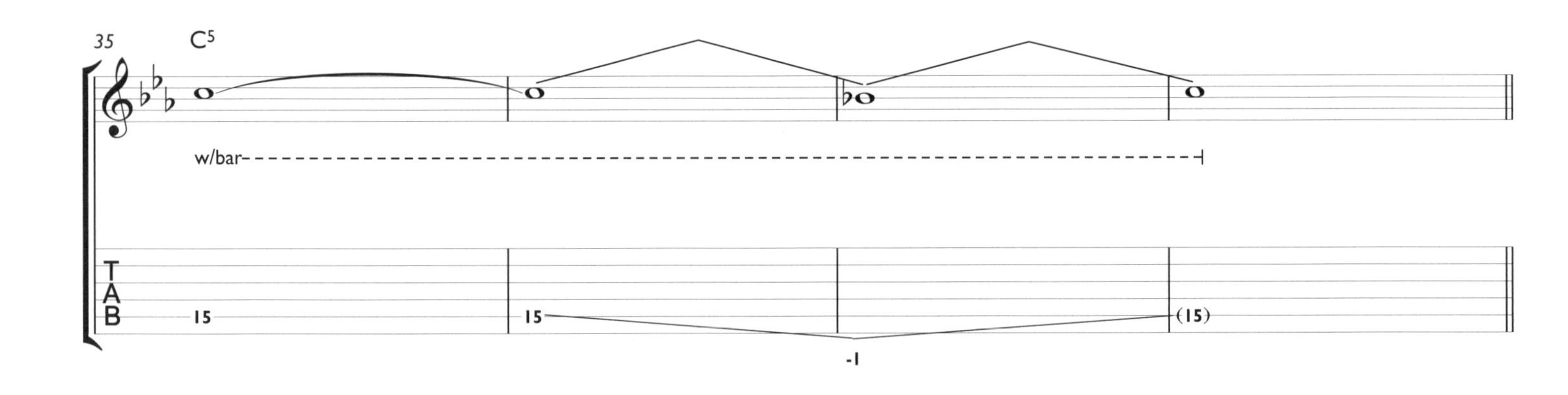
35
C5
w/bar
T
A
B
15
15
-1
(15)

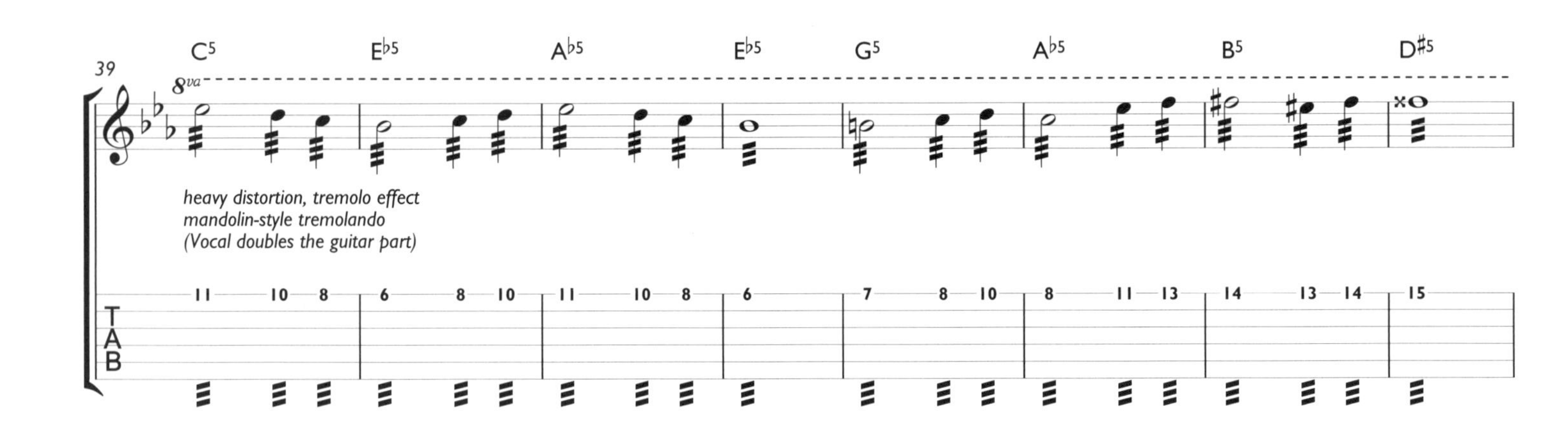
39
C5
E♭5
A♭5
E♭5
G5
A♭5
B5
D♯5
8va
heavy distortion, tremolo effect
mandolin-style tremolando
(Vocal doubles the guitar part)
T
A
B
11 10 8 6 8 10 11 10 8 6 7 8 10 8 11 13 14 13 14 15

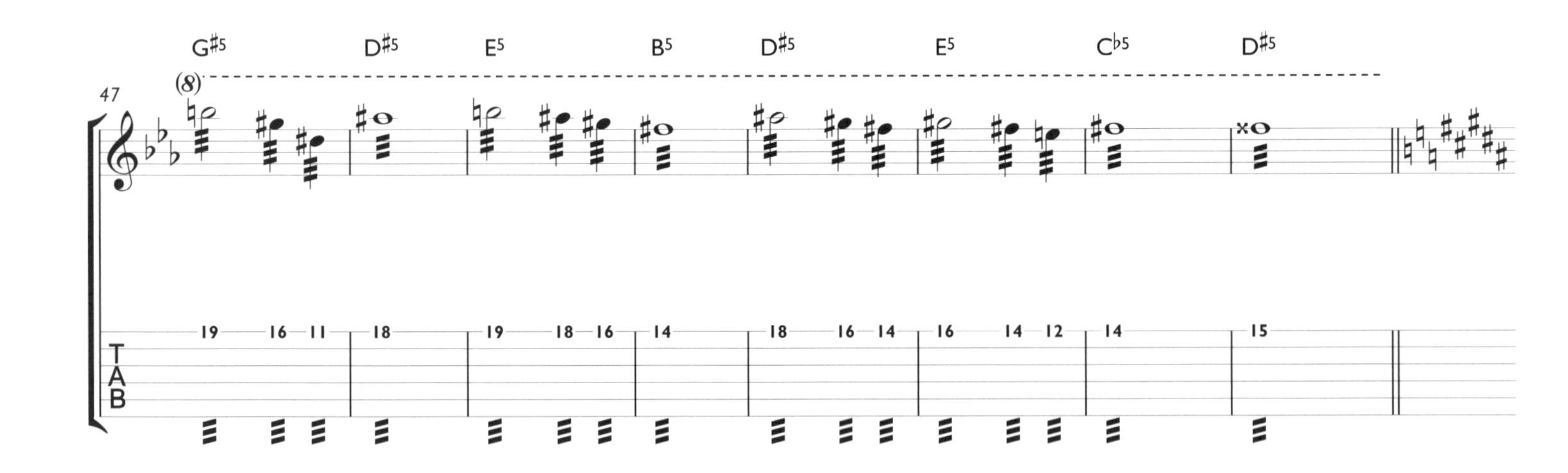
47
G♯5
D♯5
E5
B5
D♯5
E5
C♭5
D♯5
(8)
T
A
B
19 16 11 18 19 18 16 14 18 16 14 16 14 12 14 15

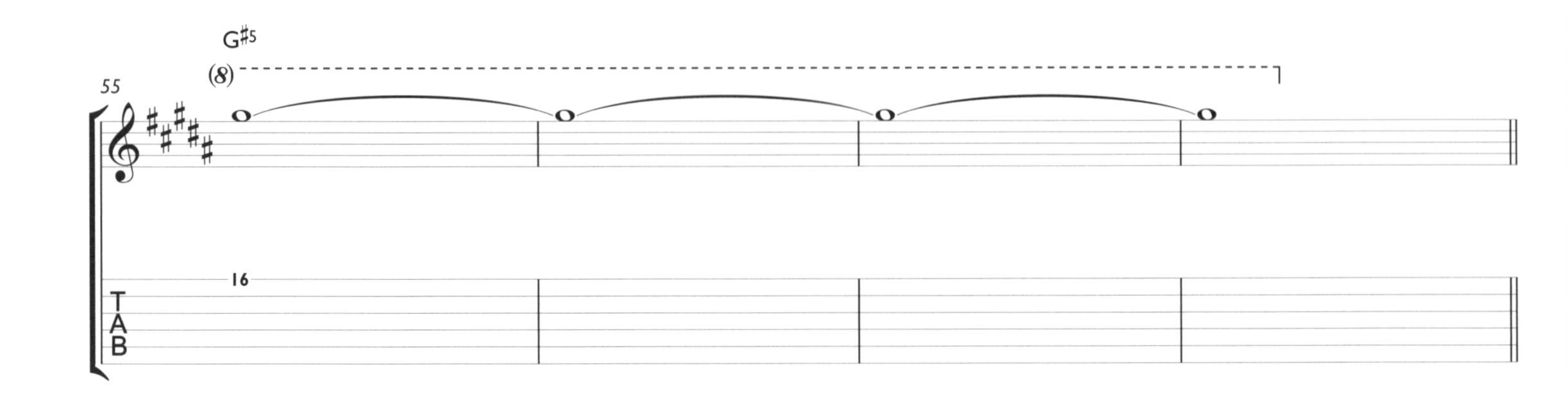
55
G♯5
(8)
T
A
B
16

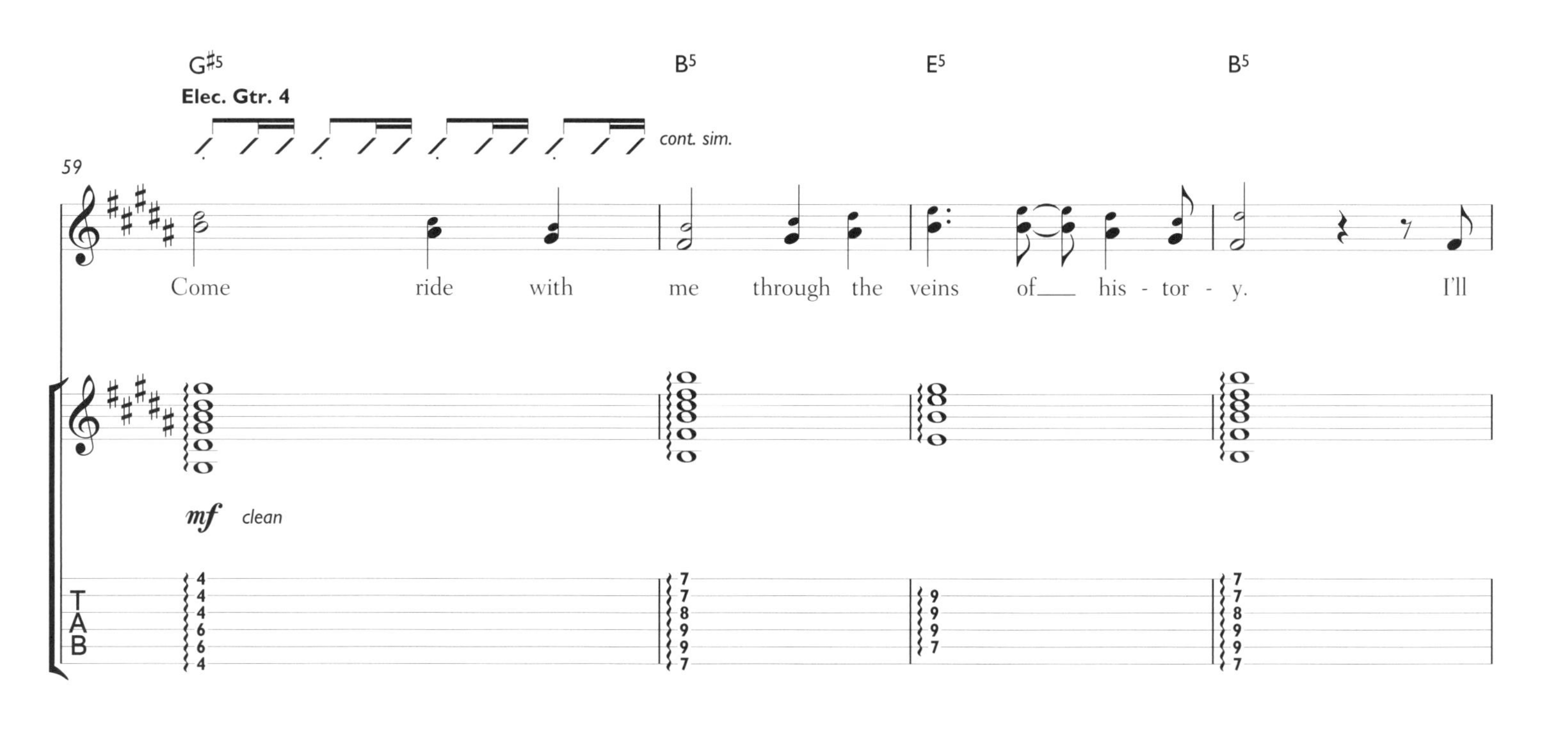
G♯5
Elec. Gtr. 4
cont. sim.
B5
E5
B5
59
Come ride with me through the veins of his - tor - y. I'll
mf clean

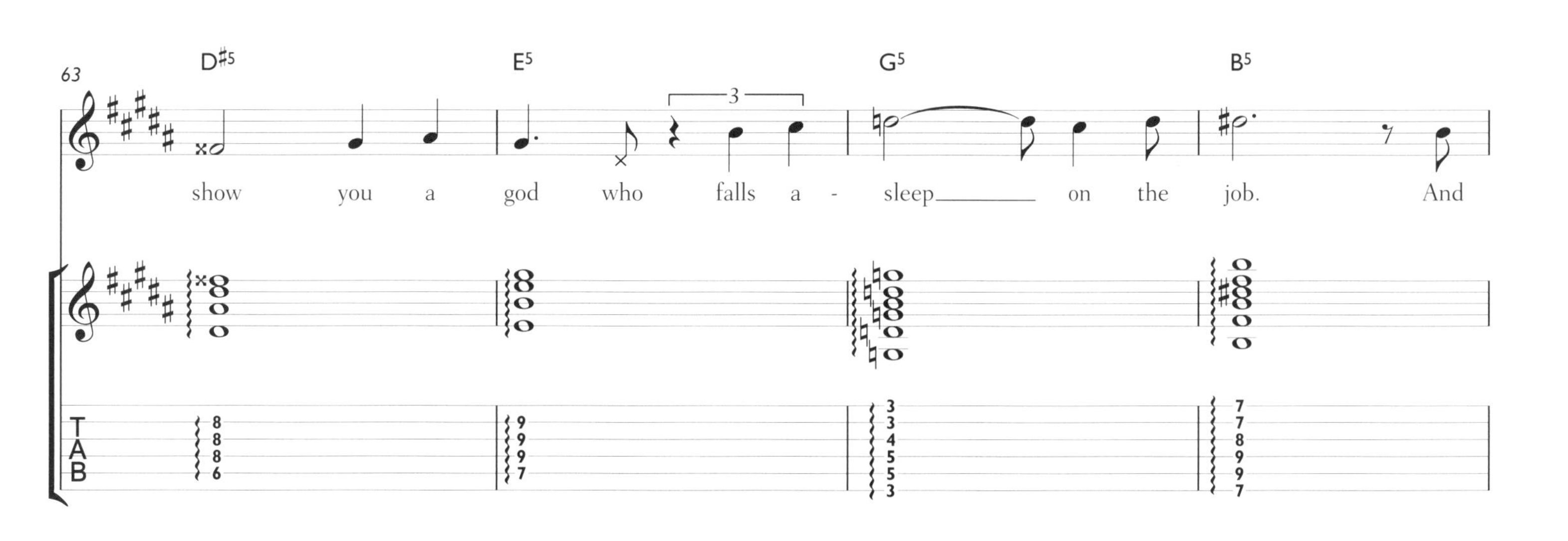
63
D♯5
E5
3
G5
B5
show you a god who falls a - sleep on the job. And

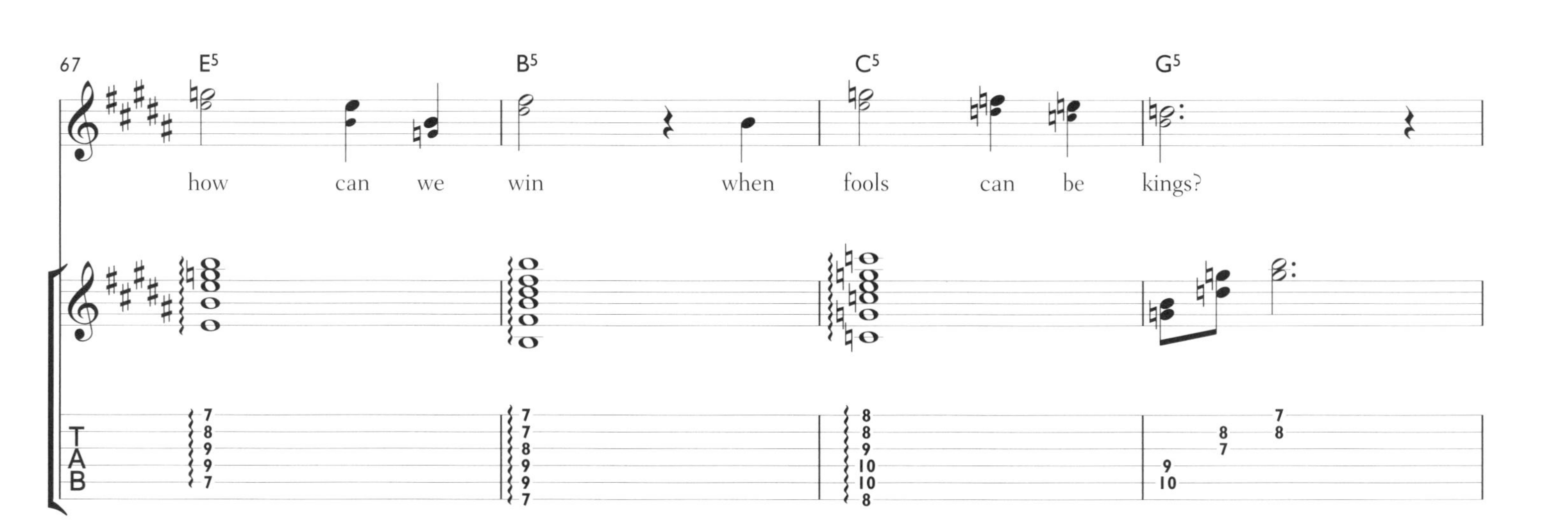
67
E5
B5
C5
G5
how can we win when fools can be kings?

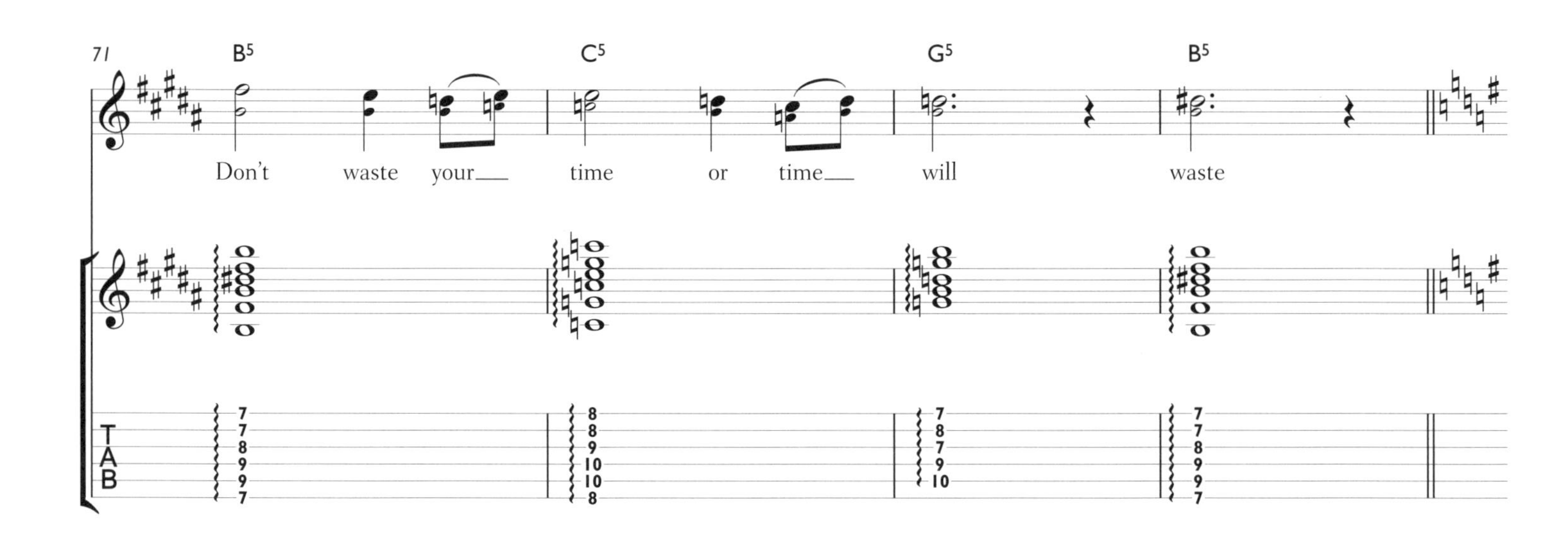
71
B5
C5
G5
B5
Don't waste your time or time will waste
T
A
B

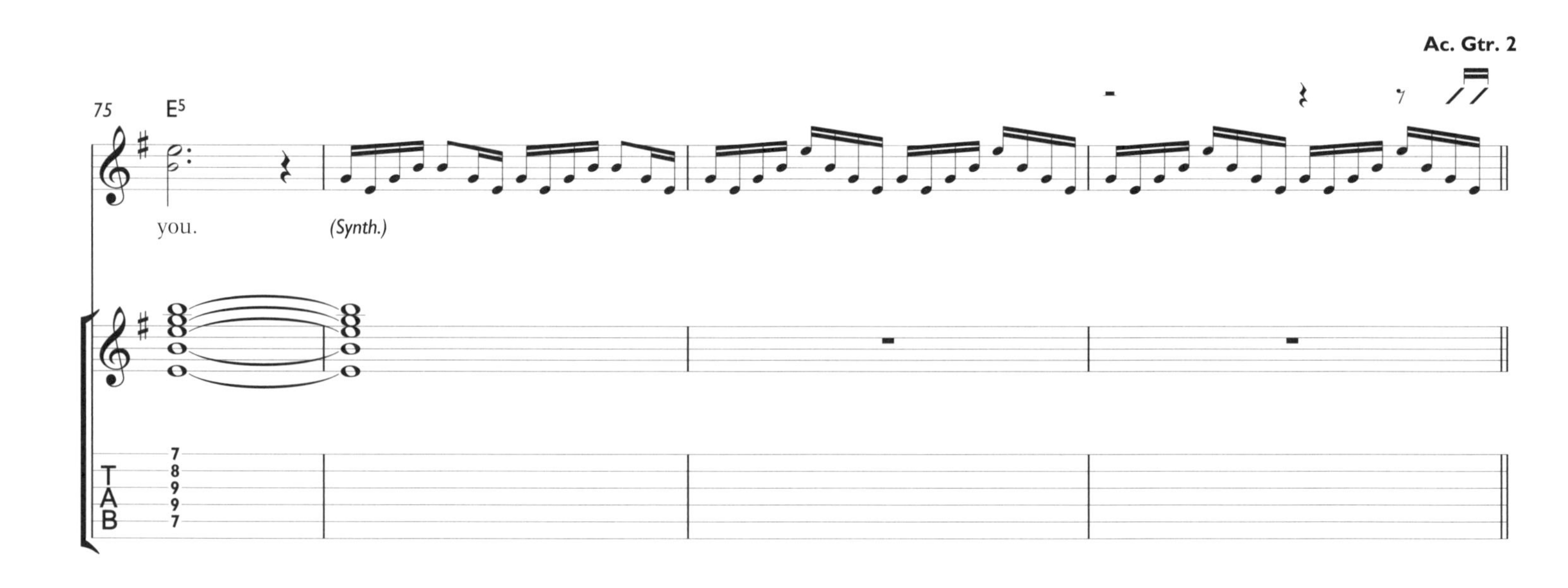
Ac. Gtr. 2
75
E5
you.
(Synth.)
T
A
B

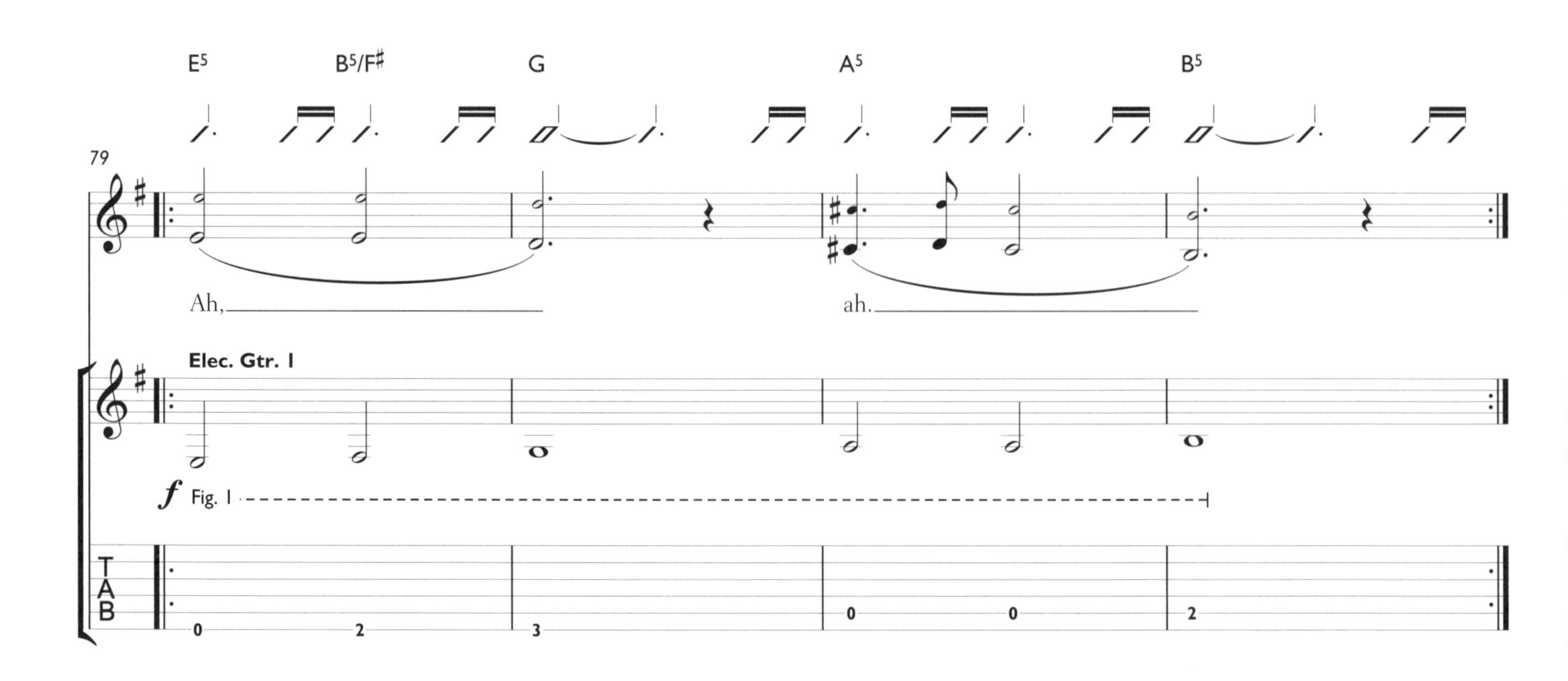
E5
B5/F♯
G
A5
B5
79
Ah,
ah.
Elec. Gtr. 1
f Fig. 1
T
A
B

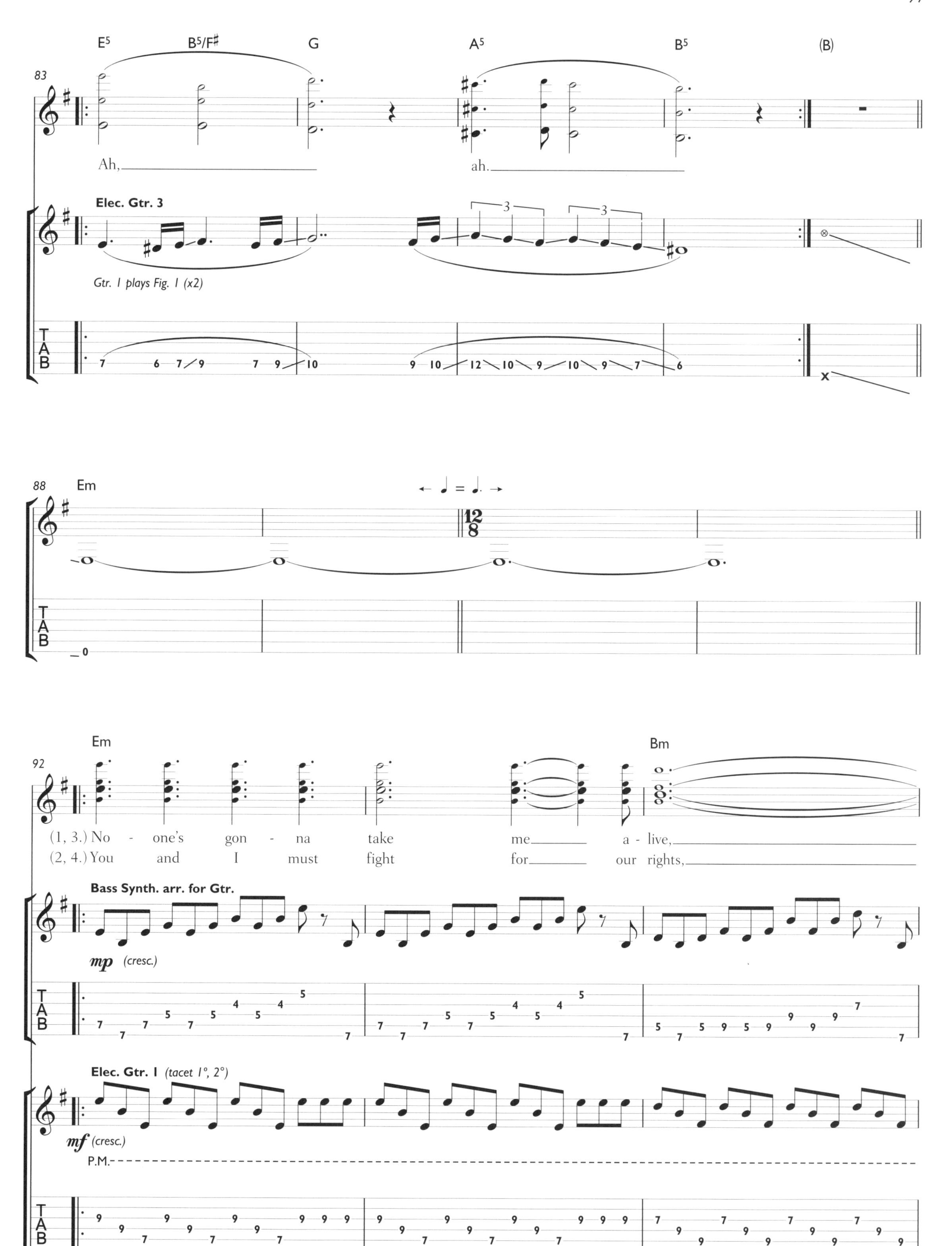
E5
B5/F♯
G
A5
B5
(B)
Ah,
ah.
Elec. Gtr. 3
Gtr. 1 plays Fig. 1 (x2)
Em
Em
Bm
(1, 3.) No - one's gon - na take me a - live,
(2, 4.) You and I must fight for our rights,
Bass Synth. arr. for Gtr.
mp (cresc.)
Elec. Gtr. 1 (tacet 1°, 2°)
mf (cresc.)
P.M.

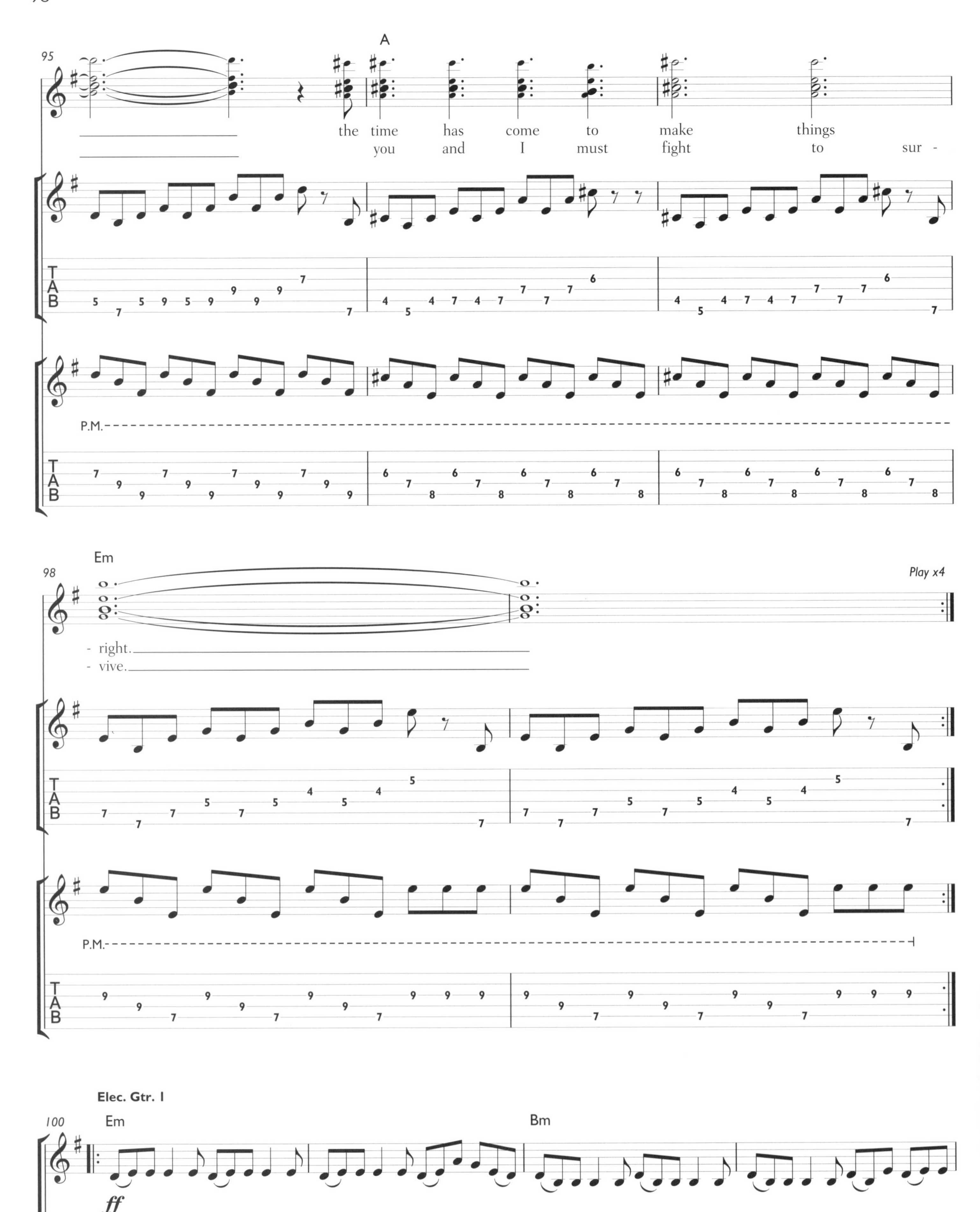
A
the time has come to make things
you and I must fight to sur -
P.M.
Em
Play x4
- right.
- vive.
P.M.
Elec. Gtr. 1
Em
ff
Bm

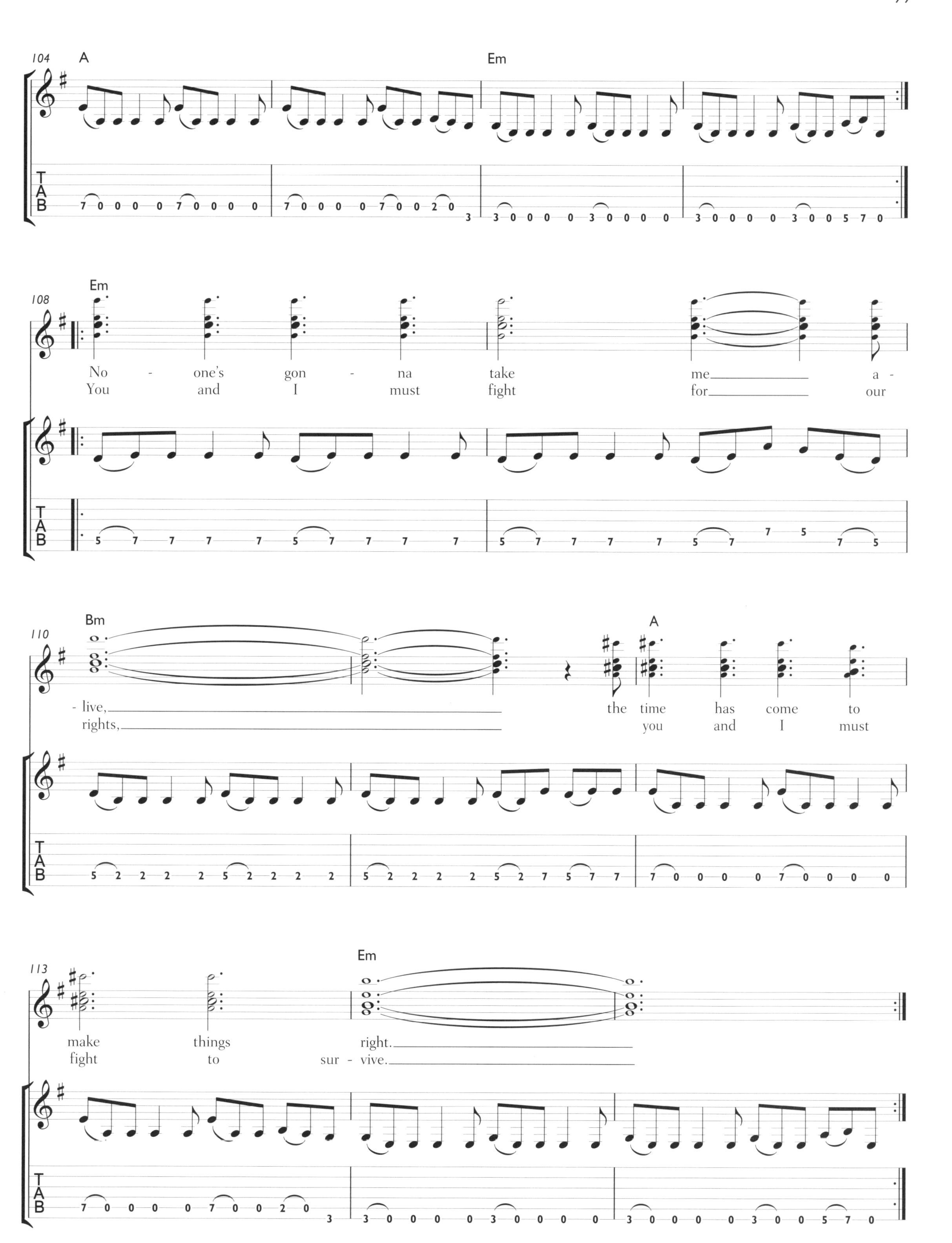
104
A
Em
108
Em
No - one's gon - na take me a -
You and I must fight for our
110
Bm
A
- live, the time has come to
rights, you and I must
113
Em
make things right.
fight to sur - vive.

Em
Bm
(Synth.)
A
Em
1.
2.
Em

LIQUID STATE

Words and Music by Chris Wolstenholme

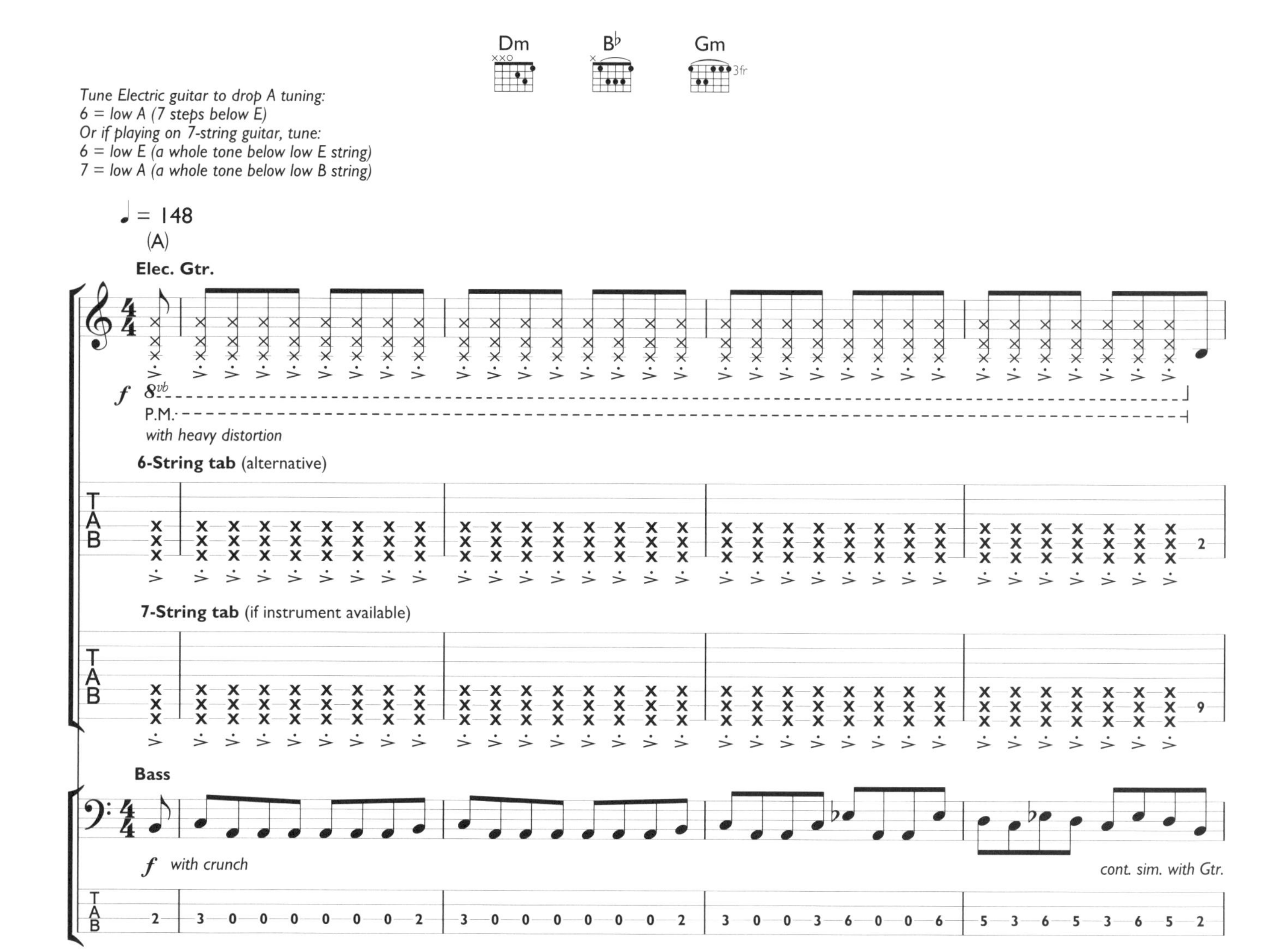

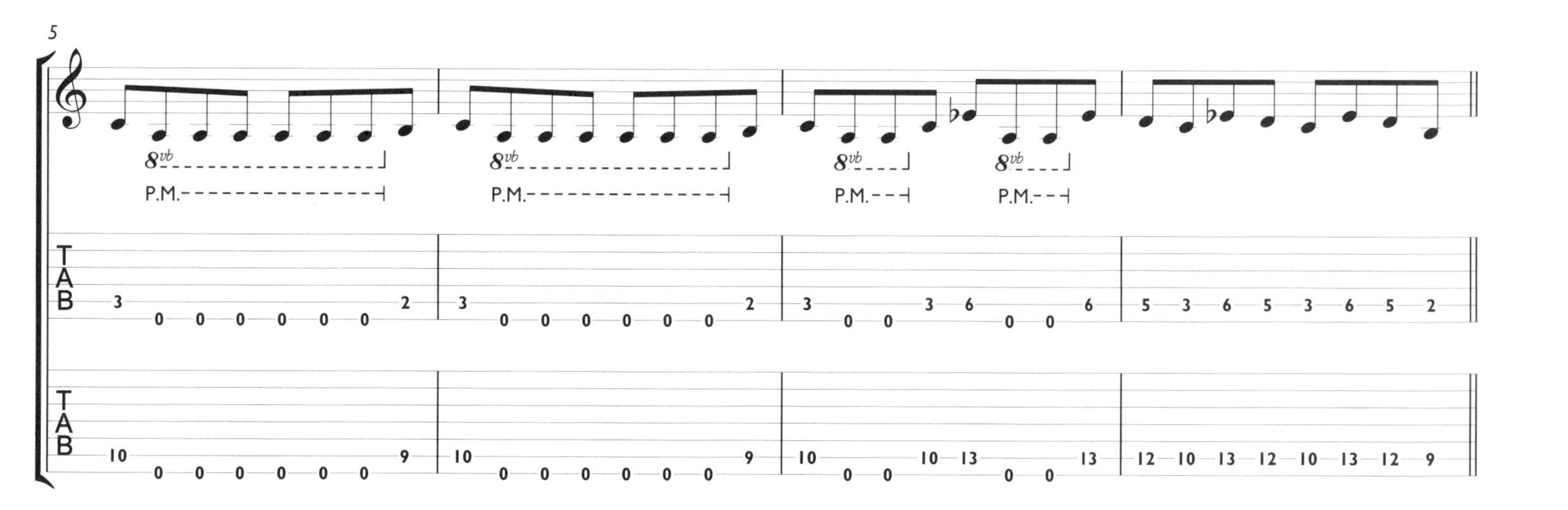

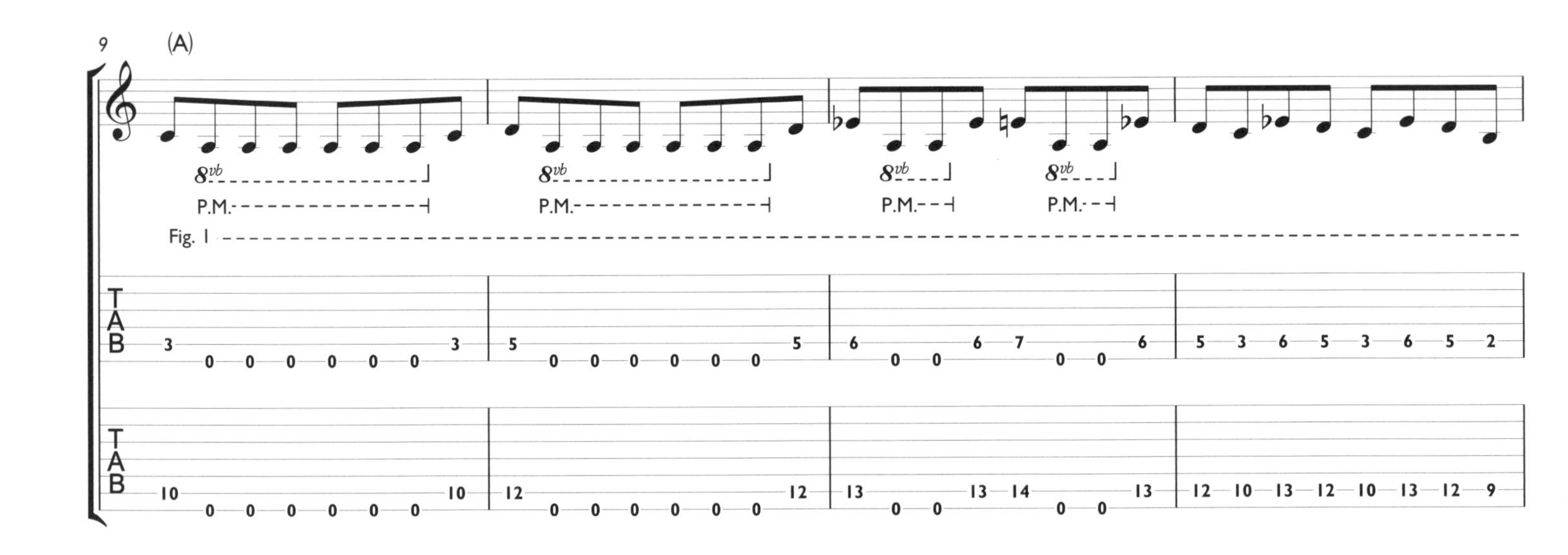
9
(A)
8vb
P.M.
Fig. 1
TAB

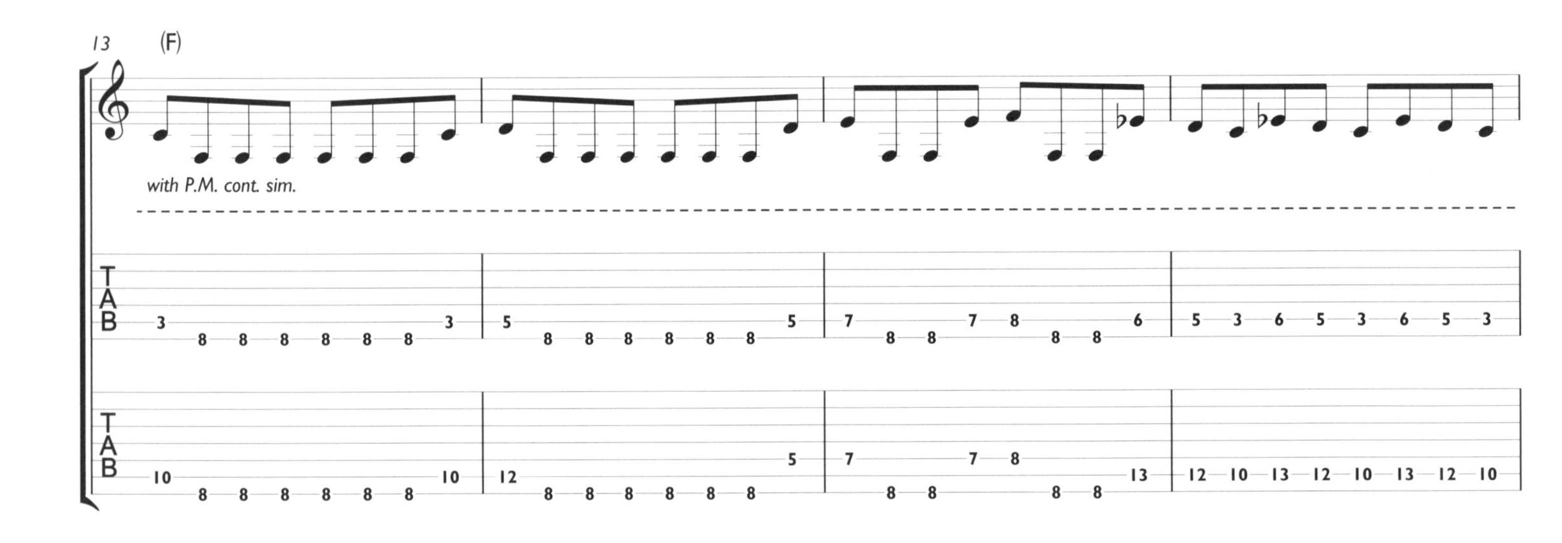
13
(F)
with P.M. cont. sim.
TAB

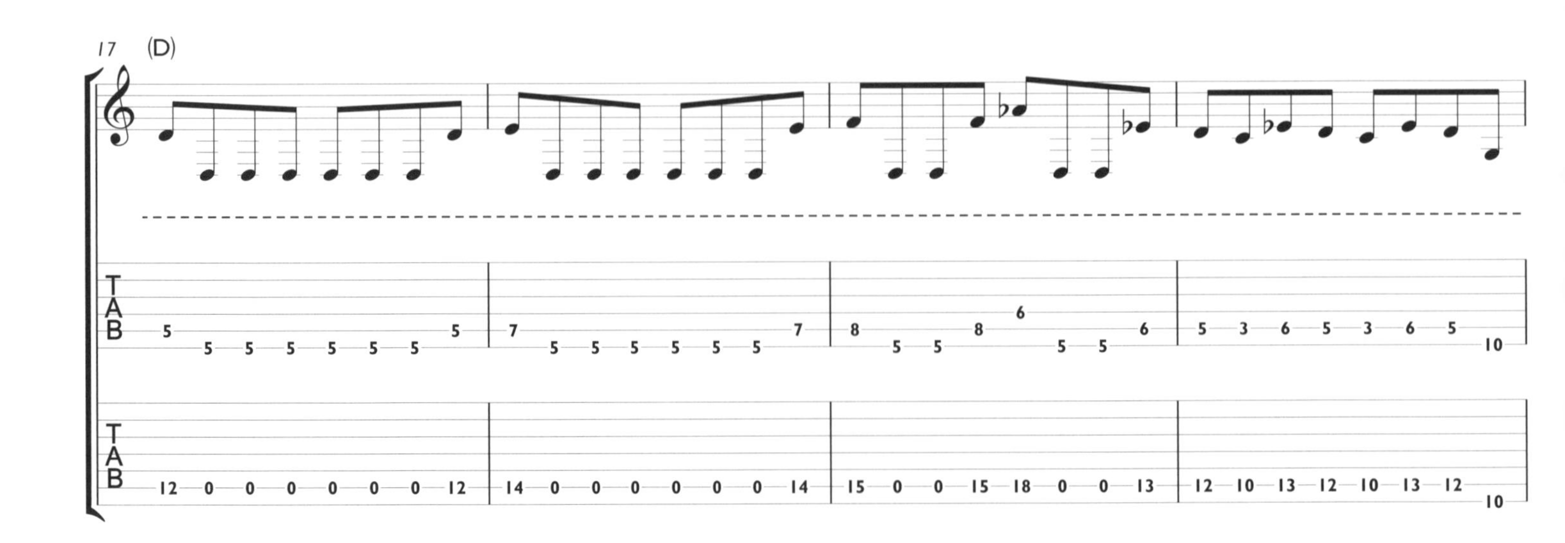
17
(D)
TAB

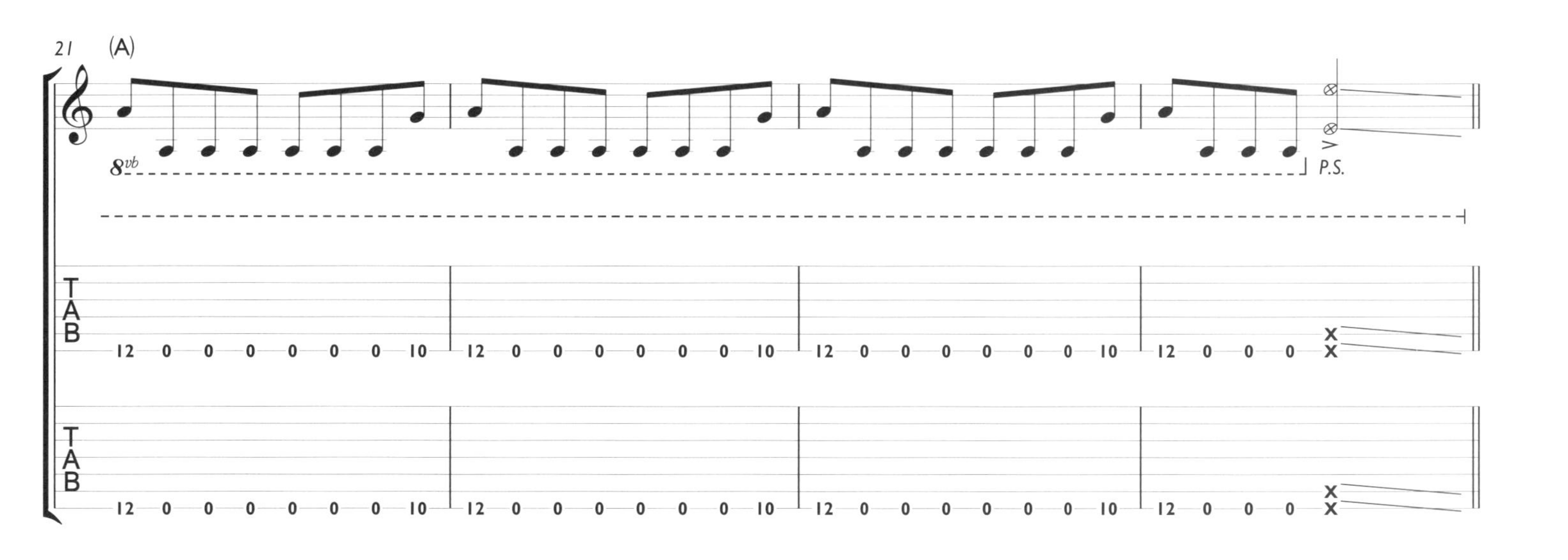
21
(A)
8vb
P.S.
T
A
B
12 0 0 0 0 0 0 10 12 0 0 0 0 0 0 10 12 0 0 0 0 0 0 10 12 0 0 0
T
A
B
12 0 0 0 0 0 0 10 12 0 0 0 0 0 0 10 12 0 0 0 0 0 0 10 12 0 0 0

25 (A)
1.Take me for a ride, break me up and steal what's left in -
Elec. Gtr. plays Fig. 1

29 (F)
- - side, and hope and pray in - i -

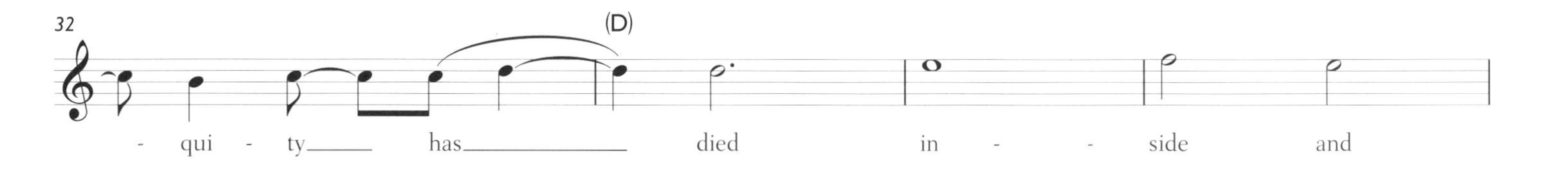
32
(D)
- qui - ty has died in - - side and

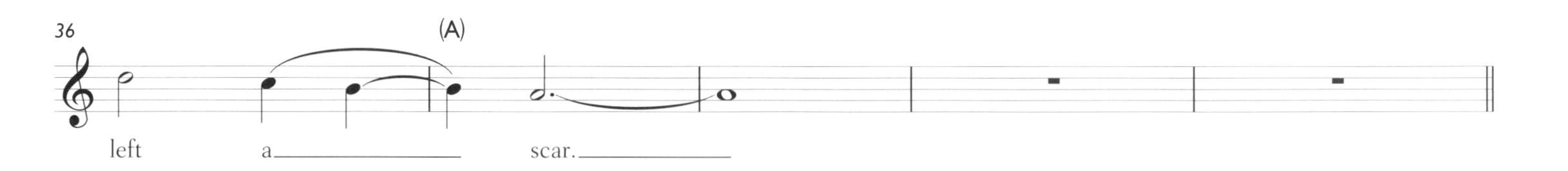
36
(A)
left a scar.

(A)
2. I'm on red a - lert, bring me peace and wash a - way my
3. Kick me when I'm down, feed me poi - son, fill me till I
Elec. Gtr. plays Fig. 1
(F)
dirt, spin me round and help
drown, wake me up be - fore
(D)
me to di - vert, and walk in -
I get pushed out and fall in -
(A)
-to the light.
-to the night.
Dm
(Sing 2°)
Force me to lose con -
Warm my heart to - night and
Elec. Gtr.
with delay
Bass

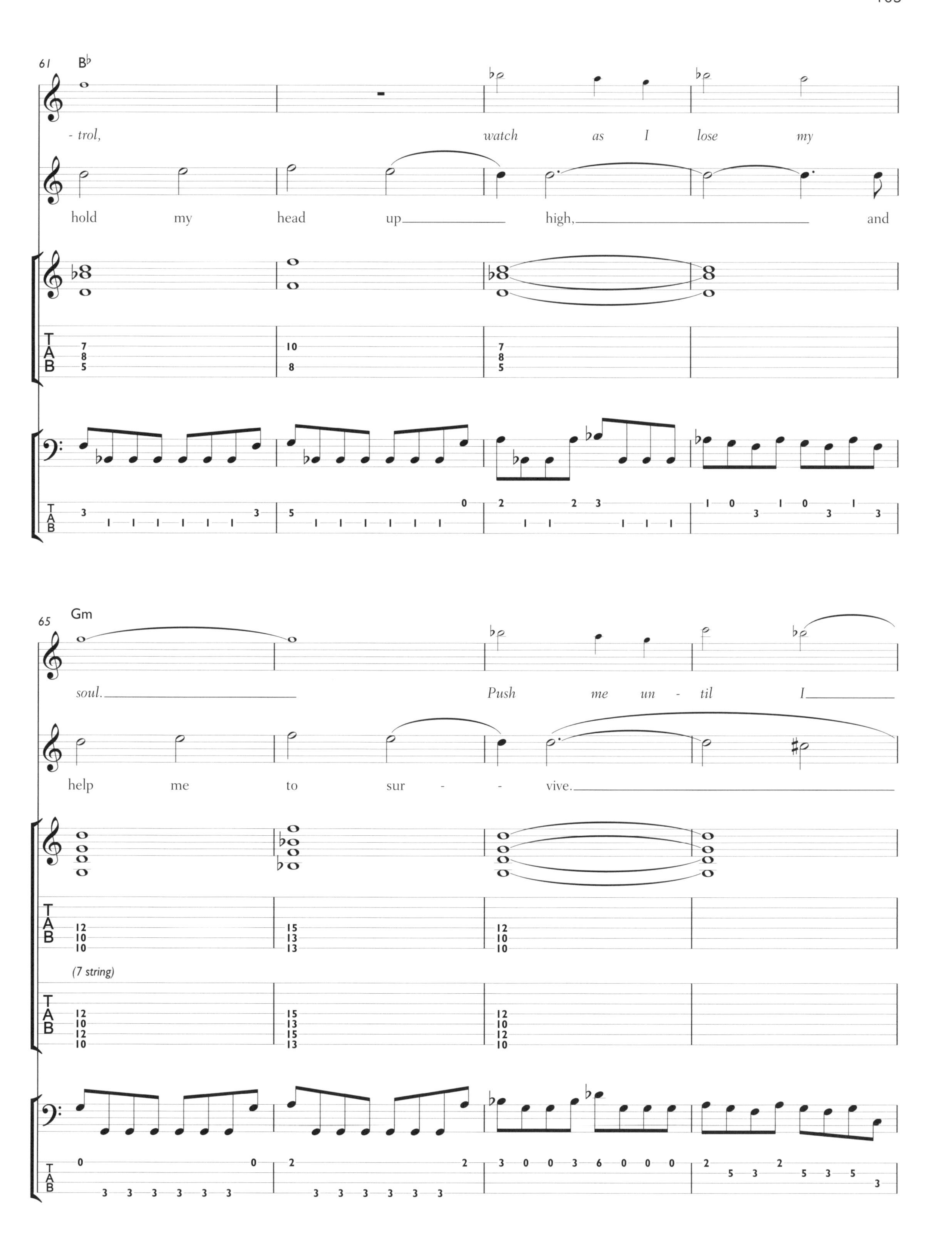
61
B♭
- trol,
watch as I lose my
hold my head up high, and
65
Gm
soul.
Push me un - til I
help me to sur - - vive.
(7 string)

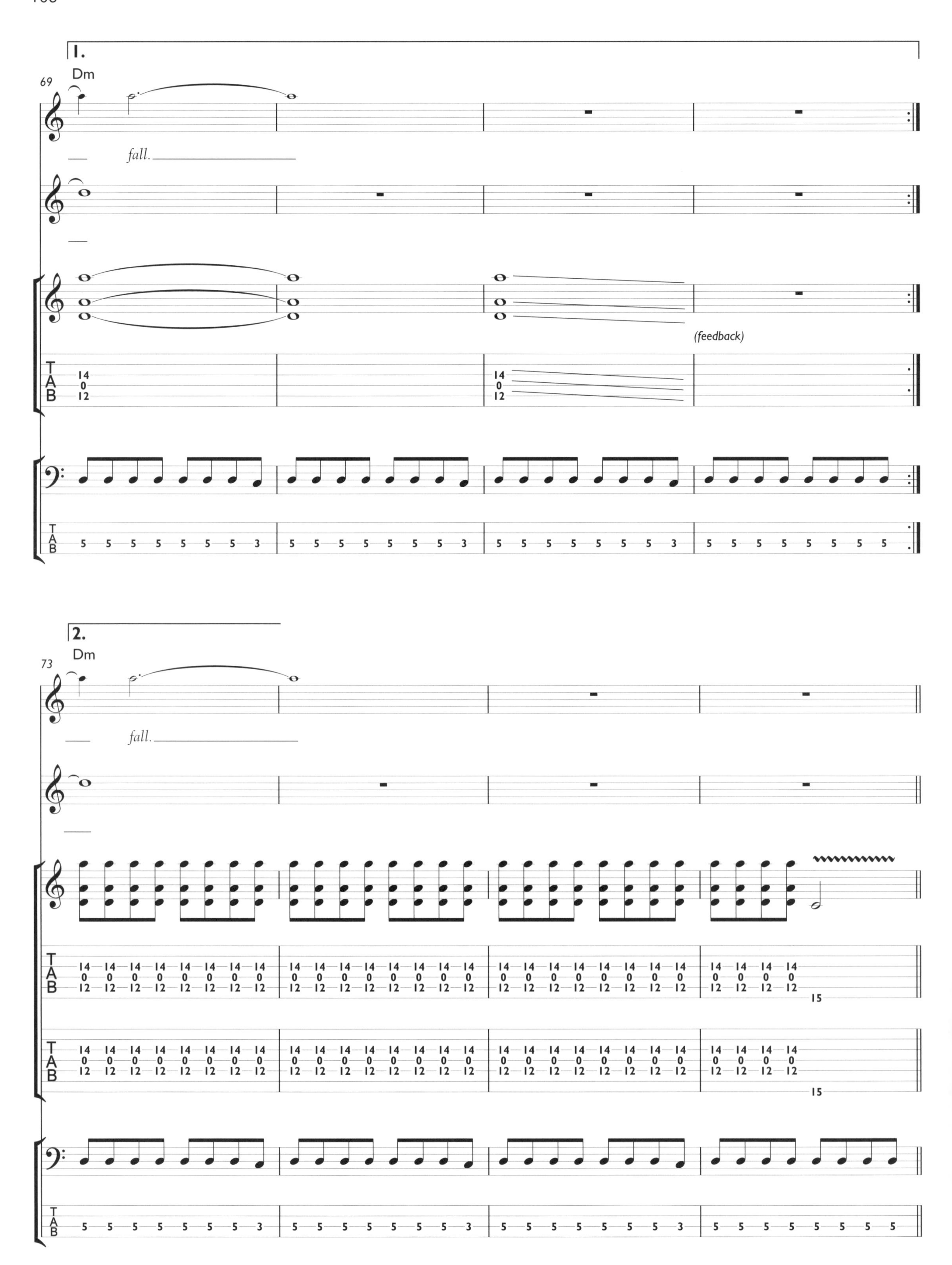
1.
69
Dm
fall.
(feedback)
2.
73
Dm
fall.

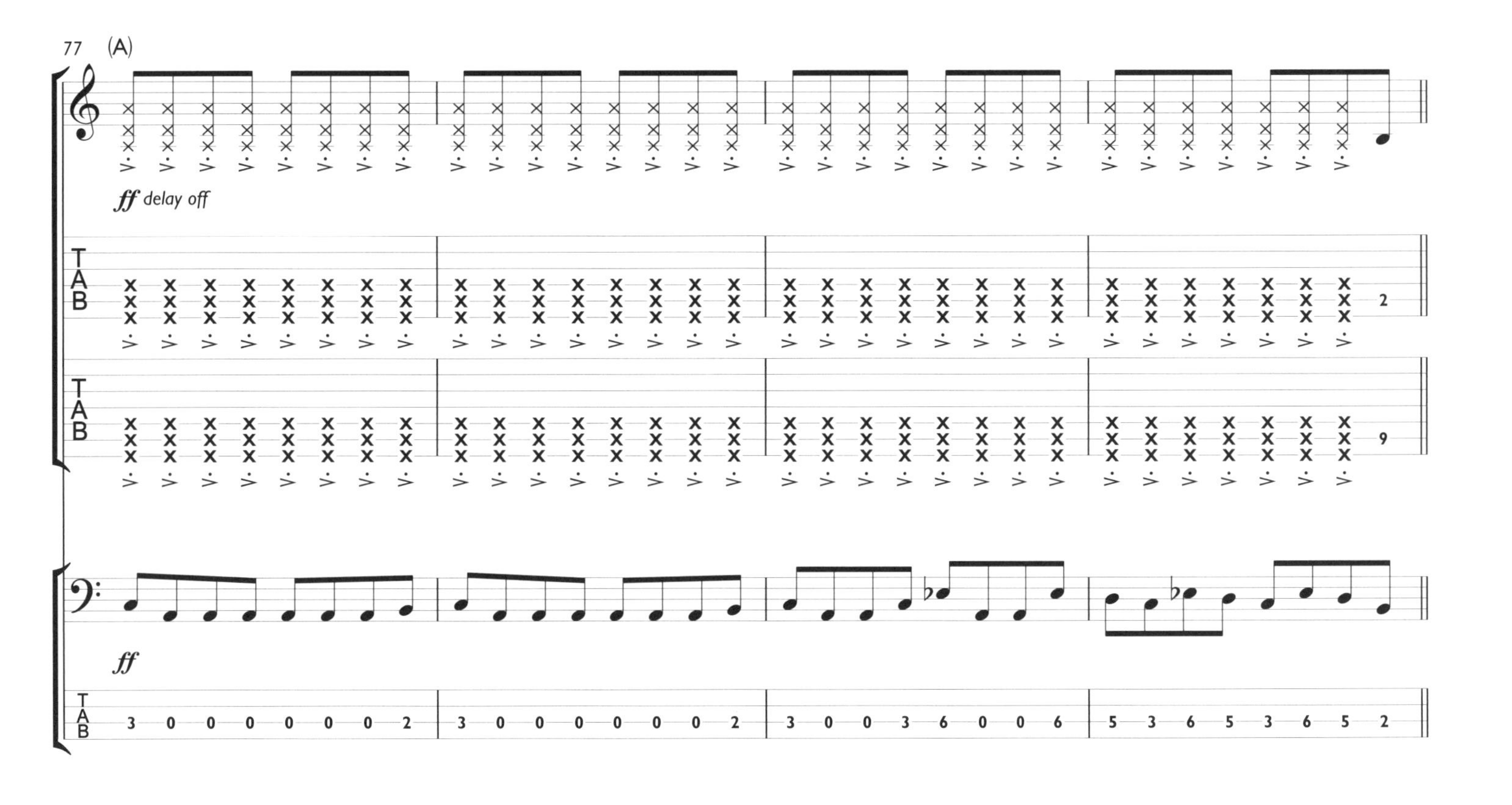
77
(A)
ff delay off
ff

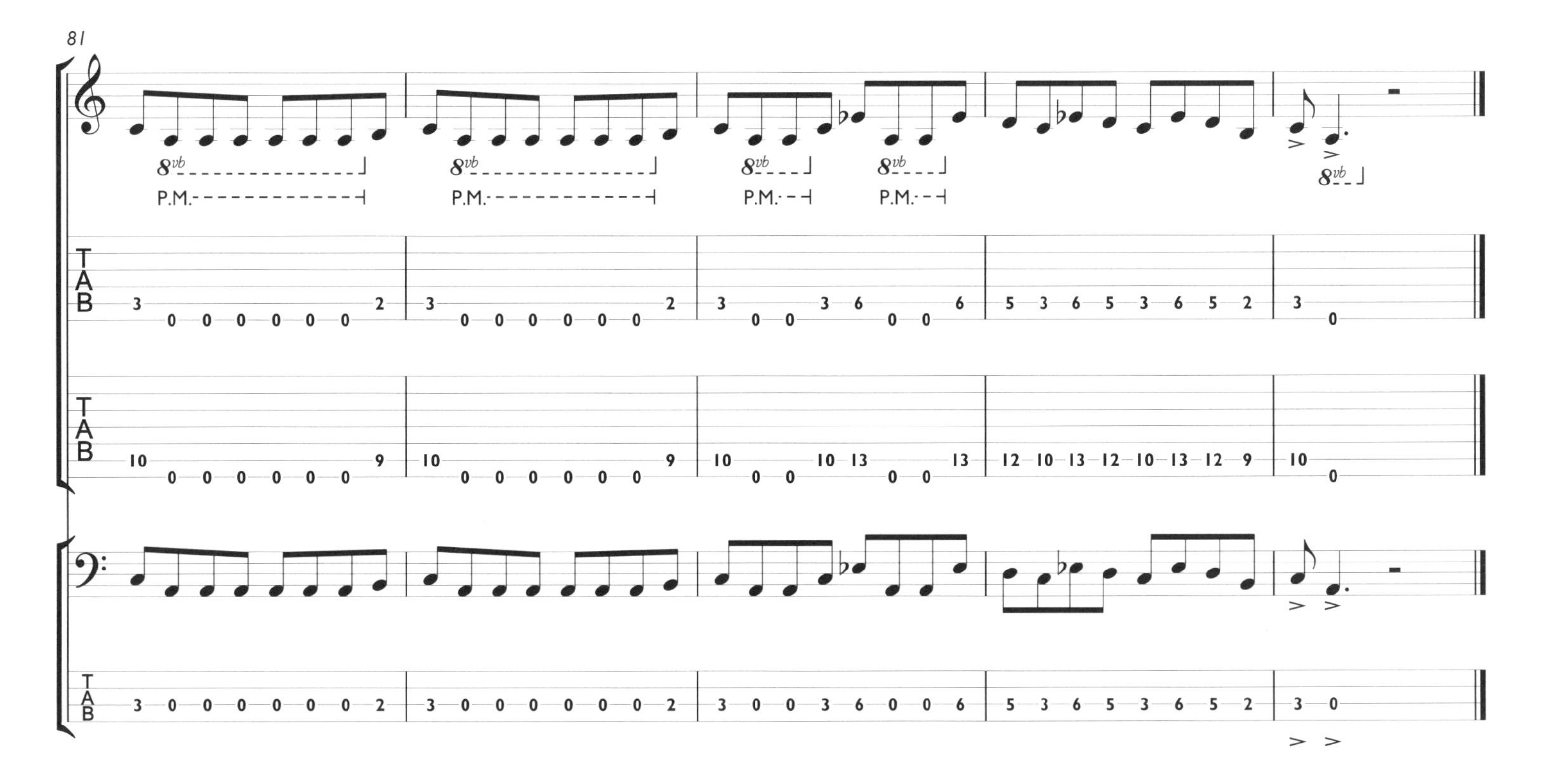
81
P.M.
P.M.
P.M.
P.M.

MICRO CUTS

Words and Music by Matthew Bellamy

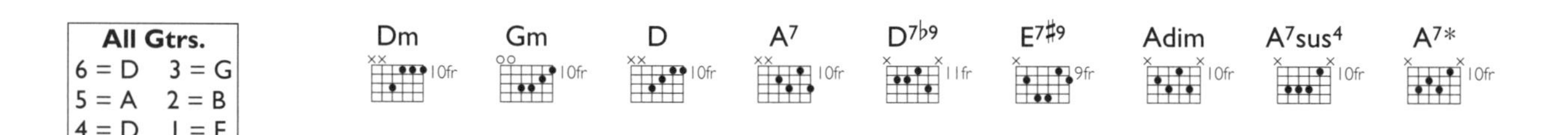

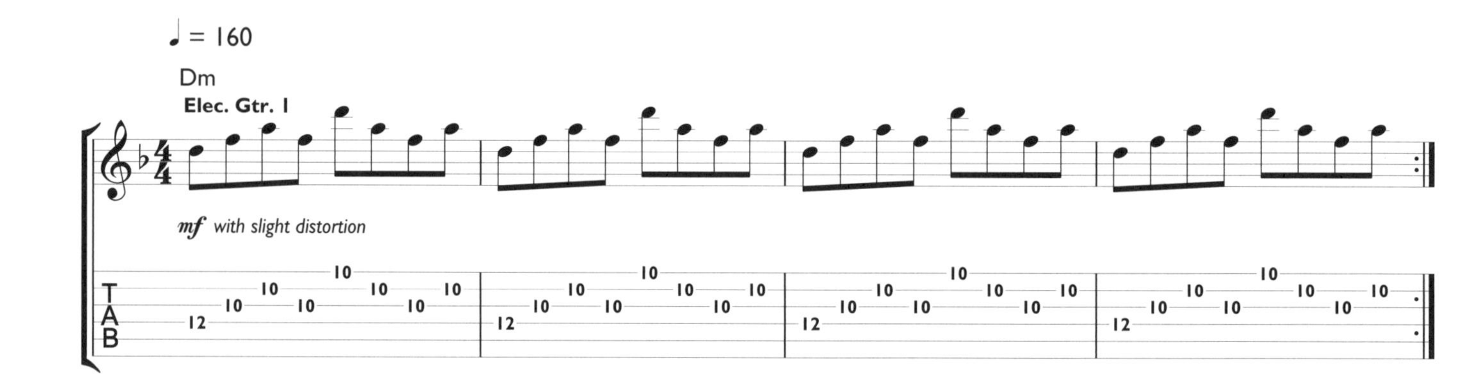

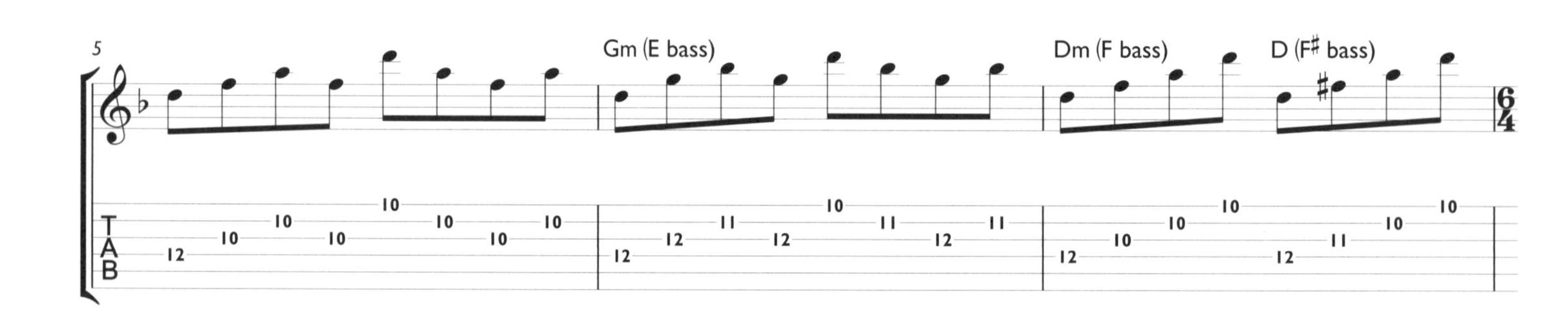

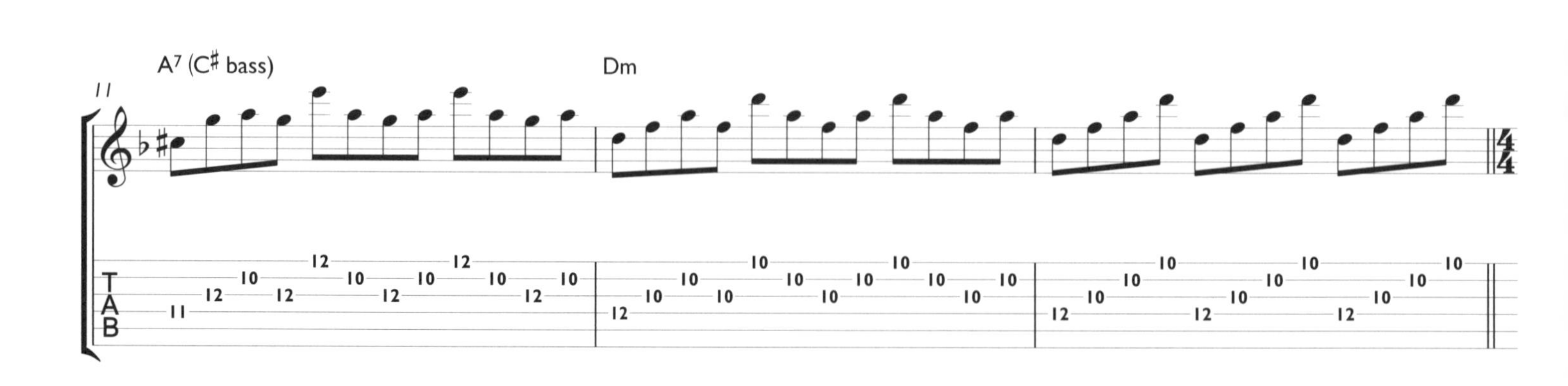

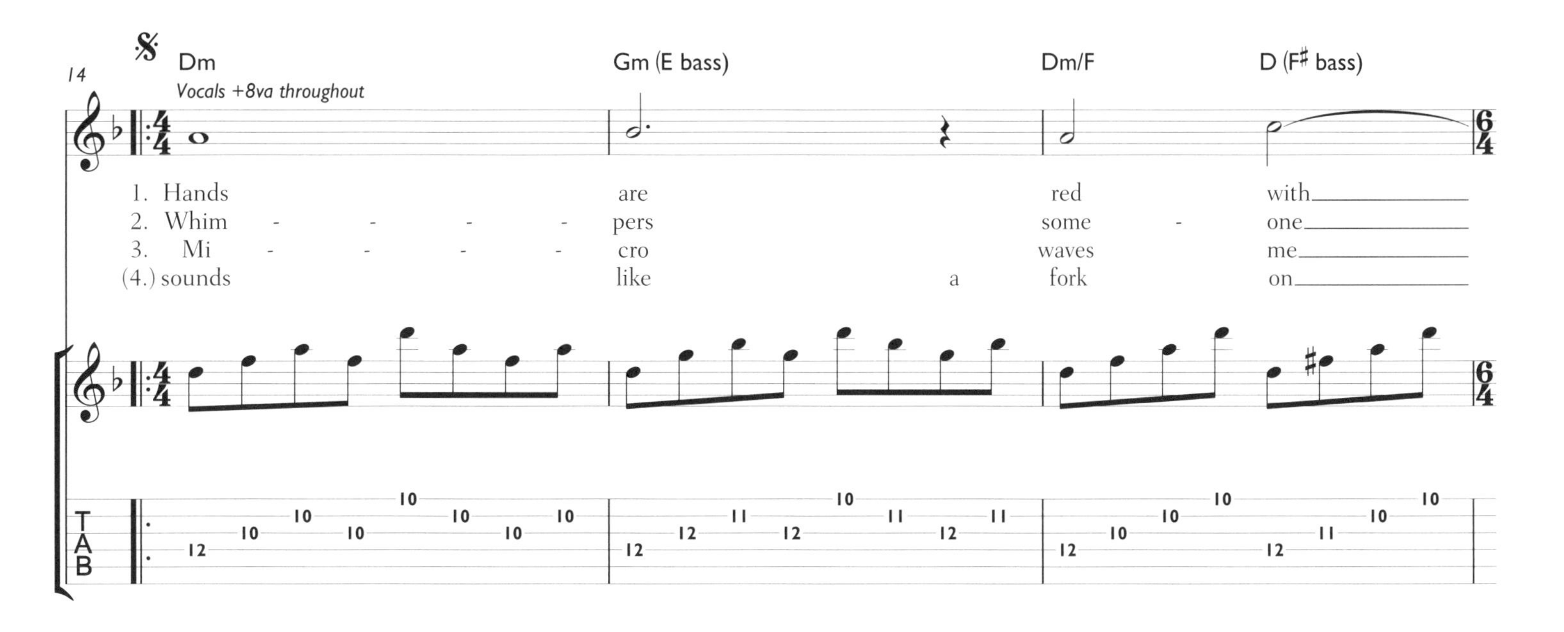
14
Dm
Gm (E bass)
Dm/F
D (F♯ bass)
Vocals +8va throughout
1. Hands are red with
2. Whim - pers some - one
3. Mi - cro waves me
(4.) sounds like a fork on
TAB

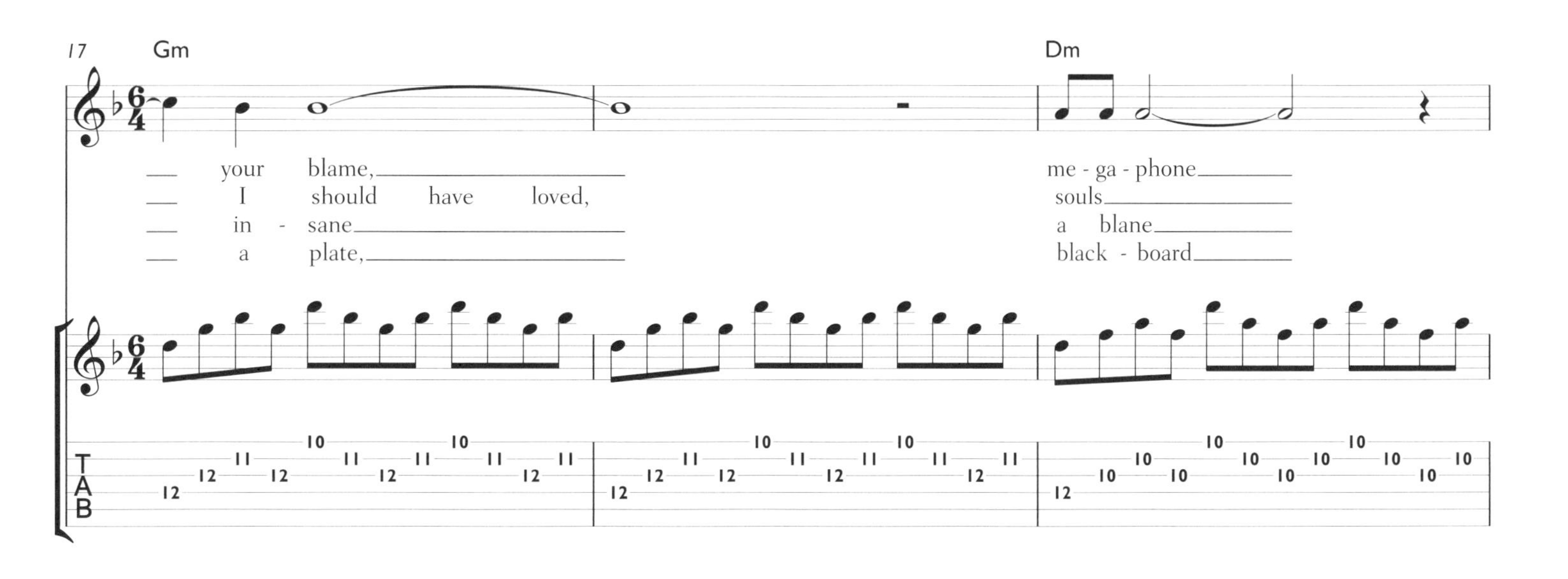
17
Gm
Dm
your blame, me - ga - phone
I should have loved, souls
in - sane a blane
a plate, black - board
TAB

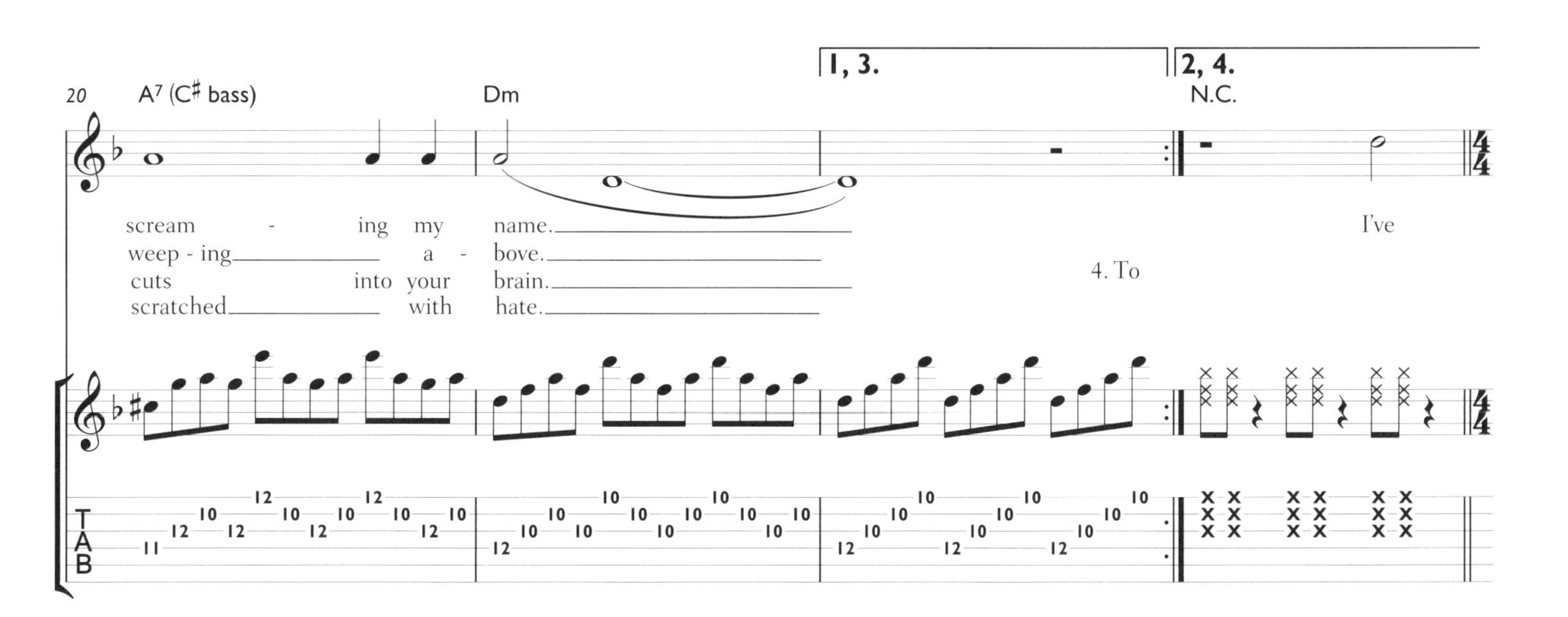
20
A7 (C♯ bass)
Dm
1, 3.
2, 4.
N.C.
scream - ing my name. I've
weep - ing a - bove.
cuts into your brain. 4. To
scratched with hate.
TAB

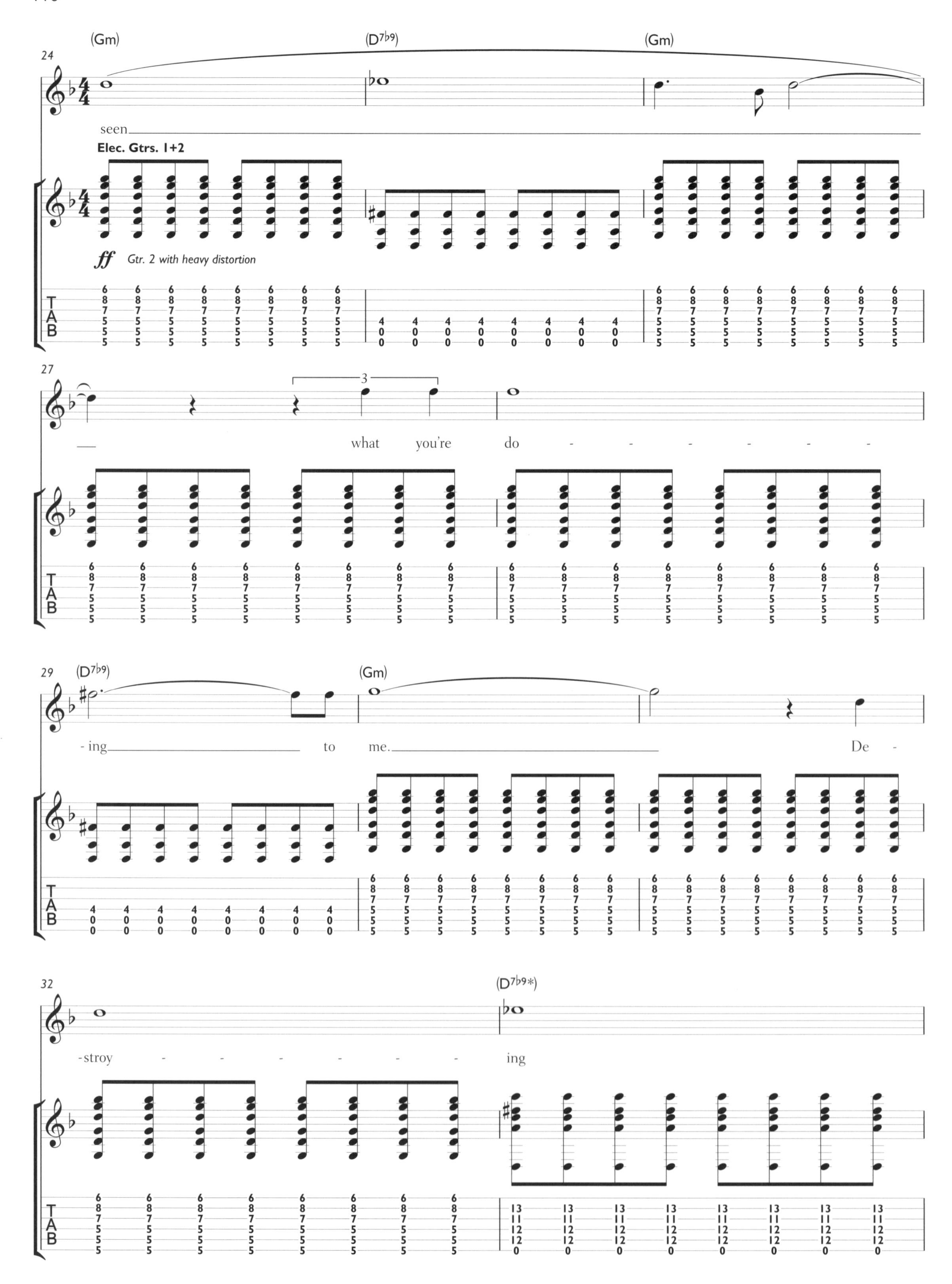

(Gm)
(D7♭9)
(Gm)
24
seen
Elec. Gtrs. 1+2
ff
Gtr. 2 with heavy distortion
27
what you're do - - - - - -
29
(D7♭9)
(Gm)
-ing to me.
De -
32
(D7♭9*)
-stroy - - - - - ing

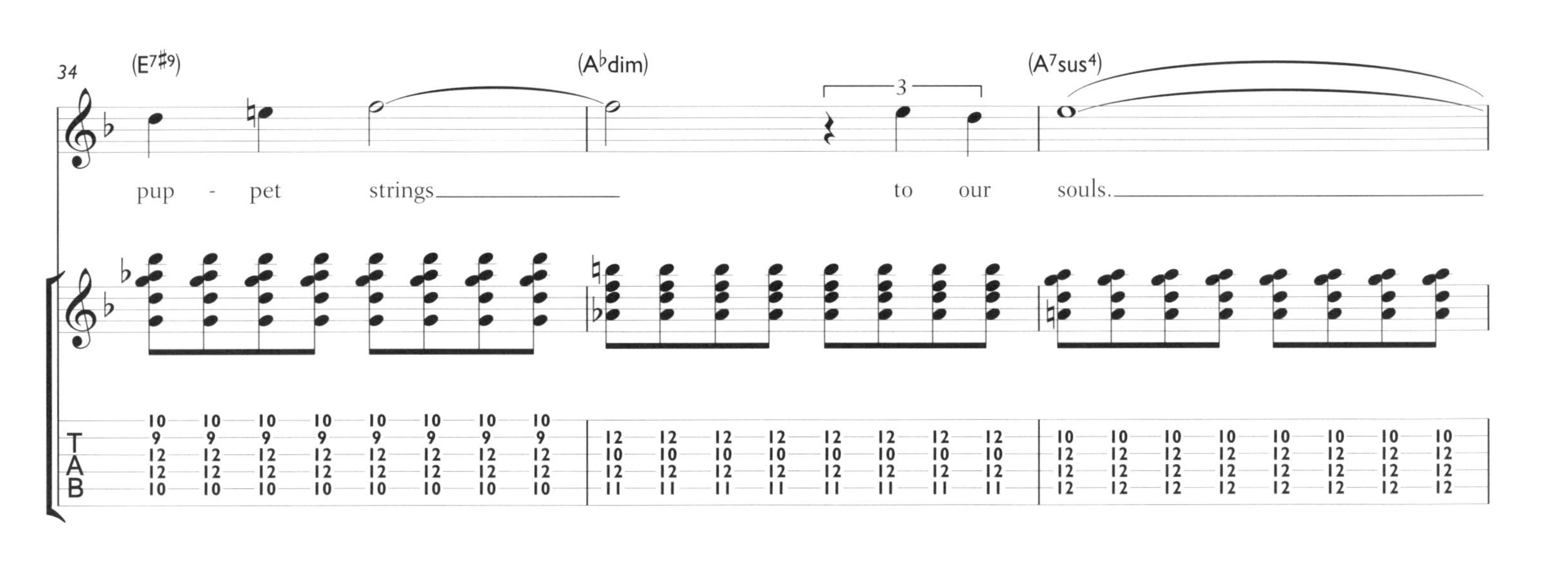

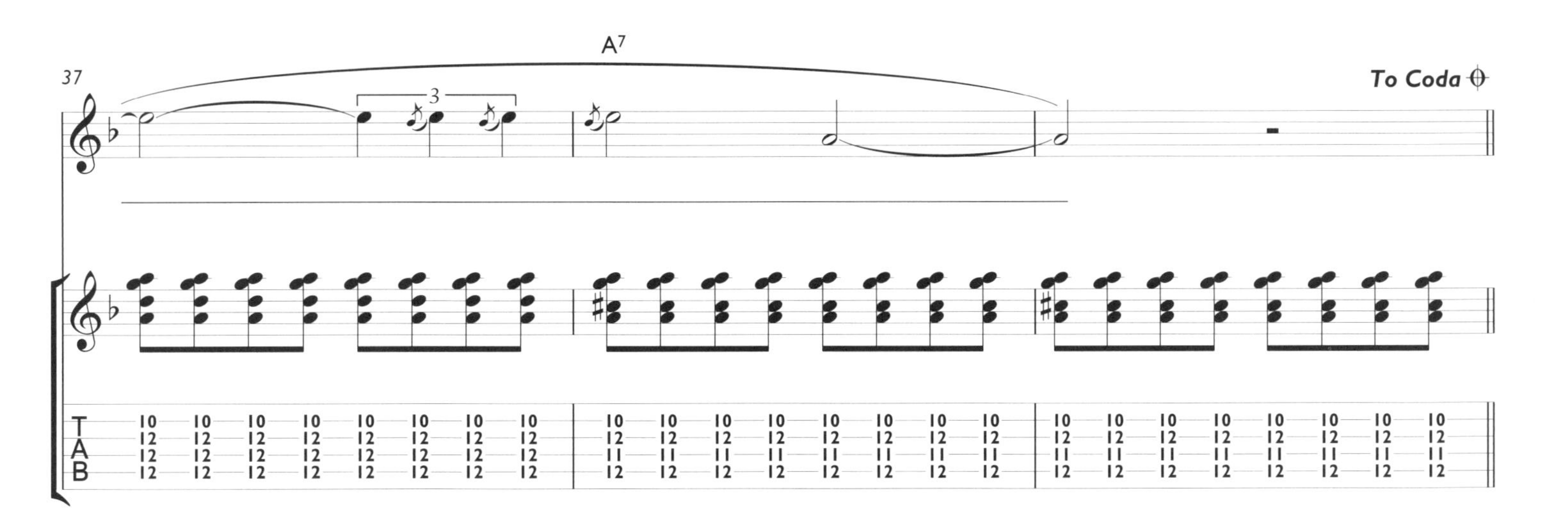

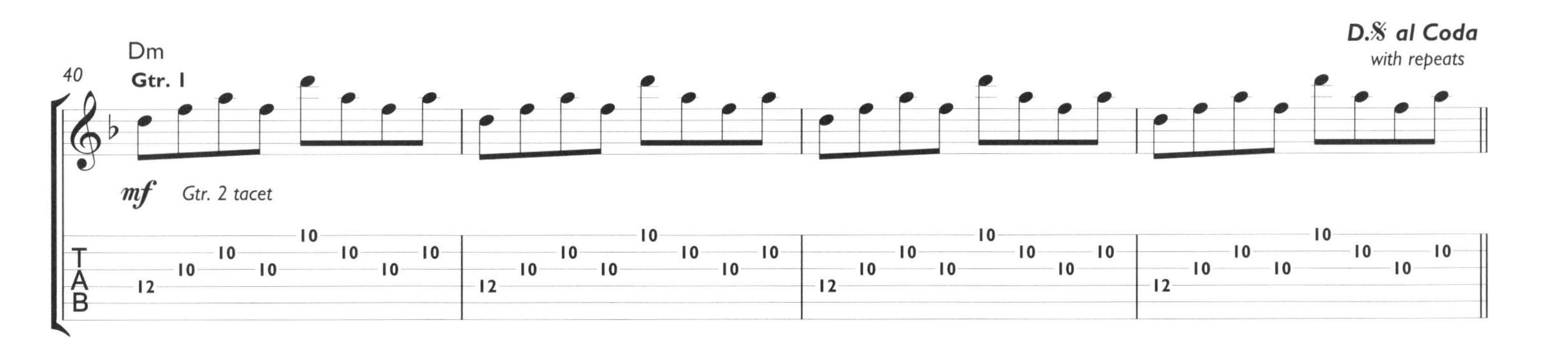

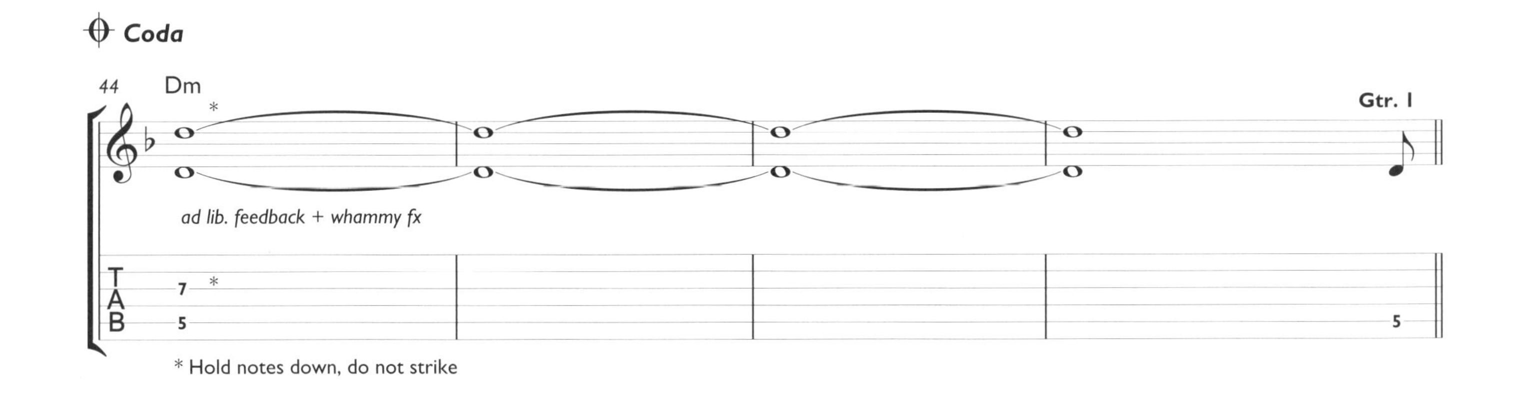

* Hold notes down, do not strike

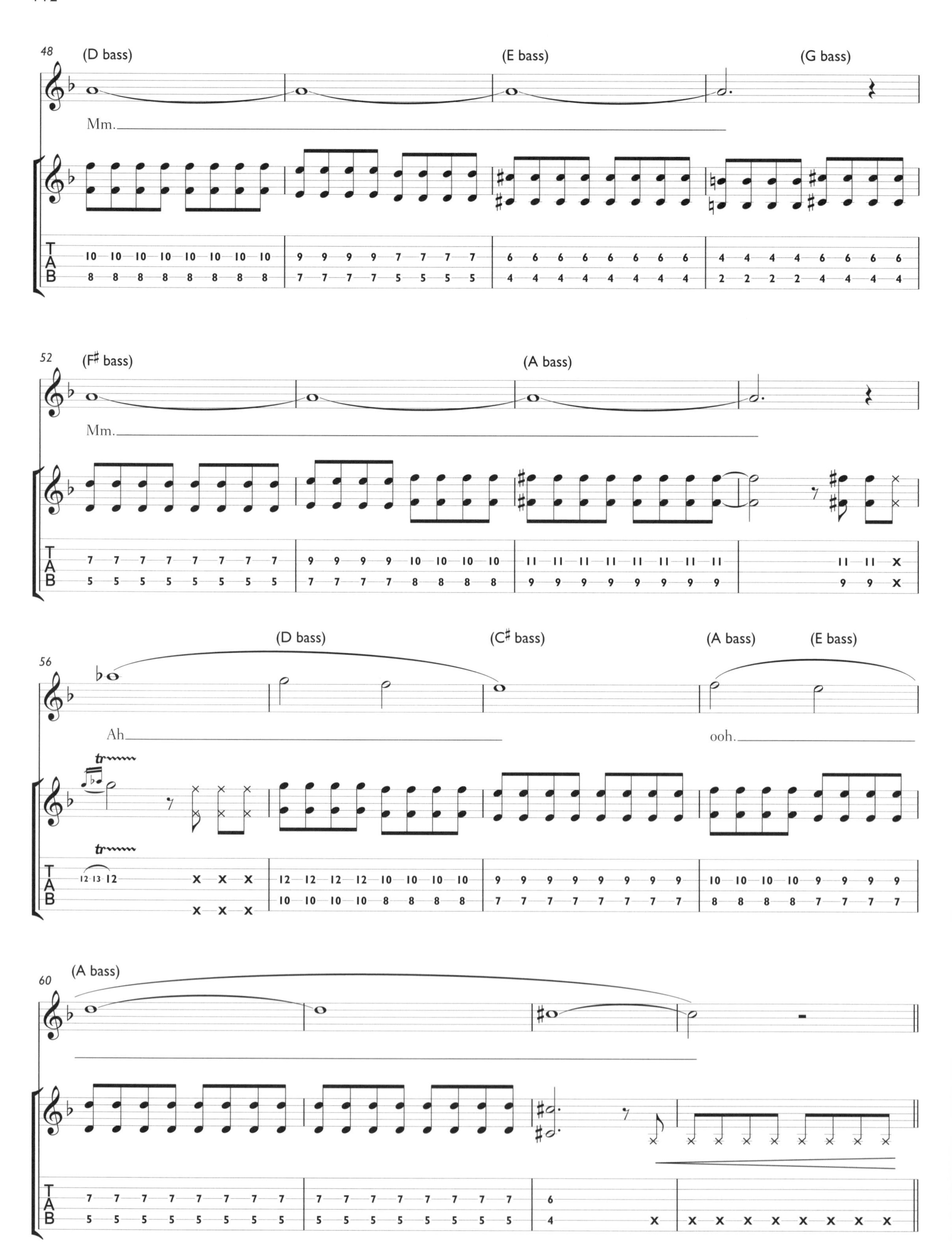
48
(D bass)
(E bass)
(G bass)
Mm.
52
(F♯ bass)
(A bass)
Mm.
56
(D bass)
(C♯ bass)
(A bass)
(E bass)
Ah
ooh.
tr
60
(A bass)

64
N.C.
ff

68

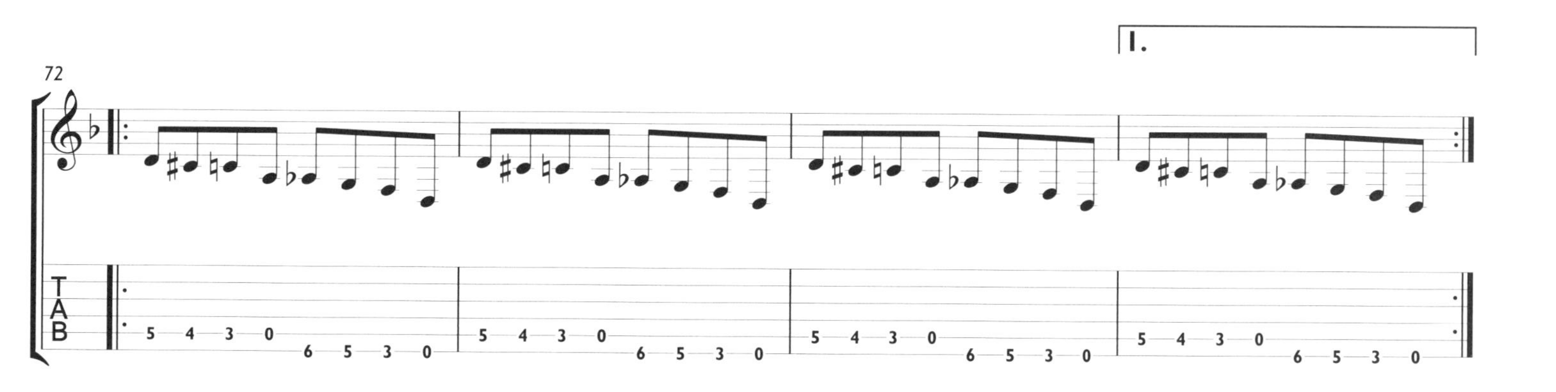
72
1.

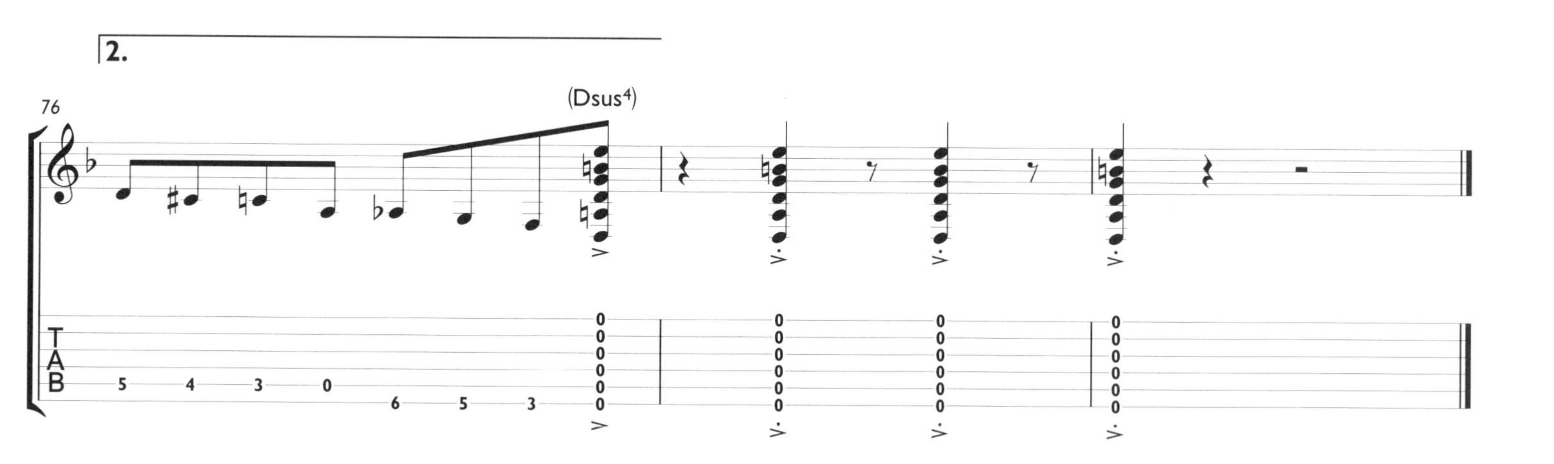
2.
76
(Dsus4)

MUSCLE MUSEUM

Words and Music by Matthew Bellamy

11
Bm
F♯m
C♯
way.
You will wait un - til it's ov - er, to re-veal what you'd nev - er
T
A
B

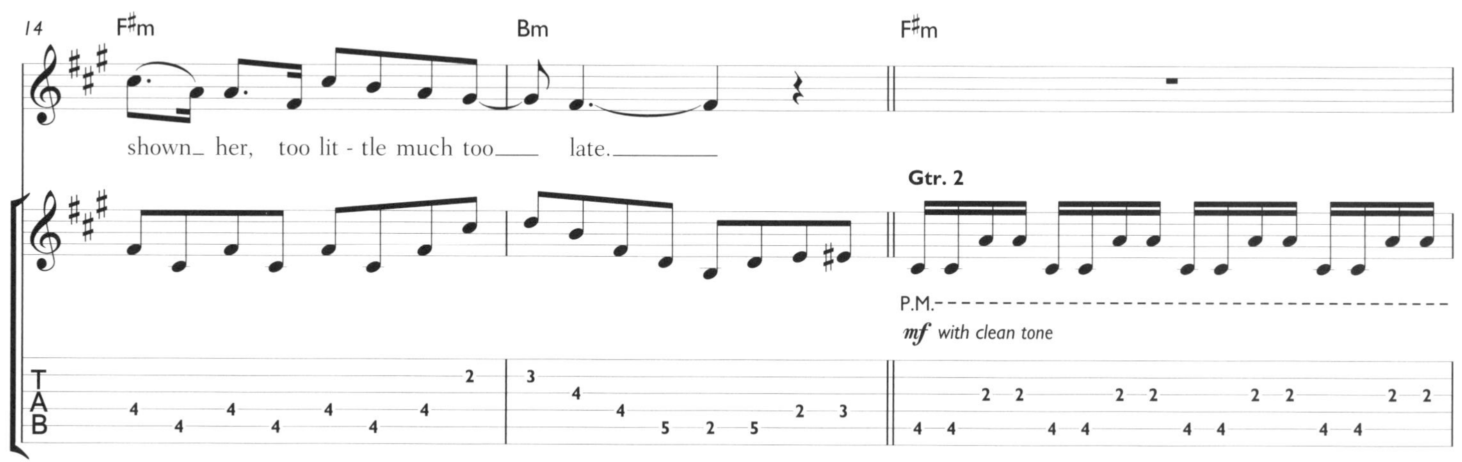
14
F♯m
Bm
F♯m
shown her, too lit - tle much too late.
Gtr. 2
P.M.
mf with clean tone
T
A
B

17
C♯
F♯m
T
A
B

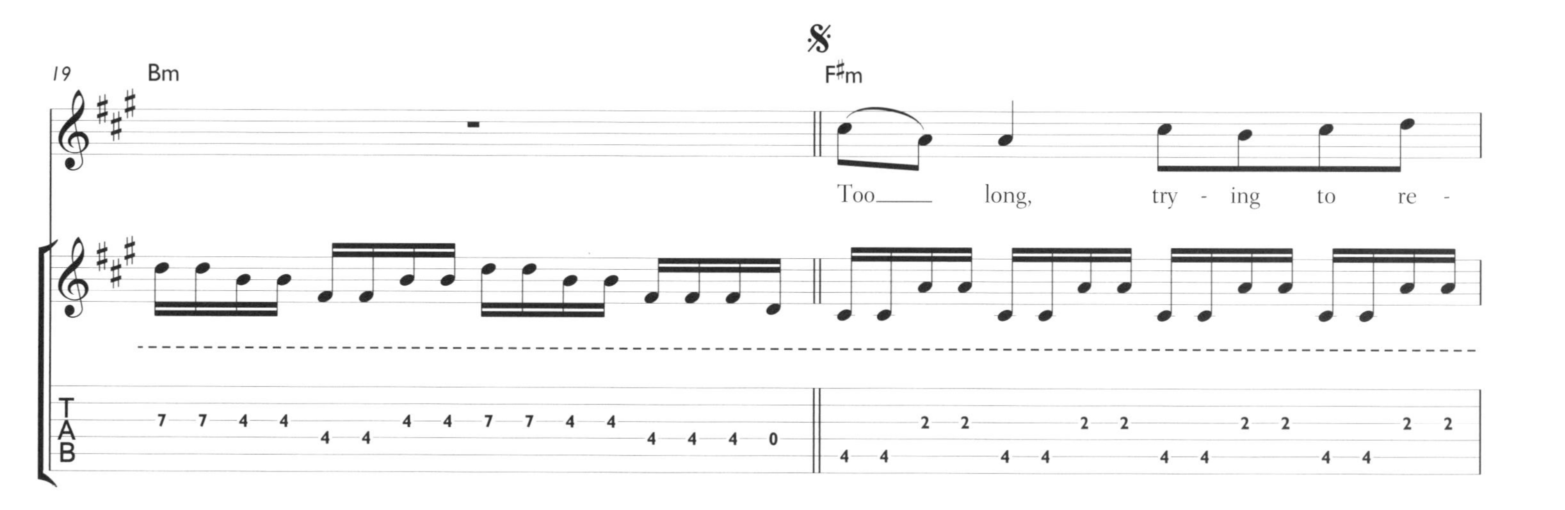
19
Bm
F♯m
Too long, try - ing to re -
T
A
B

21
C♯
F♯m
Bm
-sist it, you've just gone and missed it. It's es-caped your world.

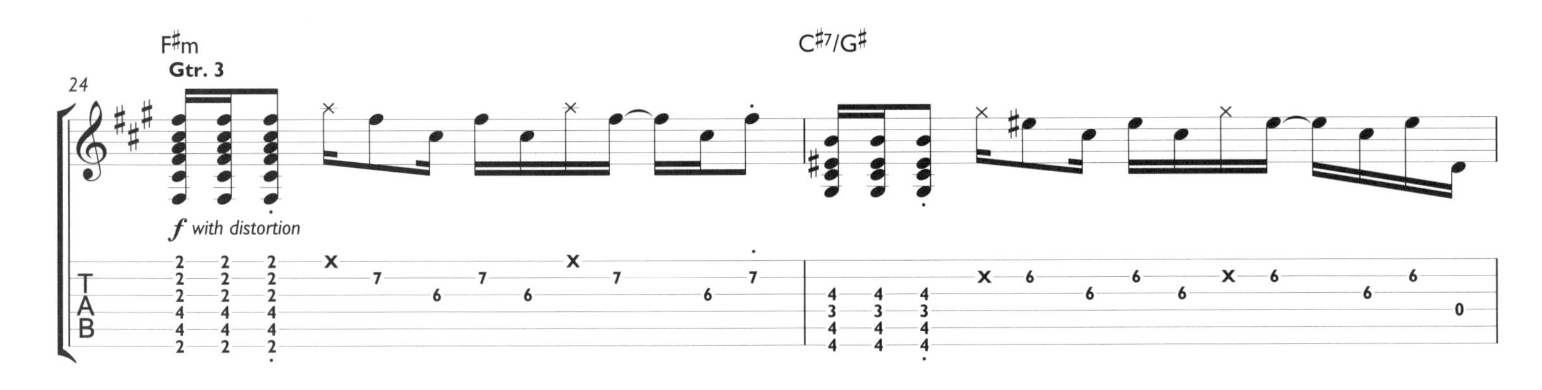
24
F♯m
Gtr. 3
C♯7/G♯
f with distortion

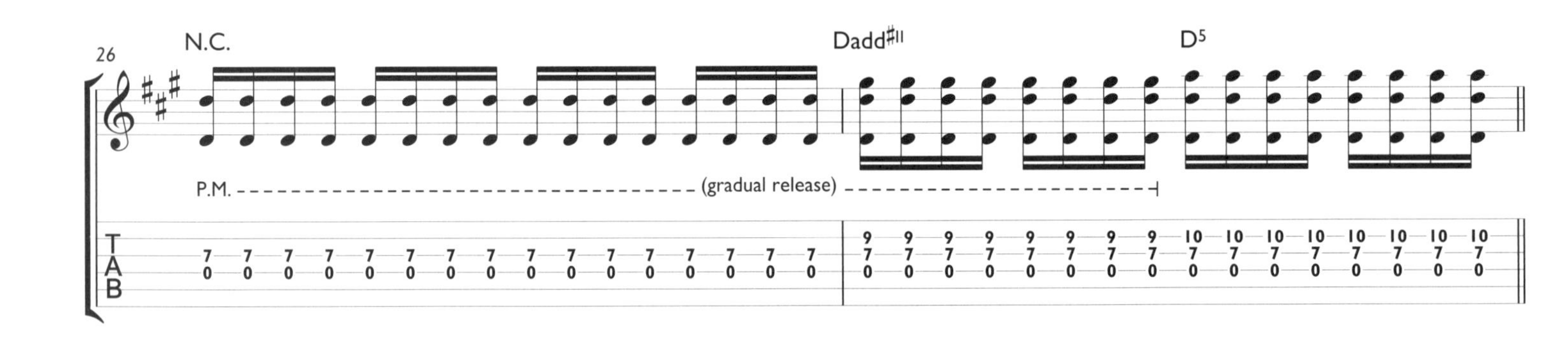
26
N.C.
Dadd♯11
D5
P.M.
(gradual release)

28
F♯m
C♯7/G♯
F♯m
Gtr. 3
sim.
Can you see that I am need-ing, beg-ging for so much more than you could ev-
Gtr. 4
let ring...
mf with slight distortion

Bm
F♯m
C♯7/G♯
- er give.
And I don't want you to a - dore me, don't want you to ig -
F♯m
Bm
E
To Coda
- nore me, when it pleas - es you. Yeah and I'll do
C♯/E♯
F♯m
Gtr. 3
it on my own.
Bass arr. for gtr.
F♯m
C♯
Gtr. 1
Gtr. 3 tacet

42
F♯m
F♯
Bm
F♯m
I have played in ev - 'ry
Bass arr. for gtr.
45
C♯7
F♯m
Bm
D.𝄋 al Coda
toi - let, but you still want to spoil it, to prove I've made a big mis - take.
Gtr. 2
Bass arr. for gtr.
sul pont.
let ring…
1/2
Coda
C♯/E♯
F♯m
F♯m7
D
48
sim.
it on my own.
Yeah.
Vocals with heavy fx.
E7
C♯/E♯
F♯m
F♯m7
51
And I'll do it on my own.

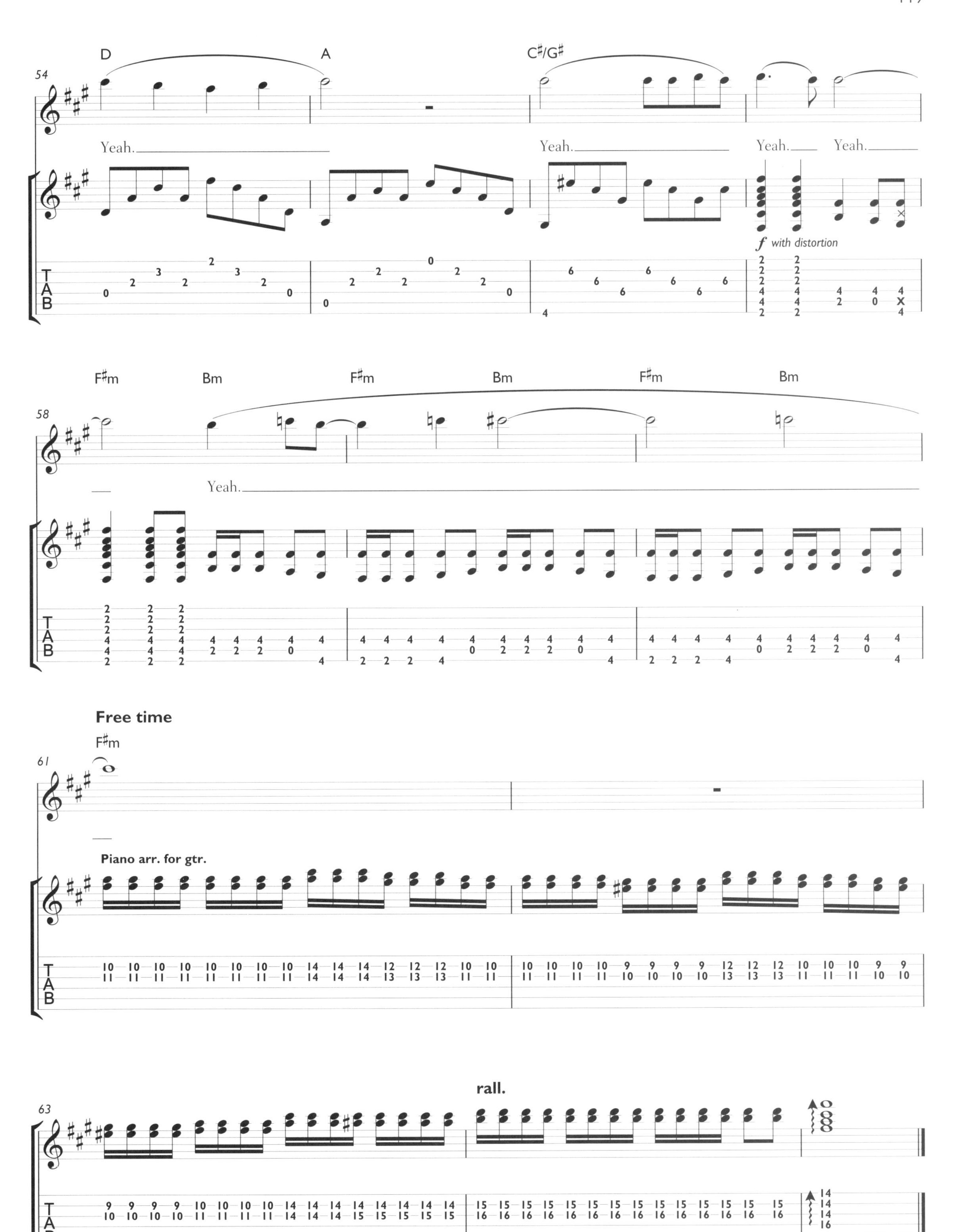
D
A
C♯/G♯
Yeah.
Yeah.
Yeah.
Yeah.
f with distortion
F♯m
Bm
F♯m
Bm
F♯m
Bm
Yeah.
Free time
F♯m
Piano arr. for gtr.
rall.

MK ULTRA

Words and Music by Matthew Bellamy

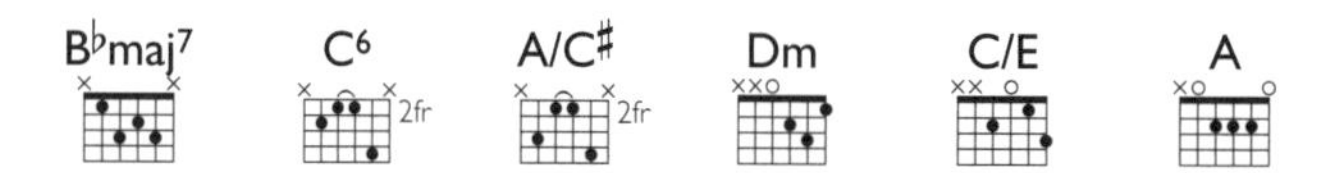

♩ = 155

Electric Guitars in drop-D tuning

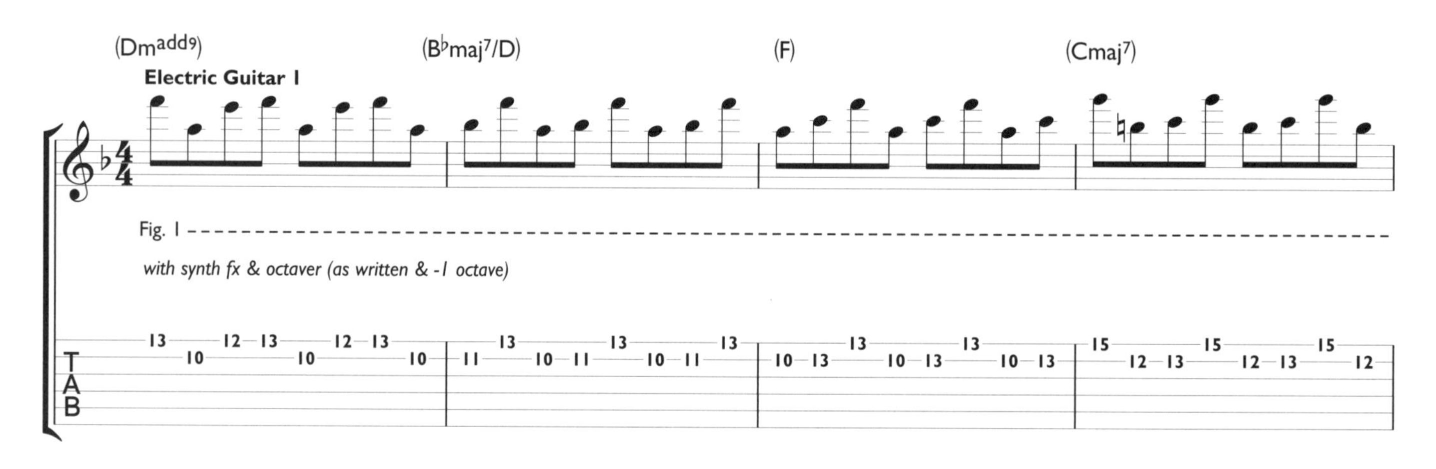

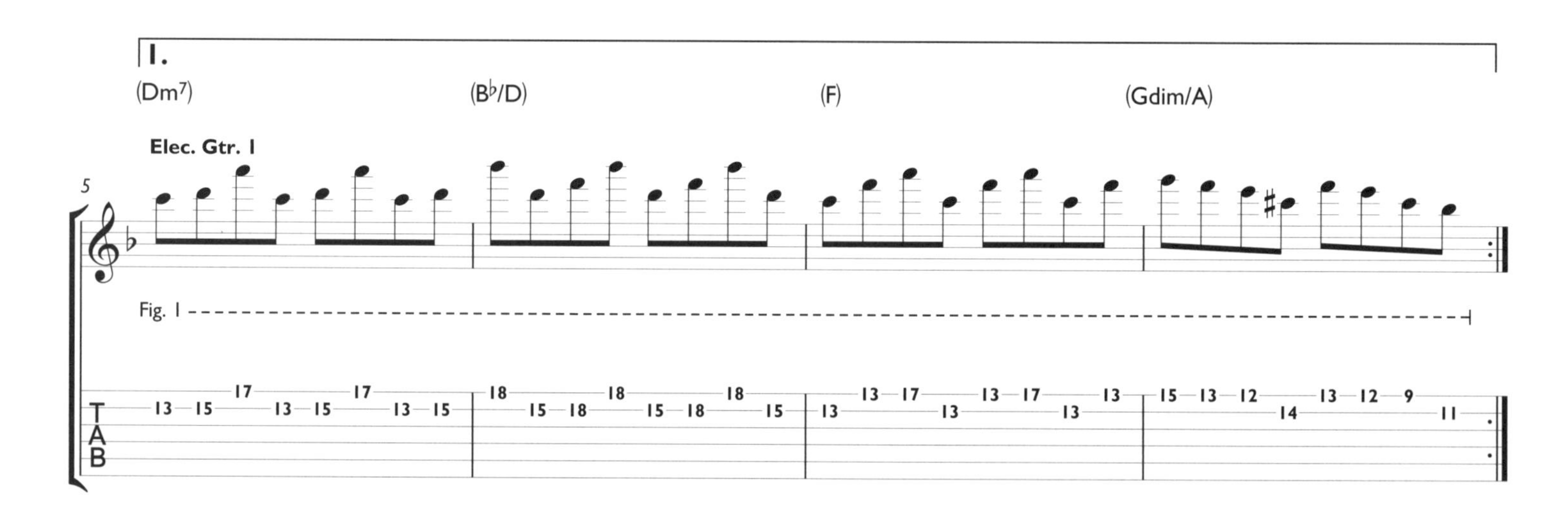

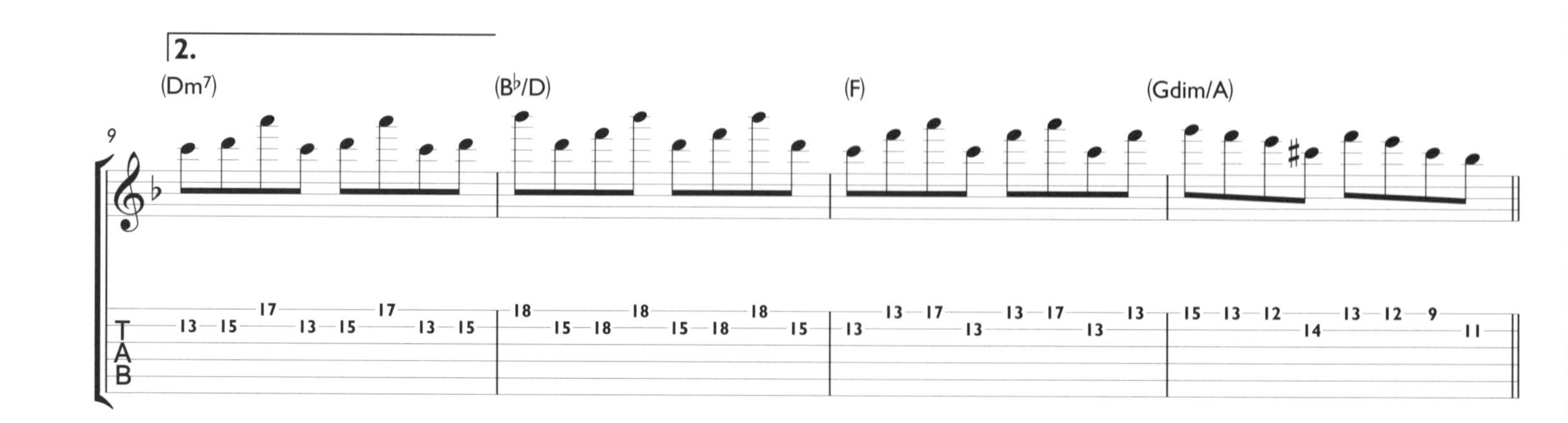

(Dmadd9)
(B♭maj7/D)
(F)
(Cmaj7)
13
1. The_ wave - length gent - ly_ grows,_ co - er-cive no - tions re - e - volve,_
Elec. Gtr. 1
Fig. 3
(Dm7)
(B♭/D)
(F)
(Gdim/A)
17
_ a u - ni - verse is trapped_ in - side_ a tear._
Fig. 3
21
_ It_ re - so - nates_ the_ core,_ cre - ates_ un - na - tu - ral laws,
25
_ re - pla - ces love_ and hap - pi - ness_ with fear._

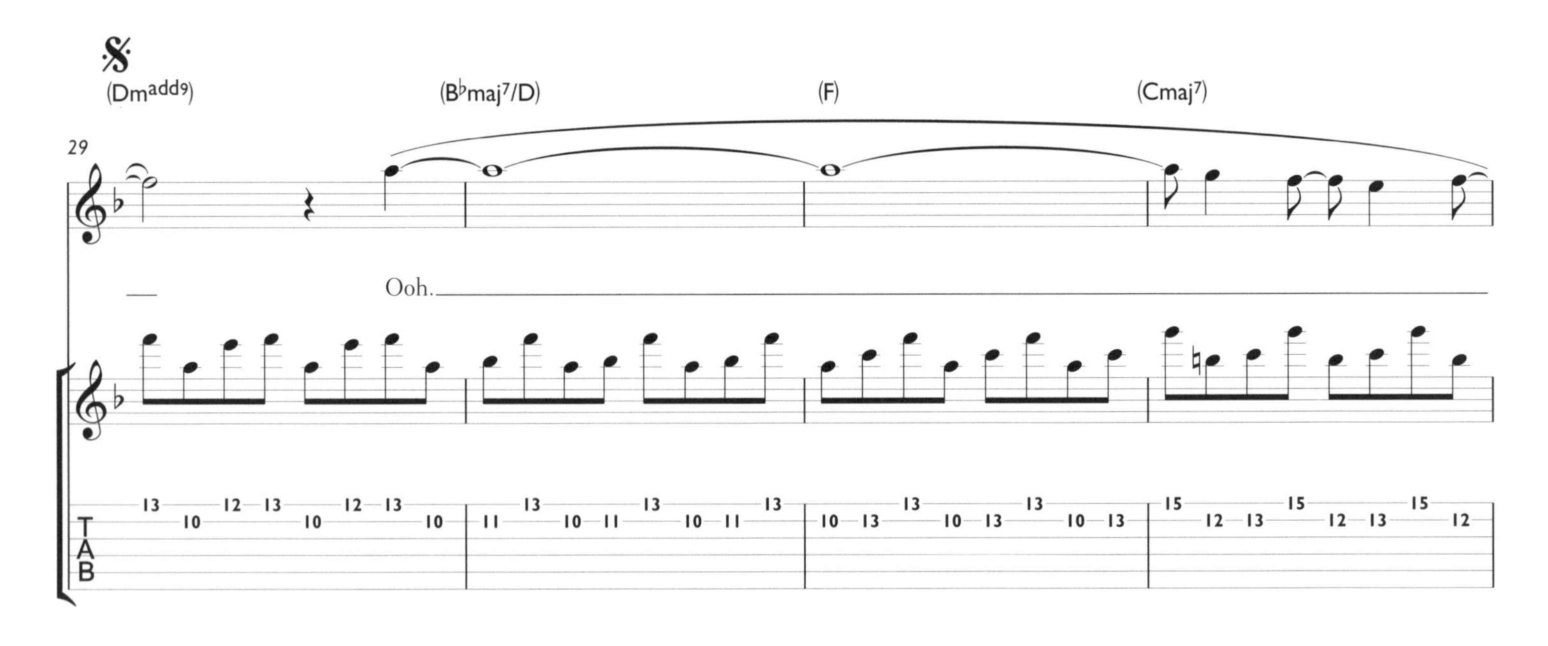
(Dmadd9)
(B♭maj7/D)
(F)
(Cmaj7)
29
Ooh.
13 10 12 13 10 12 13 10
11 13 10 11 13 10 11 13
10 13 13 10 13 13 10 13
15 12 13 15 12 13 15 12

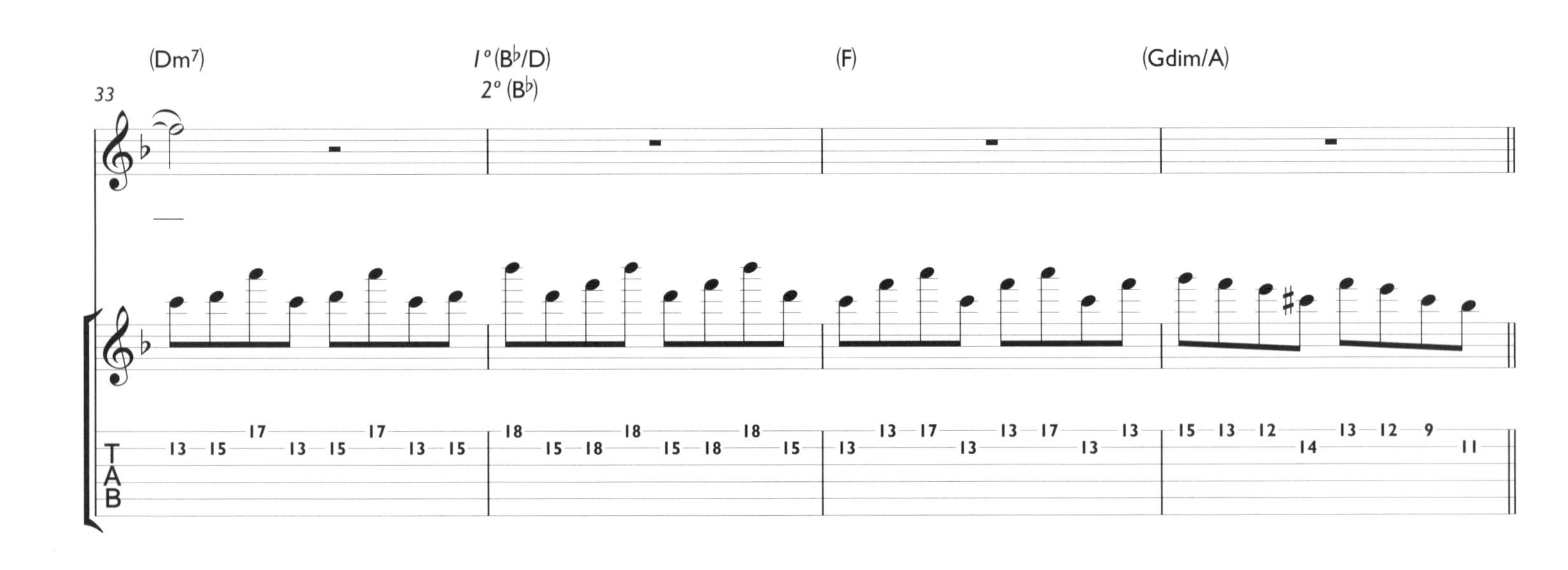
(Dm7)
1° (B♭/D)
2° (B♭)
(F)
(Gdim/A)
33
13 15 17 13 15 17 13 15
18 15 18 18 15 18 18 15
13 13 17 13 13 17 13 13
15 13 12 14 13 12 9 11

B♭maj7
C6
Electric Guitar 2
with overdrive
37
How much de - cep - tion can you take?
How ma - ny lies will you cre - ate?
Elec. Gtr. 1
10 10 10 10 10 10 10 10

A/C♯
Dm
How much long - er un - til you break?
Your mind's a - bout to fall.
C/E
C6
To Coda
And they are break - ing
(Dm)
(Ddim)
(A/C♯)
through.
Ooh, ooh, ooh, ooh.
They are break - ing
Elec. Gtr. 2
P.M.
Synth Strings (+1 octave)

53
(Cm6)
(G/B)
through. Ooh, ooh, ooh, ooh. And they are breaking
P.M.
P.M.
TAB
57
(Gm/B♭)
(D/A)
(Dm/A)
through. Ooh, ooh, ooh, ooh, ooh, ooh.
P.M.
P.M.
61
(A)
We are lo - sing con - trol. And they are breaking
8vb
P.M.
P.M.

(Dm)
(Ddim)
(A/C♯)
65
through.
They are breaking
Elec. Gtr. 2
P.M.
T A B
12 12 12
12
12 12 12
11
Synth Strings (+1 octave)
(Cm6)
(G/B)
69
through.
They are breaking
10 10 10
10
9 9 9
9
(Gm/B♭)
(D/A)
(Dm/A)
73
through.
Now we're falling,
8 8 8
8
7 7 7
7

77
(A)
we are lo - sing con - trol.
P.M.
P.M.
T
A
B
(Dm)
81
Elec. Gtr. 2
(Dmadd9)
(B♭maj7/D)
(F)
(Cmaj7)
1° Elec. Gtr. 2
open
⑥
85
Vocals 2° only
2. In - vi - si - ble to all, the mind be - comes a wall,
1° Elec. Gtr. 1 plays Fig. 3
2° Elec. Gtr. 1 plays Fig. 1

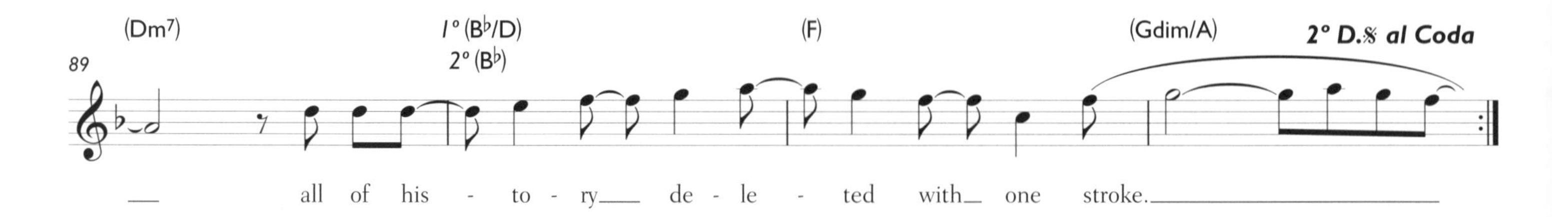
(Dm7)
1° (B♭/D)
2° (B♭)
(F)
(Gdim/A)
2° D.𝄋 al Coda
89
all of his - to - ry de - le - ted with one stroke.

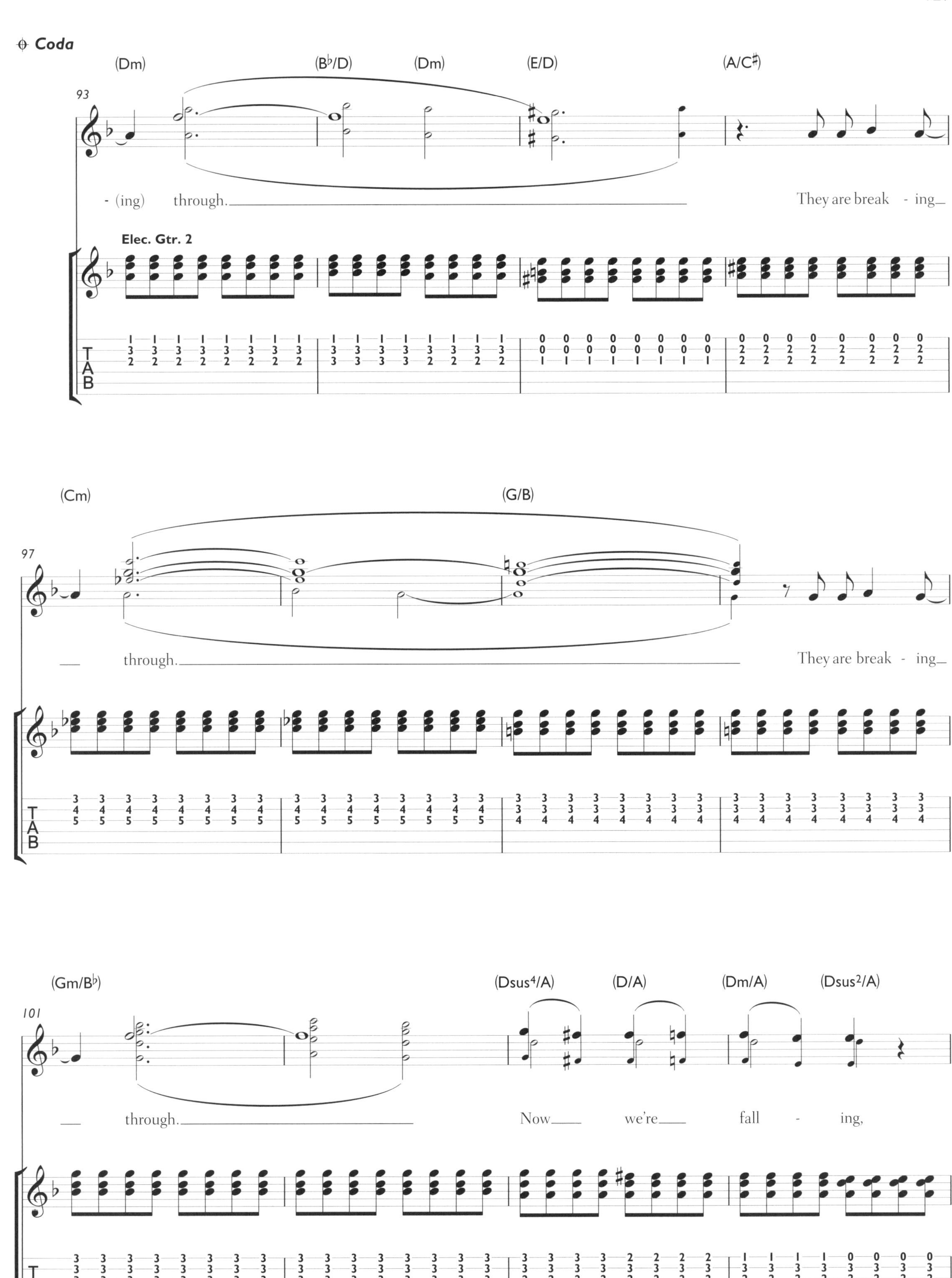
Coda
(Dm)
(B♭/D)
(Dm)
(E/D)
(A/C♯)
93
- (ing) through.
They are break - ing
Elec. Gtr. 2
(Cm)
(G/B)
97
through.
They are break - ing
(Gm/B♭)
(Dsus4/A)
(D/A)
(Dm/A)
(Dsus2/A)
101
through.
Now we're fall - ing,

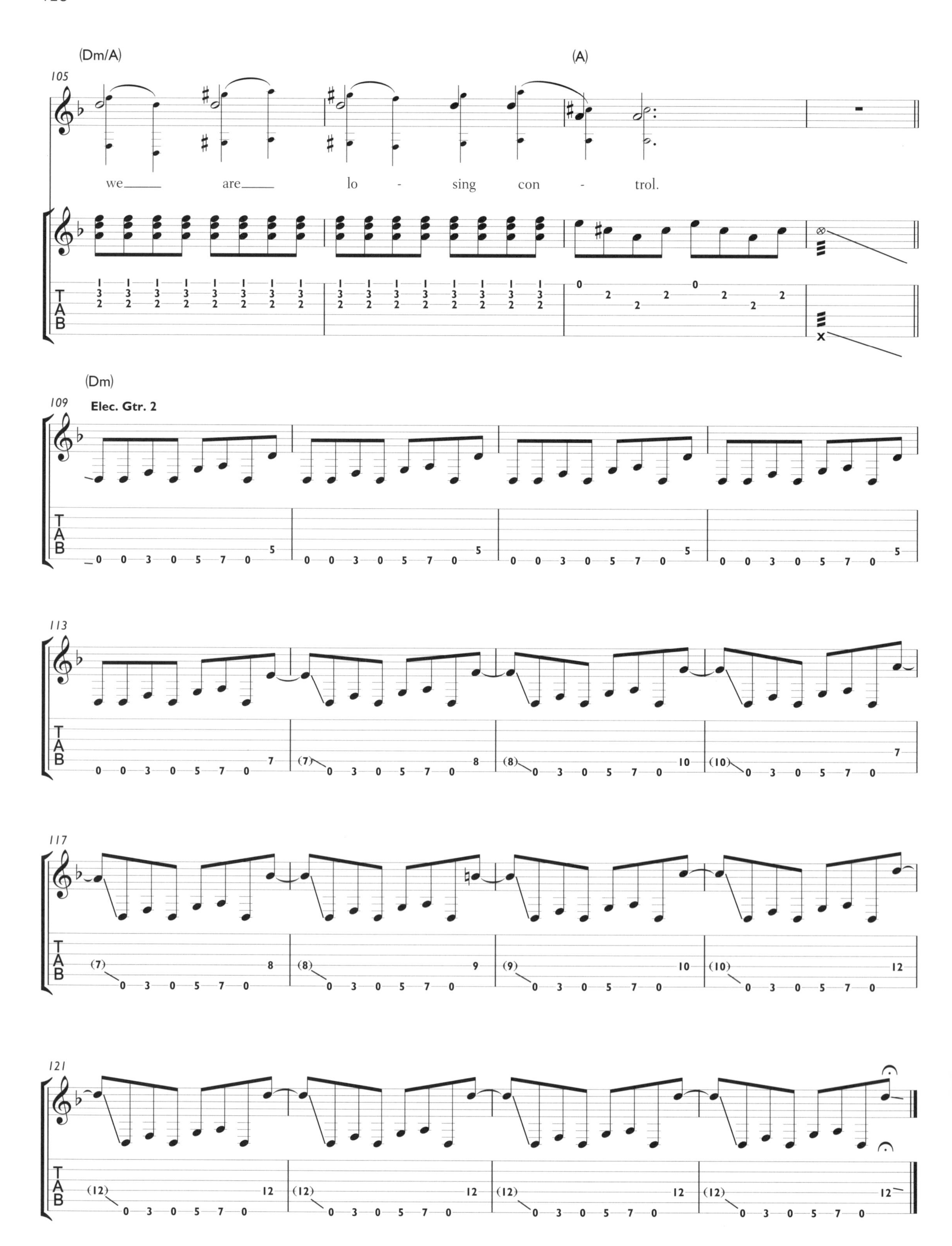
(Dm/A)
(A)
we___ are___ lo - sing con - trol.
(Dm)
Elec. Gtr. 2

NEW BORN

Words and Music by Matthew Bellamy

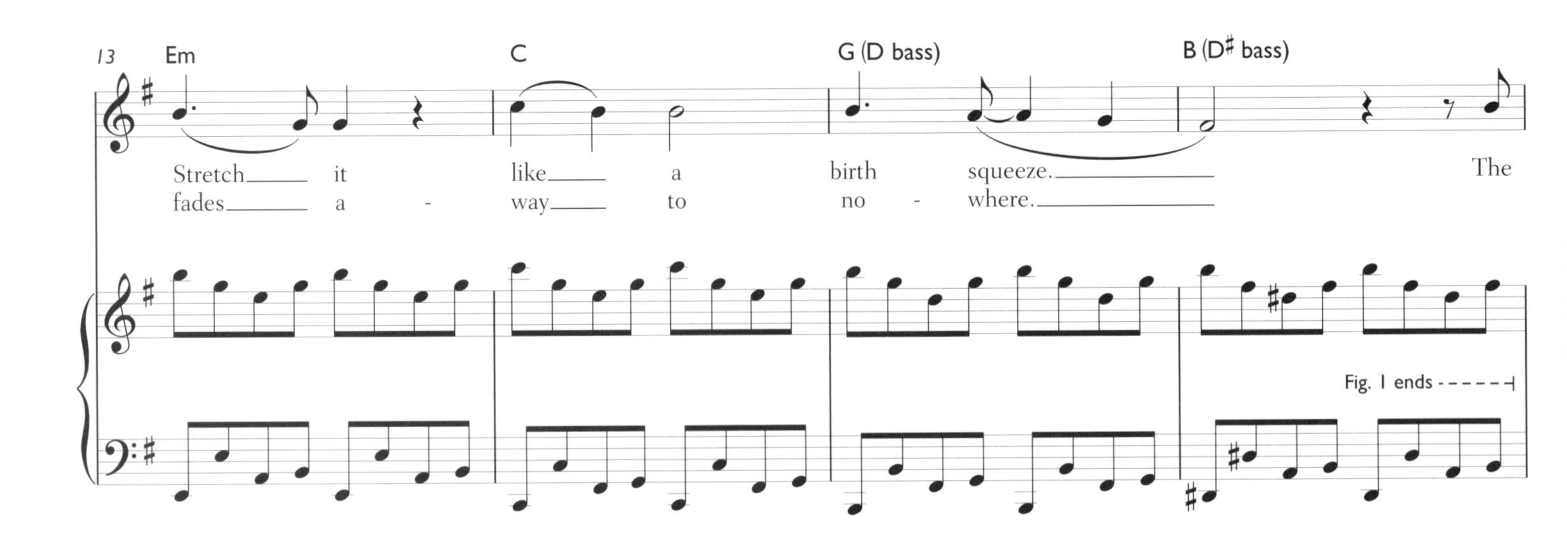
13
Em
C
G (D bass)
B (D♯ bass)
Stretch it like a birth squeeze. The
fades a - way to no - where.
Fig. 1 ends

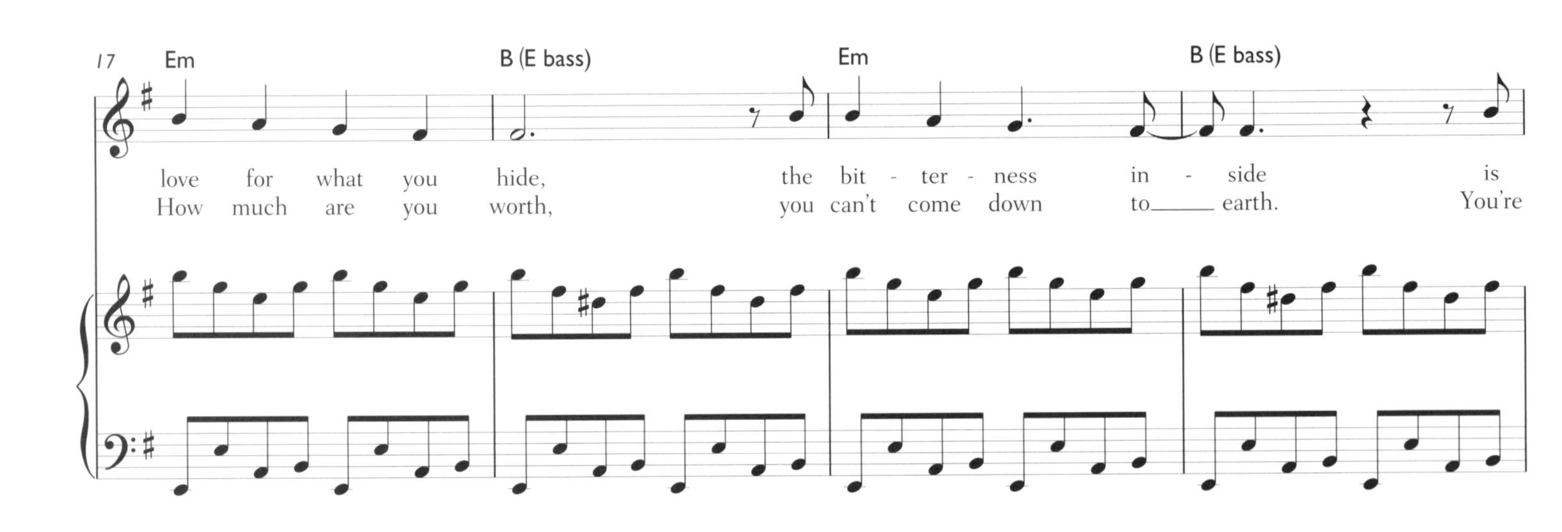
17
Em
B (E bass)
Em
B (E bass)
love for what you hide, the bit - ter - ness in - side is
How much are you worth, you can't come down to earth. You're

21
Em
C
G (D bass)
grow - ing like the new - born.
swell - ing up, you're un - stop - a - ble.

B (D♯ bass)
Em
3° Gtr. 3
cont. sim.
24
When you've
'Cause you've
seen,
2° & 3° Elec. Gtr. 4
with whammy pedal -8ve
Fig. 3
T
A
B
B (E bass)
Em
B (E bass)
Em
26
seen
too
2° & 3° Gtr. 4 with Fig. 3 (x2)
C
G (B bass)
B (D♯ bass)
30
much,
too
2° & 3° Gtr. 4 with Fig. 3 (x3)

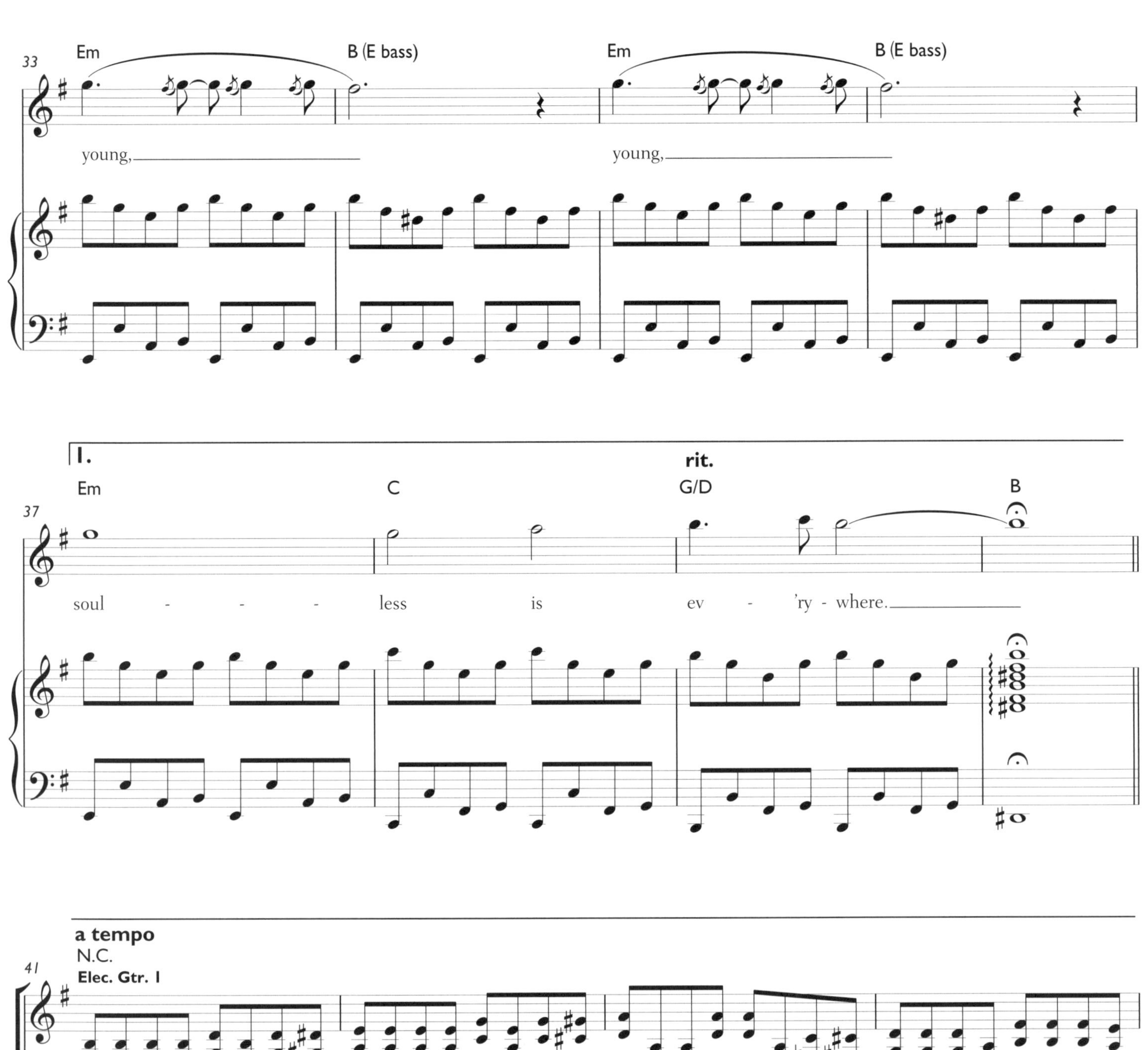
33
Em
B (E bass)
Em
B (E bass)
young,
young,
1.
rit.
Em
C
G/D
B
37
soul - - - less is ev - 'ry - where.

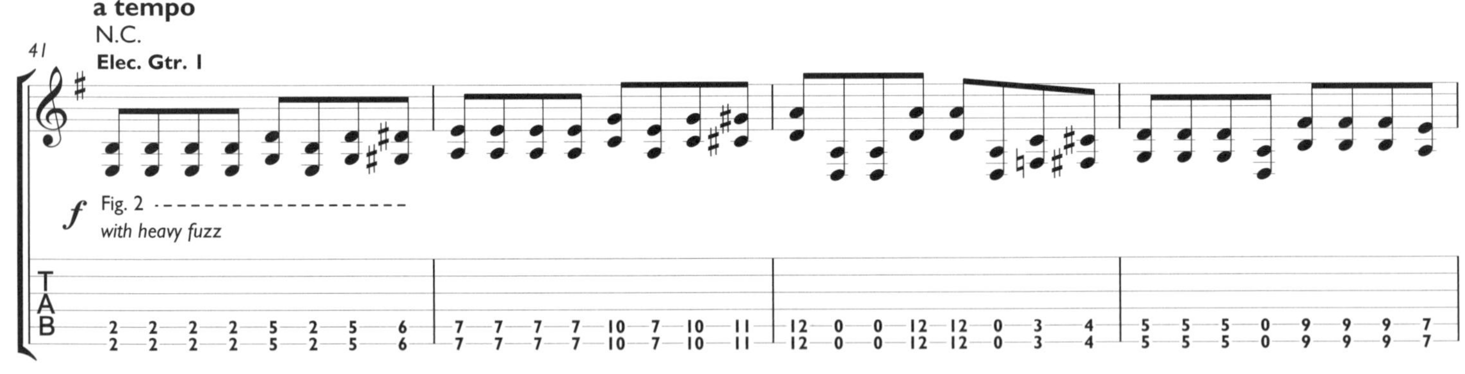
a tempo
N.C.
41
Elec. Gtr. 1
Fig. 2
with heavy fuzz
TAB

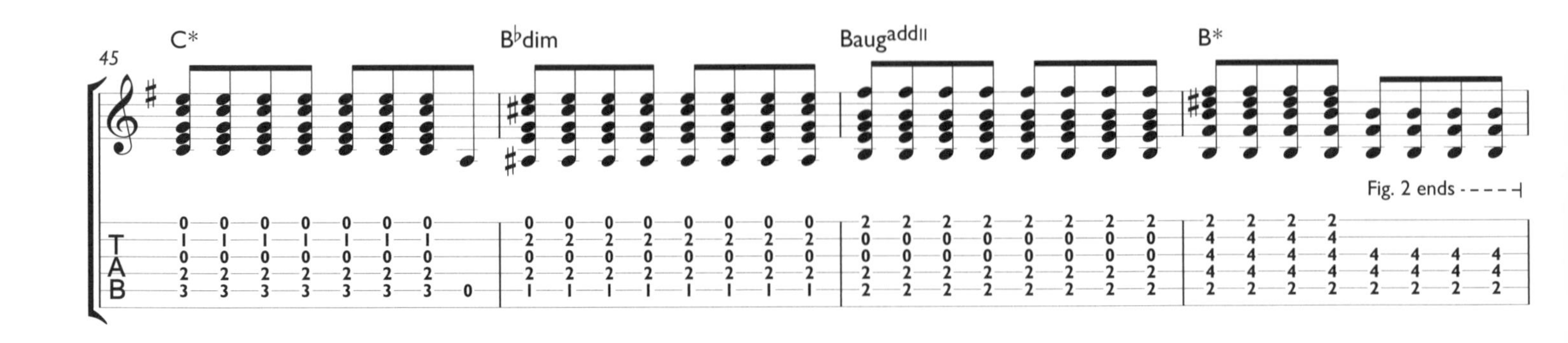
45
C*
B♭dim
Baugadd11
B*
Fig. 2 ends
TAB

49
N.C.
Elec. Gtr. 2
with distortion
Gtr. 1 with Fig. 2 (x2)
T
A
B
2 2 2 2 5 2 5 6
7 7 7 7 10 7 10 11
12 0 0 12 0 0 3 4
5 5 5 5 2 2 0 2

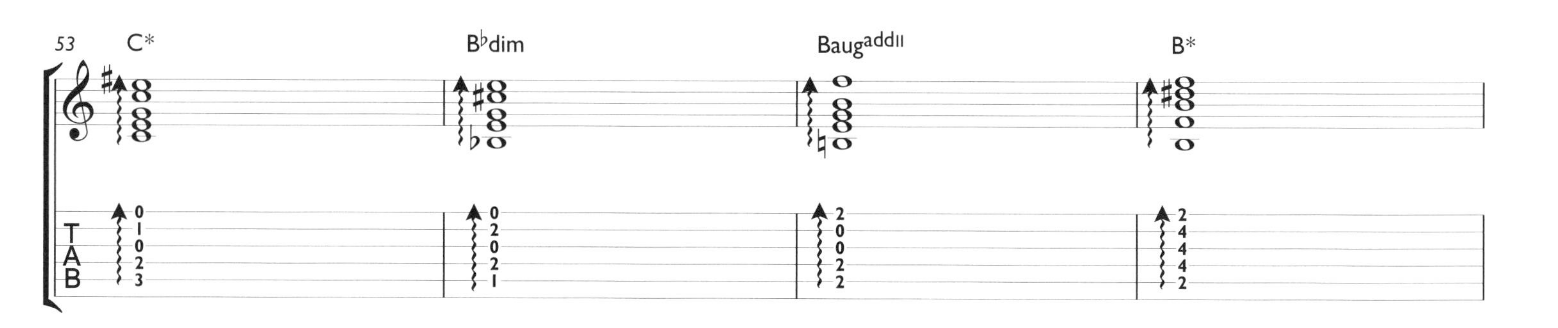
53
C*
B♭dim
Baugadd11
B*
T
A
B

57
N.C.
T
A
B
2 2 2 2 5 2 5 6
7 7 7 7 10 7 10 11
12 0 0 12 0 0 3 4
5 5 5 5 2 2 0 2

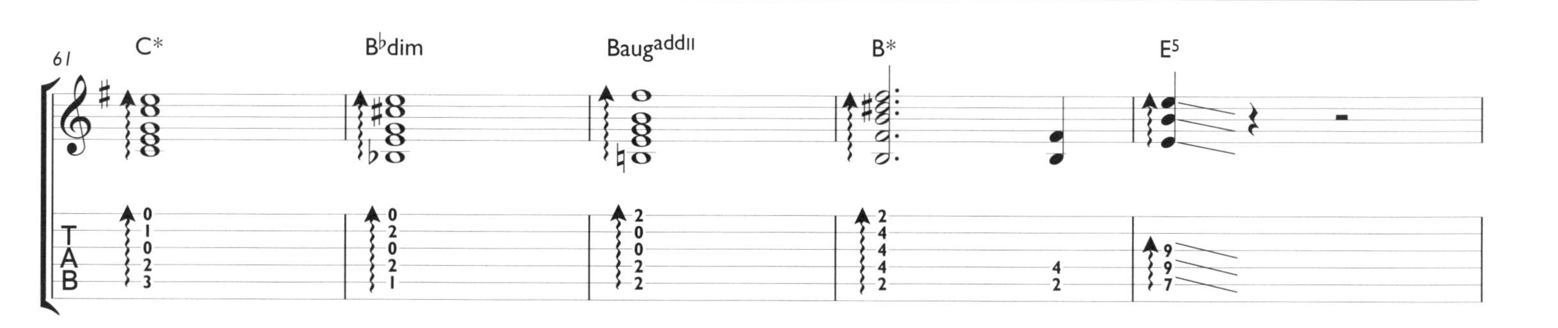
61
C*
B♭dim
Baugadd11
B*
E5
T
A
B

66
Bass arr. for gtr. (standard tunings)
T
A
B

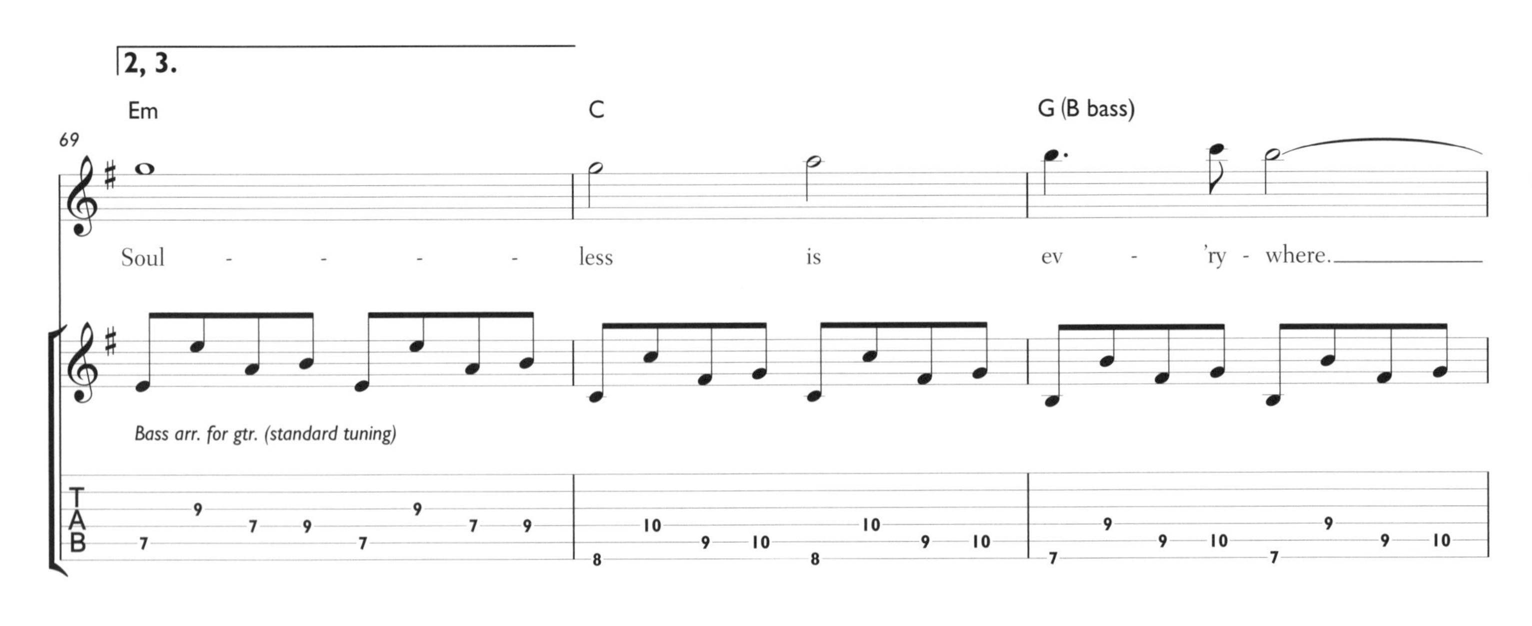
2, 3.
Em
C
G (B bass)
Soul - - - - less is ev - 'ry - where.
Bass arr. for gtr. (standard tuning)
TAB

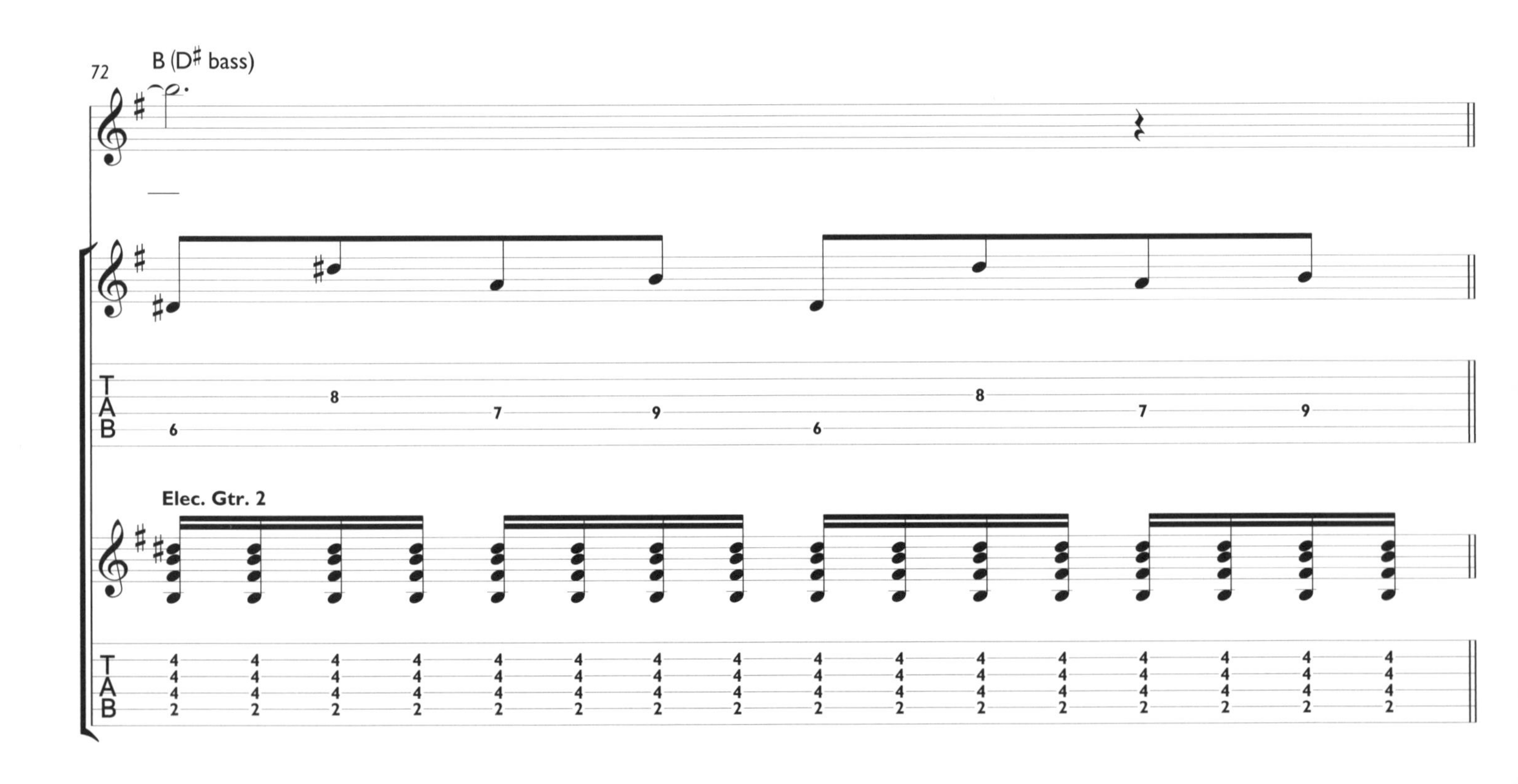
B (D♯ bass)
TAB
Elec. Gtr. 2
TAB

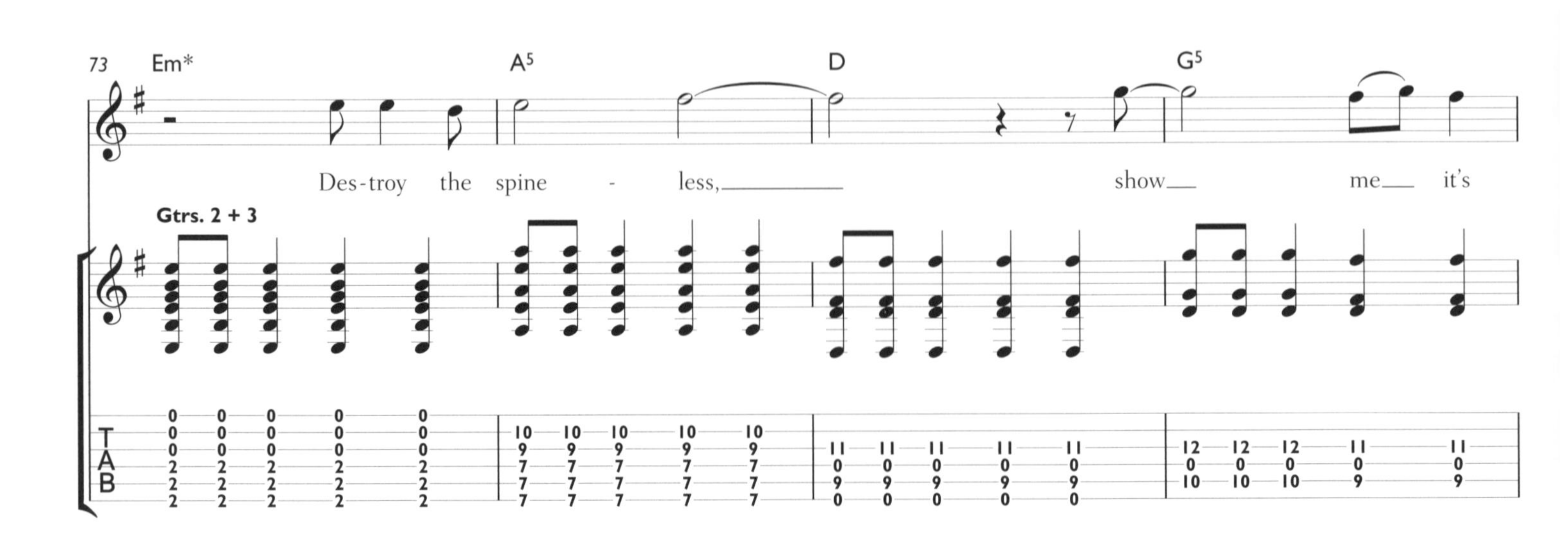
Em*
A5
D
G5
Des-troy the spine - less, show me it's
Gtrs. 2 + 3
TAB

77
C**
B♭dim
Baugadd11
B*
real. Wast - ing our last chance to come a - way,
81
Em*
A5
D
G5
just break the si - lence, 'cause I'm drift - ing a -
85
C**
B♭dim
To Coda
Baugadd11*
B*
- way a - way from you. Ooh yeah.
89
N.C.
Gtr. 2
Gtr. 3 tacet
N.H.
Harm. just above 3rd fret
N.H.
Harm. just above 2nd and 3rd fret
8va
N.H.
Harm. just below 2nd fret

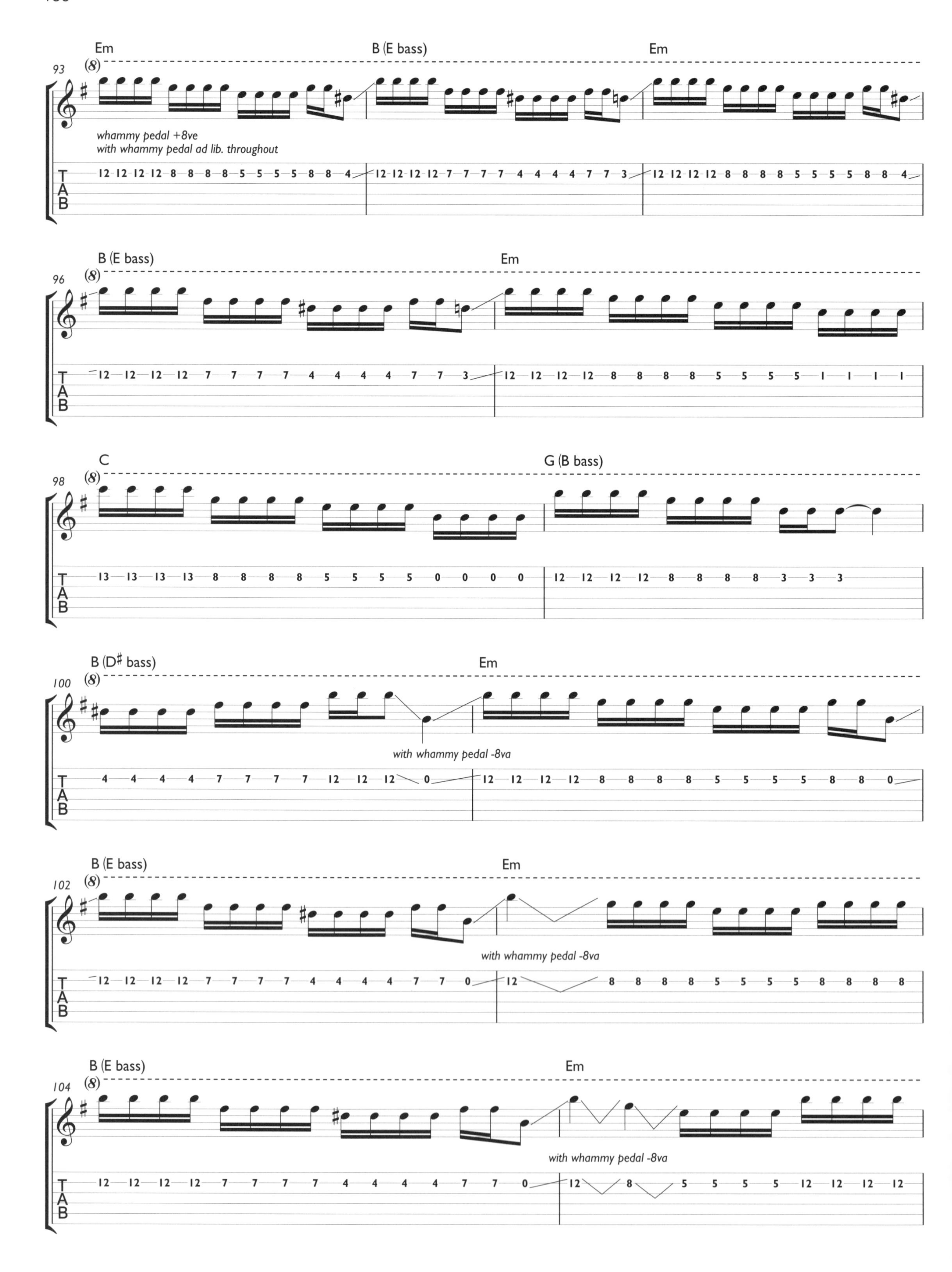

Em
B (E bass)
Em
whammy pedal +8ve
with whammy pedal ad lib. throughout
B (E bass)
Em
C
G (B bass)
B (D♯ bass)
Em
with whammy pedal -8va
B (E bass)
Em
with whammy pedal -8va
B (E bass)
Em
with whammy pedal -8va

D.𝄋 al Coda
C
G (B bass)
B (D♯ bass)
106
with whammy pedal
Coda
B*
N.C.
109
Ooh
yeah.
Gtr. 1 with Fig. 2 (x3)
Gtr. 3 tacet
113
C*
B♭dim
Baugadd11
B*
118
N.C.
122
C*
B♭dim
Baugadd11
B*
Em*
Gtr. 1 tacet
-½ bend neck away from body
T
A
B

PLUG IN BABY

Words and Music by Matthew Bellamy

13
(F♯)
ba - - by. The un - der - neath's no
ba - by you're gon - na lose your own
16
(G)
(D)
big sur - prise, now it's time for
game.
Gtr. 1
19
(F♯)
chan - - ging and cleans - ing ev -
Change me, re - place the en -
22
(G)
(D)
- 'ry - thing to for - get your love.
- vy - ing to for - get your love.
TAB

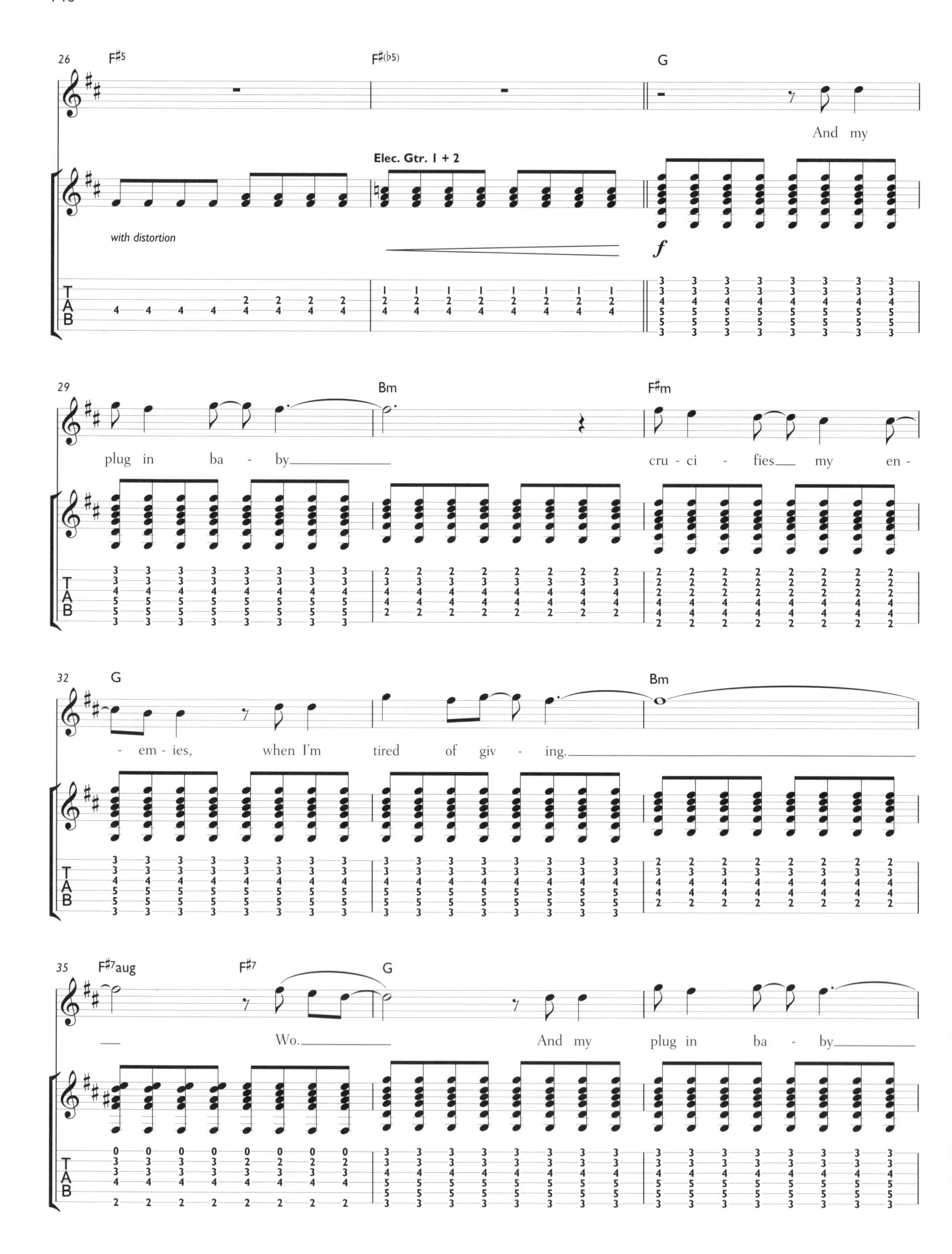
F♯5
F♯(♭5)
G
Elec. Gtr. 1 + 2
with distortion
And my
plug in ba - by
Bm
F♯m
cru - ci - fies my en -
- em - ies, when I'm tired of giv - ing.
F♯7aug
F♯7
Wo.
And my plug in ba - by

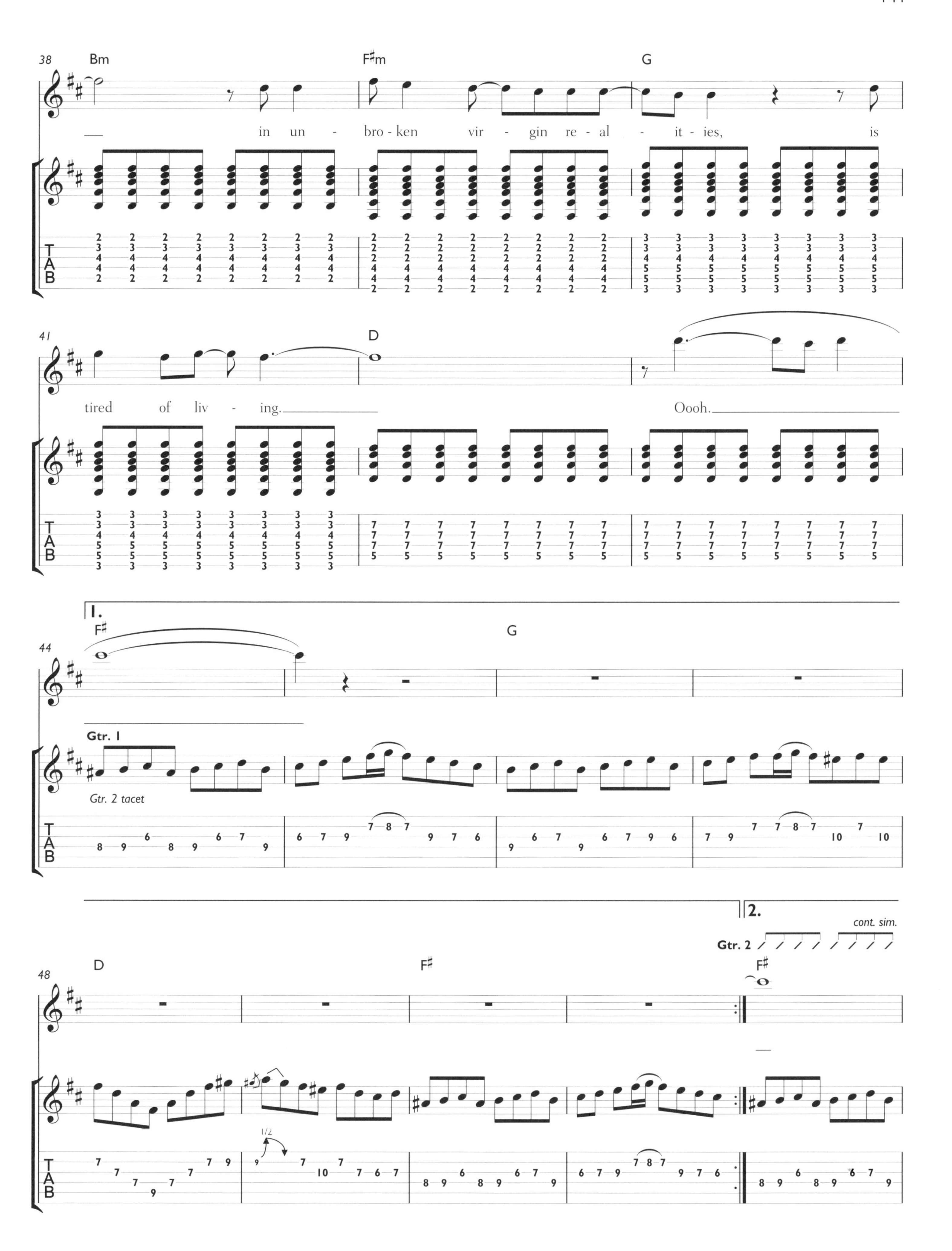
38
Bm
F♯m
G
in un - bro - ken vir - gin re - al - it - ies, is
41
D
tired of liv - ing.
Oooh.
1.
F♯
G
44
Gtr. 1
Gtr. 2 tacet
2.
cont. sim.
Gtr. 2
48
D
F♯
F♯
1/2

G
D
And I've seen your lov - ing, mine is gone,
F♯
G
and I've been in trou - ble.
8va
D
F♯
Woo - - aahhh.
G
D
F♯
G
1/2

STARLIGHT

Words and Music by Matthew Bellamy

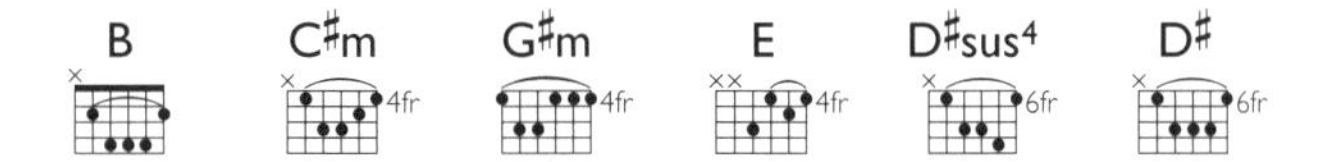

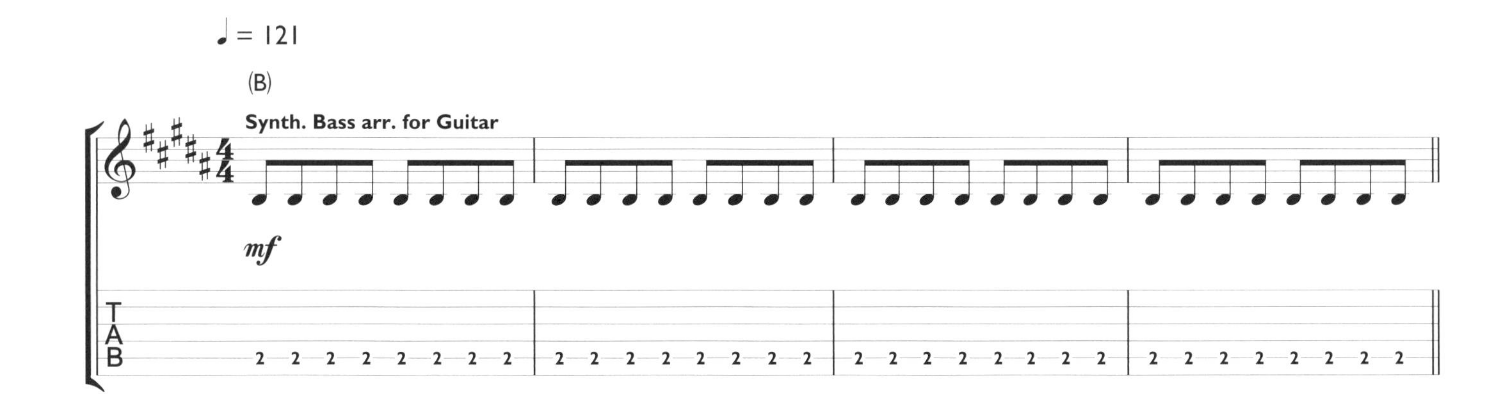

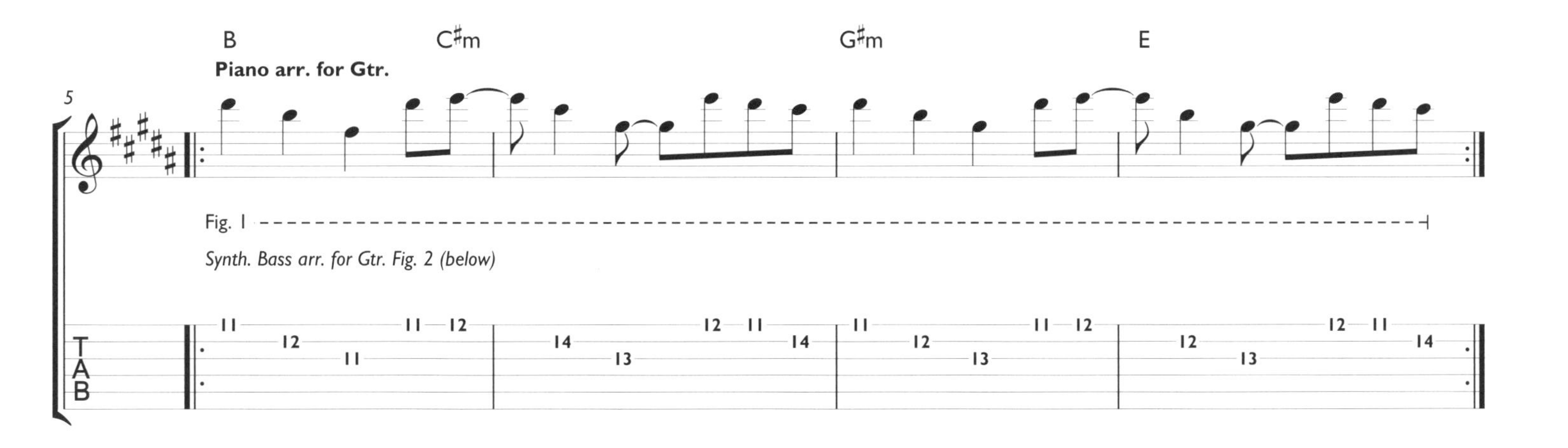

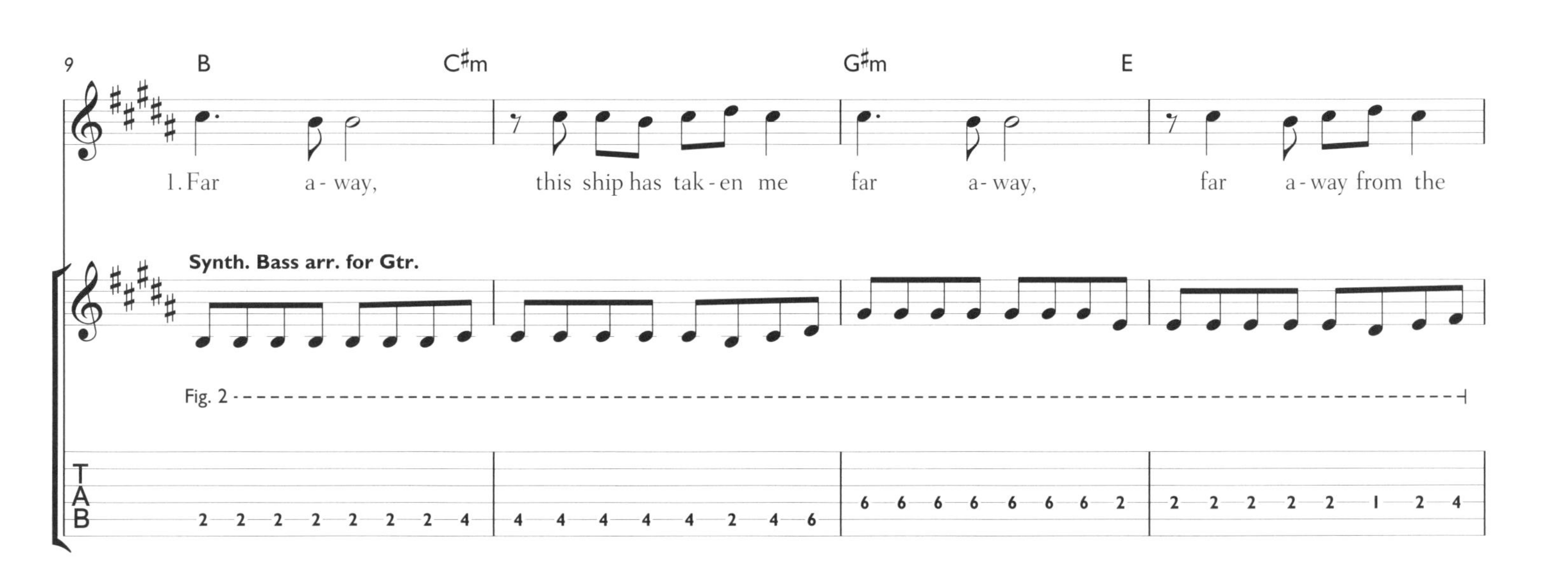

13
B
C♯m
G♯m
E
me - mo-ries of the peo-ple who care if I live or die. A
17
star - light, I will be chas-ing a star - light, un-til the end of my
21
life. I don't know if it's worth it an-y - more.
25
Hold you in my arms, I just want-ed to
Piano arr. for Gtr. plays Fig. 1
TAB

To Coda
29
B
C♯m
G♯m
E
hold you in my arms.
33
2. My life, you el - ec - tri - fy my life. Let's con-spire to ig -
Elec. Gtr. 1
mf overdrive, let ring
hold bend
1/2
37
nite all the souls that would die just to feel a - live.
Gtr. 2
distortion
T
A
B

41
C♯5
F♯5
D♯5
G♯5
I'll ne - ver let you go if you pro - mise not to
f
45
A5
E5
A5
D♯5
fade a - way, ne - ver fade a - way.
49
G♯m
D♯sus4
D♯
E
B
And our hopes and ex - pec - ta - - - - tions,
Elec. Gtr. 1
p with echo, let ring
bracketed note (2° only)
(1° only)

1.
53
G♯m
D♯sus4
D♯
E
B
black holes and re - ve - la - - - - tions.
T
A
B

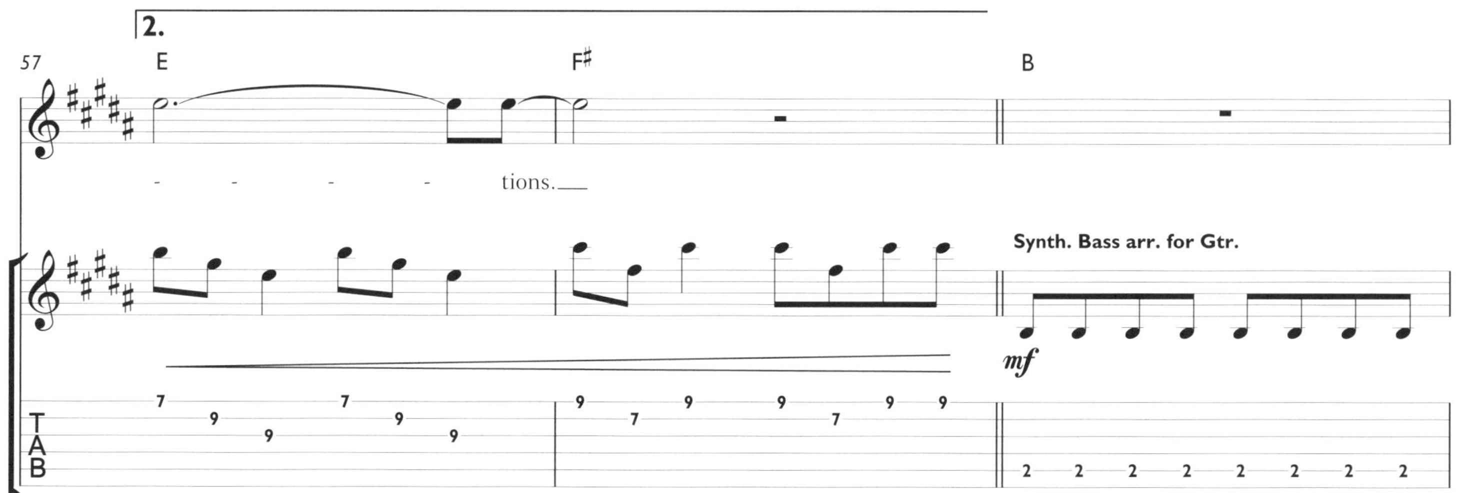
2.
57
E
F♯
B
- - - - tions.
Synth. Bass arr. for Gtr.
mf
T
A
B

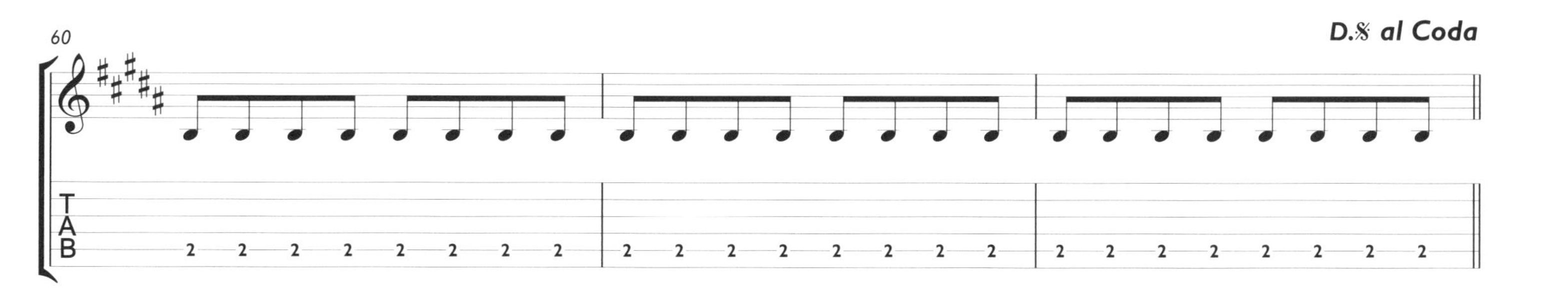
60
D.𝄋 al Coda
T
A
B

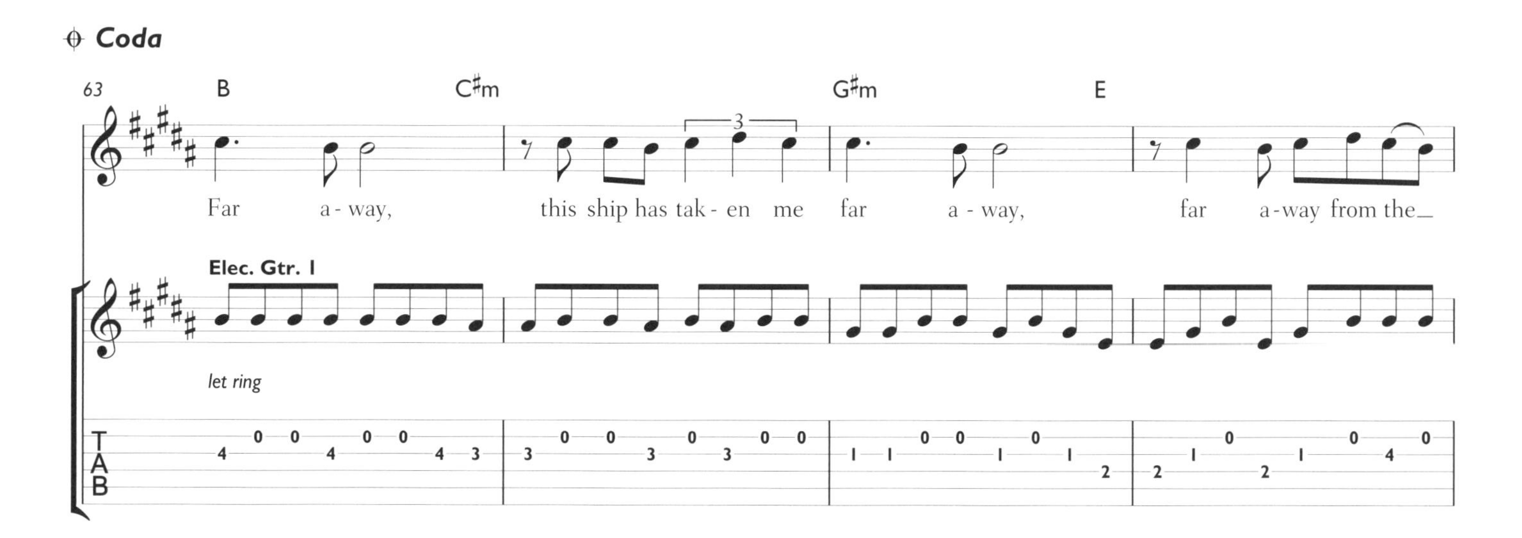
Coda
63
B
C♯m
G♯m
E
Far a - way, this ship has tak - en me far a - way, far a-way from the
Elec. Gtr. 1
let ring
T
A
B

67
B
C♯m
G♯m
E
me - mo-ries of the peo-ple who care if I live or die.
71
C♯5
F♯5
D♯5
G♯5
I'll ne - ver let you go if you pro - mise not to
Elec. Gtr. 2
f overdrive
75
A5
E5
A5
D♯5
fade a - way, ne-ver fade a - way.
79
G♯5
D♯5
E5
B5
And our hopes and ex-pec - ta - - - - tions,

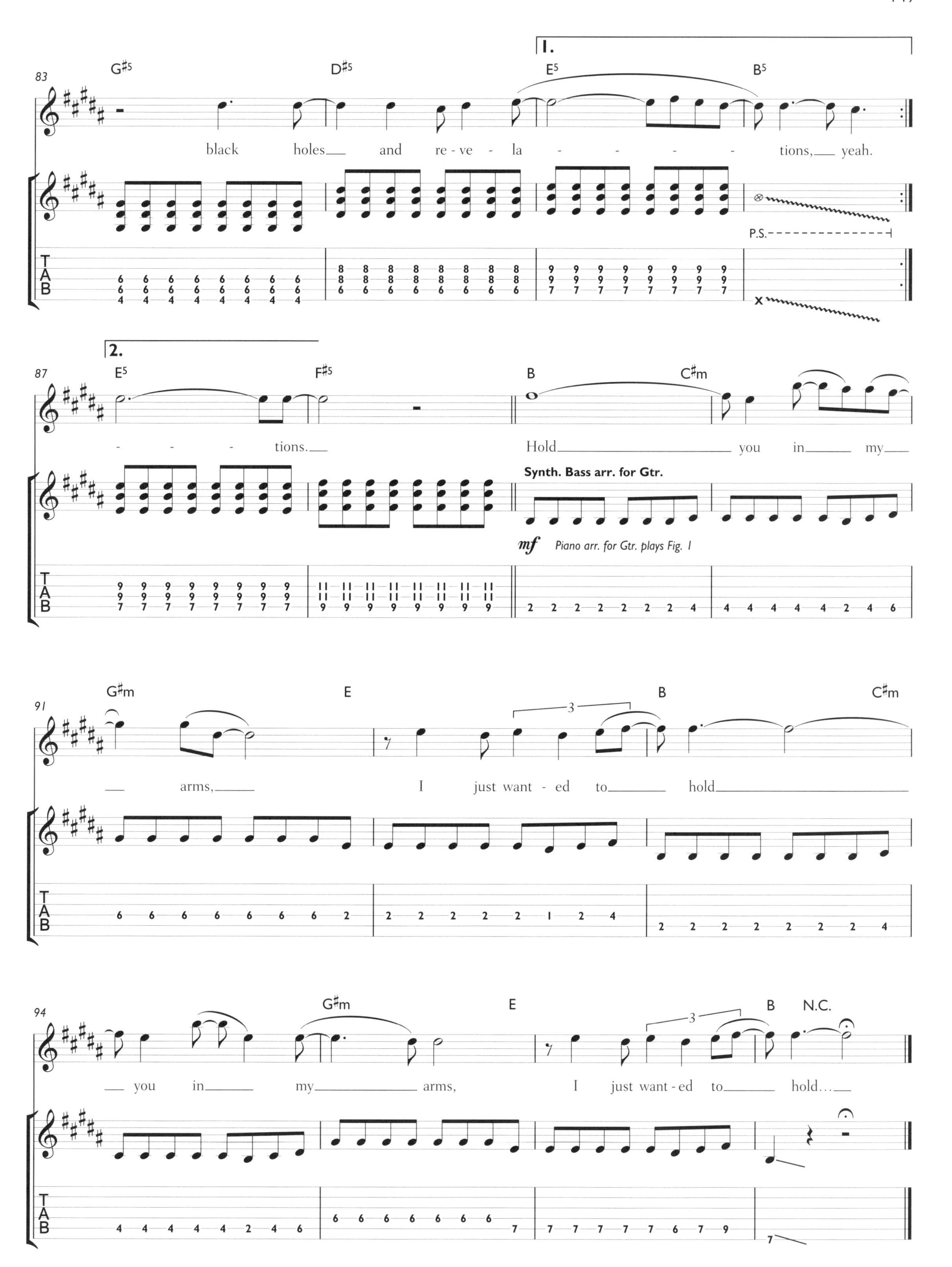
83
G♯5
D♯5
1.
E5
B5
black holes and re-ve - la - - - - tions, yeah.
P.S.
2.
87
E5
F♯5
B
C♯m
- - - tions.
Hold you in my
Synth. Bass arr. for Gtr.
mf
Piano arr. for Gtr. plays Fig. 1
91
G♯m
E
B
C♯m
arms, I just want - ed to hold
94
G♯m
E
B
N.C.
you in my arms, I just want-ed to hold…

STOCKHOLM SYNDROME

Words and Music by Matthew Bellamy

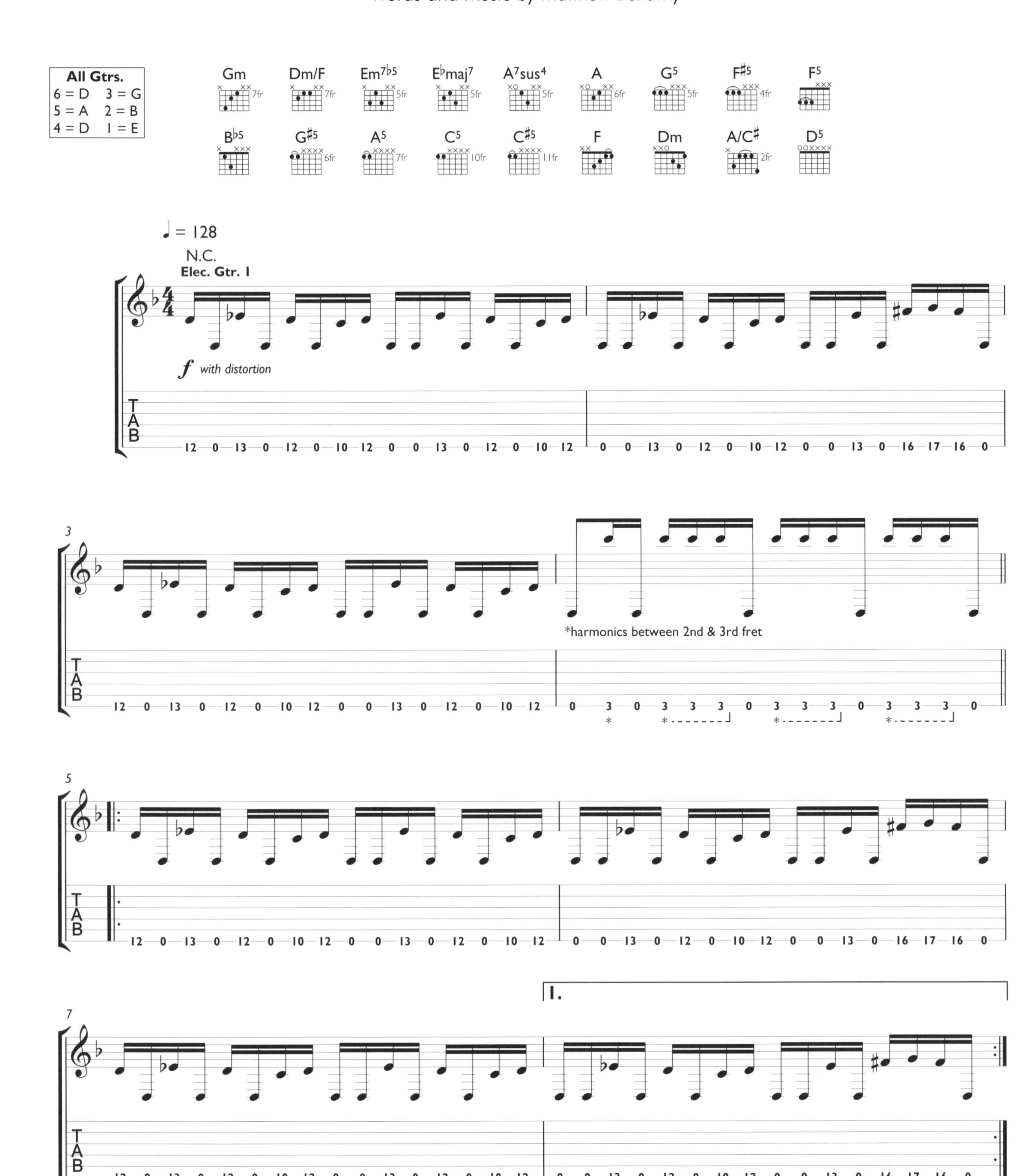

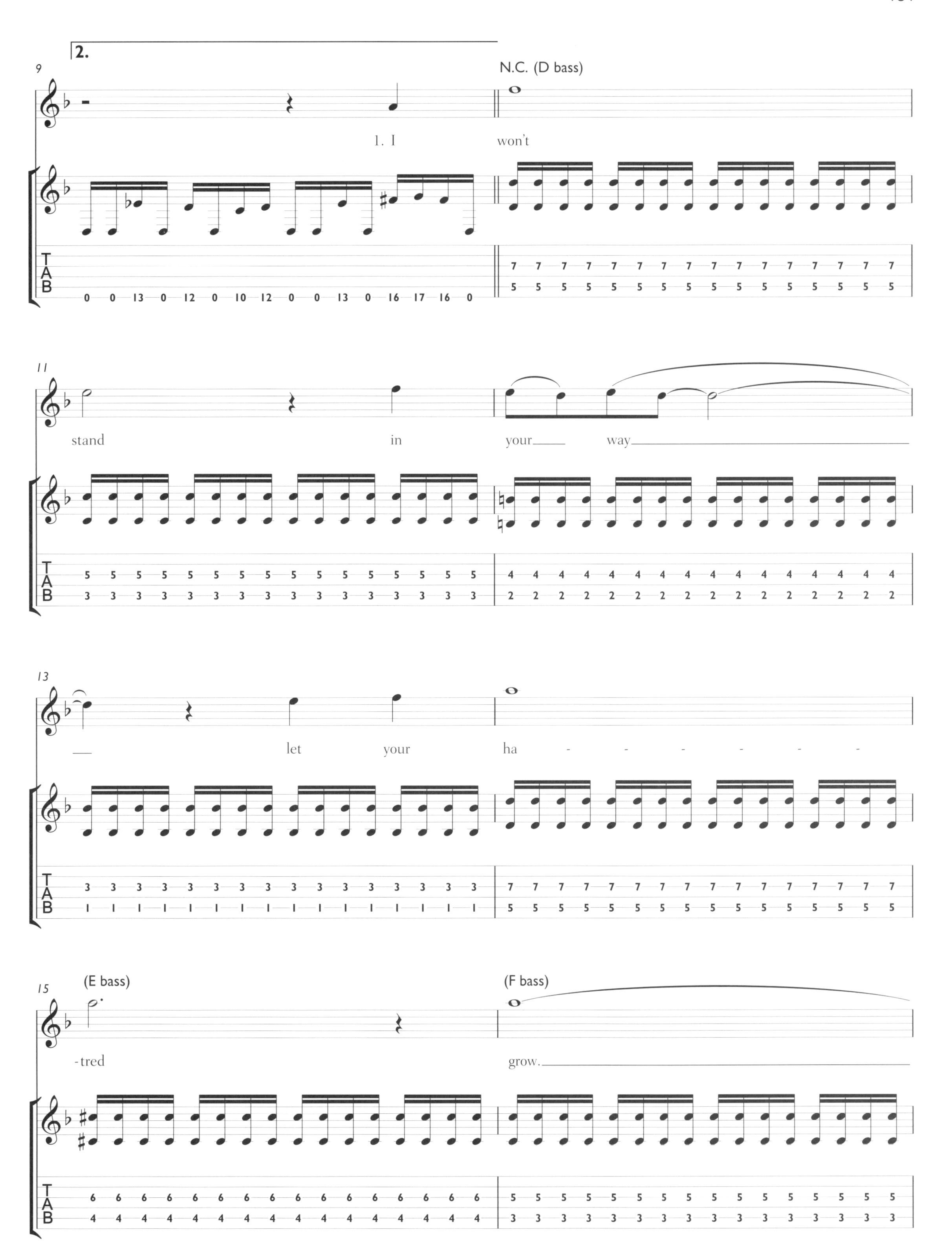
2.
9
N.C. (D bass)
1. I
won't
11
stand
in
your
way
13
let
your
ha
15
(E bass)
-tred
(F bass)
grow.

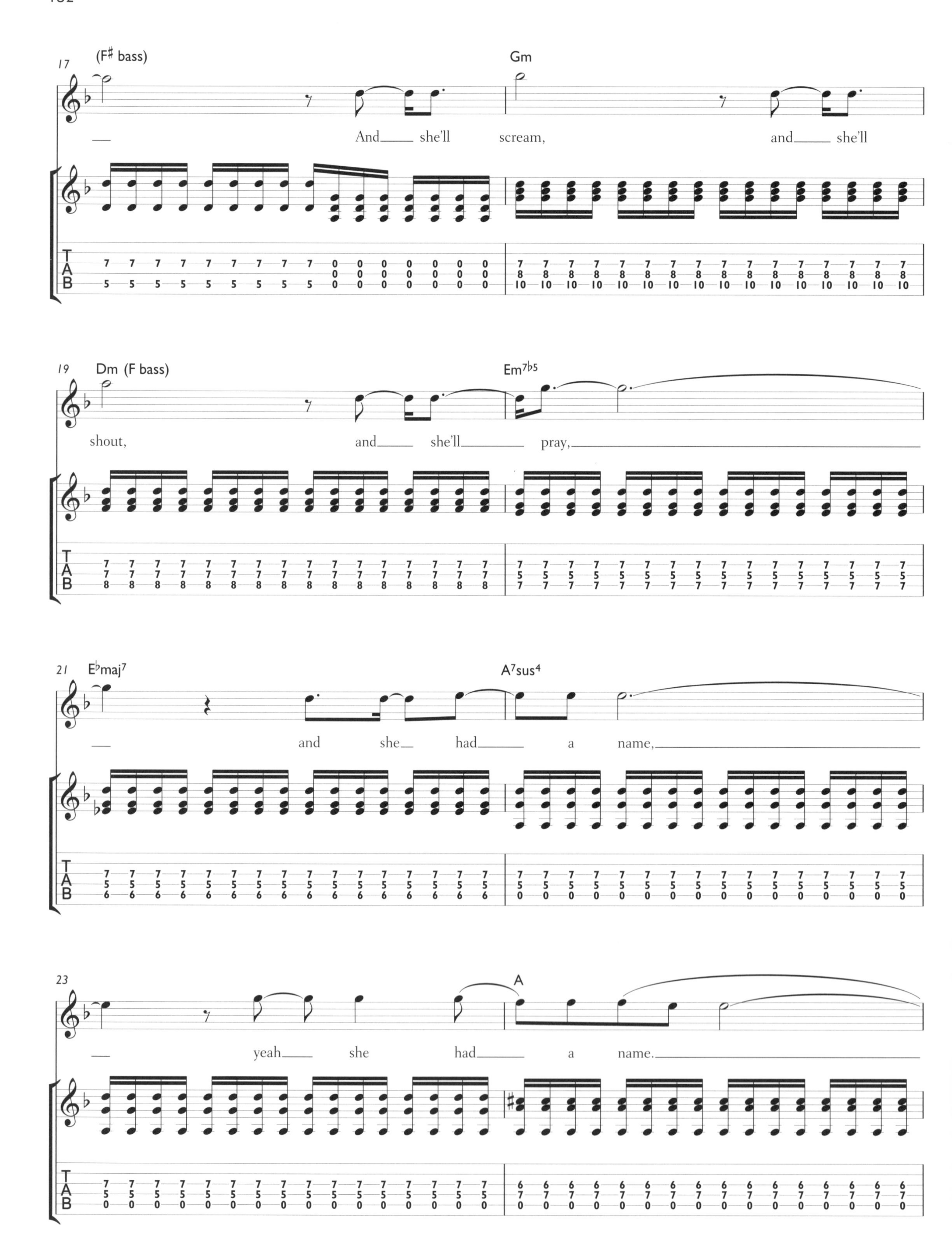
17
(F♯ bass)
Gm
And she'll scream, and she'll
19
Dm (F bass)
Em7♭5
shout, and she'll pray,
21
E♭maj7
A7sus4
and she had a name,
23
A
yeah she had a name.
TAB

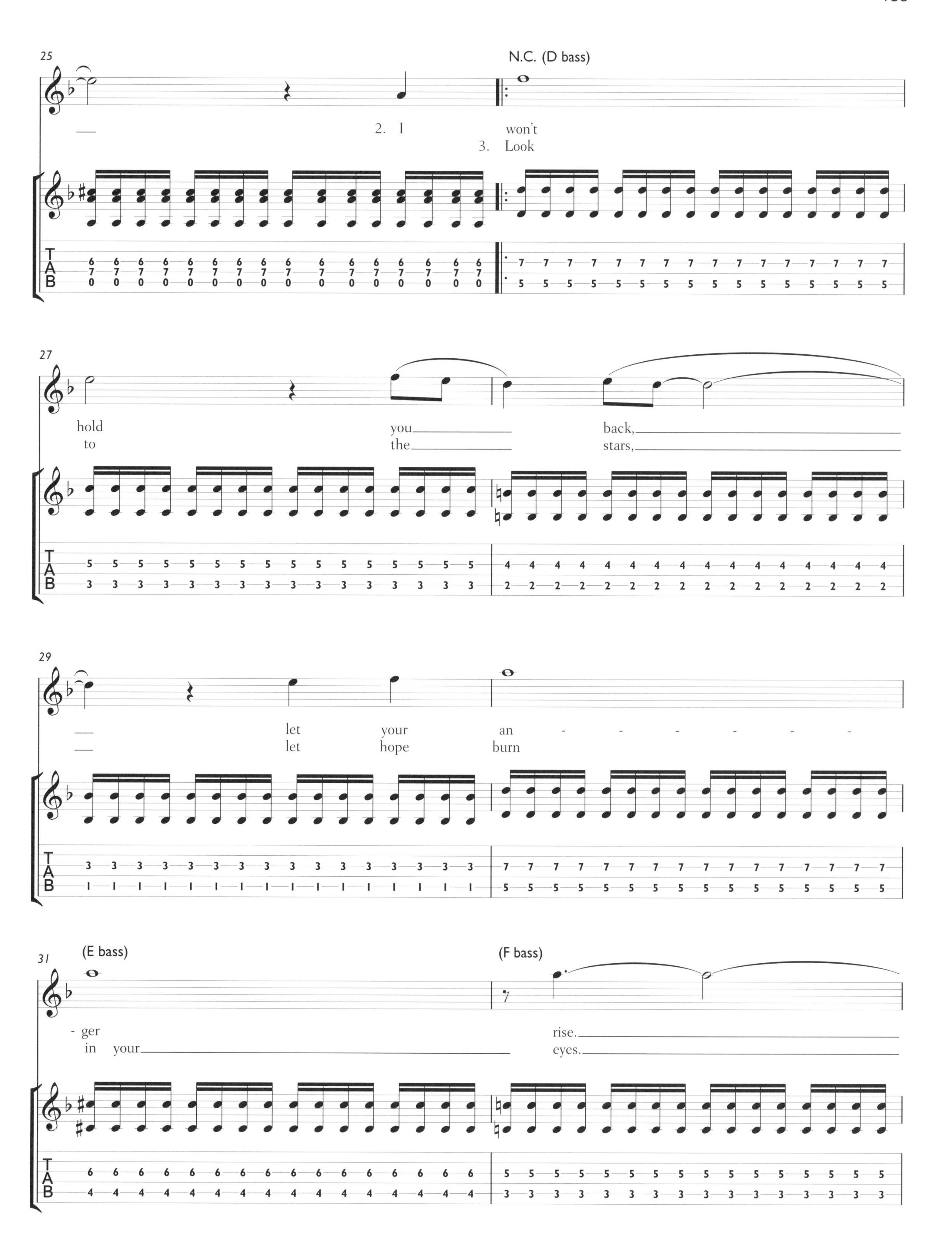
25
N.C. (D bass)
2. I won't
3. Look
27
hold you back,
to the stars,
29
let your an - - - - - -
let hope burn
31
(E bass)
(F bass)
- ger rise.
in your eyes.

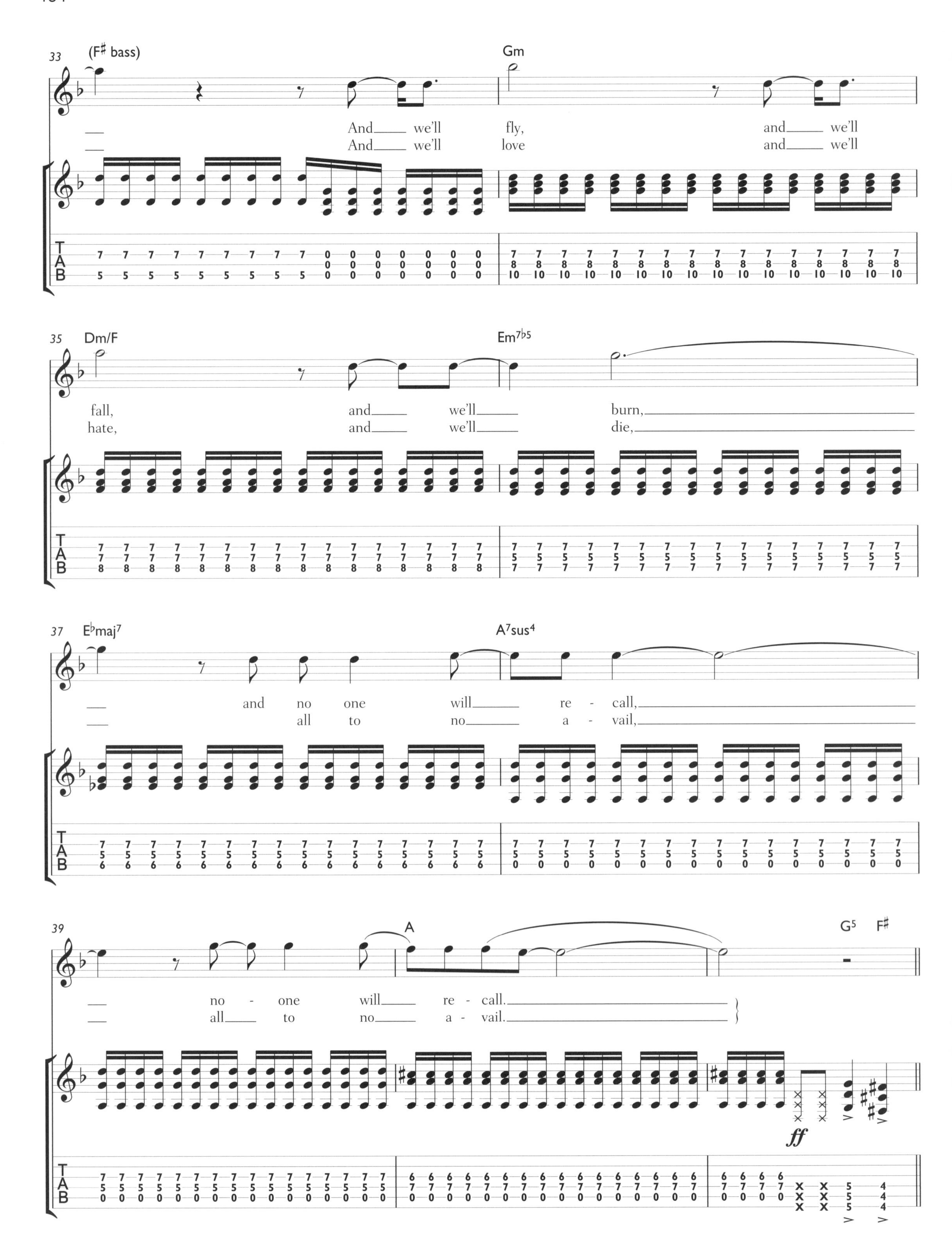
(F♯ bass)
Gm
And we'll fly, and we'll
And we'll love and we'll
Dm/F
Em7♭5
fall, and we'll burn,
hate, and we'll die,
E♭maj7
A7sus4
and no one will re - call,
all to no a - vail,
A
G5 F♯
no - one will re - call.
all to no a - vail.
ff
TAB

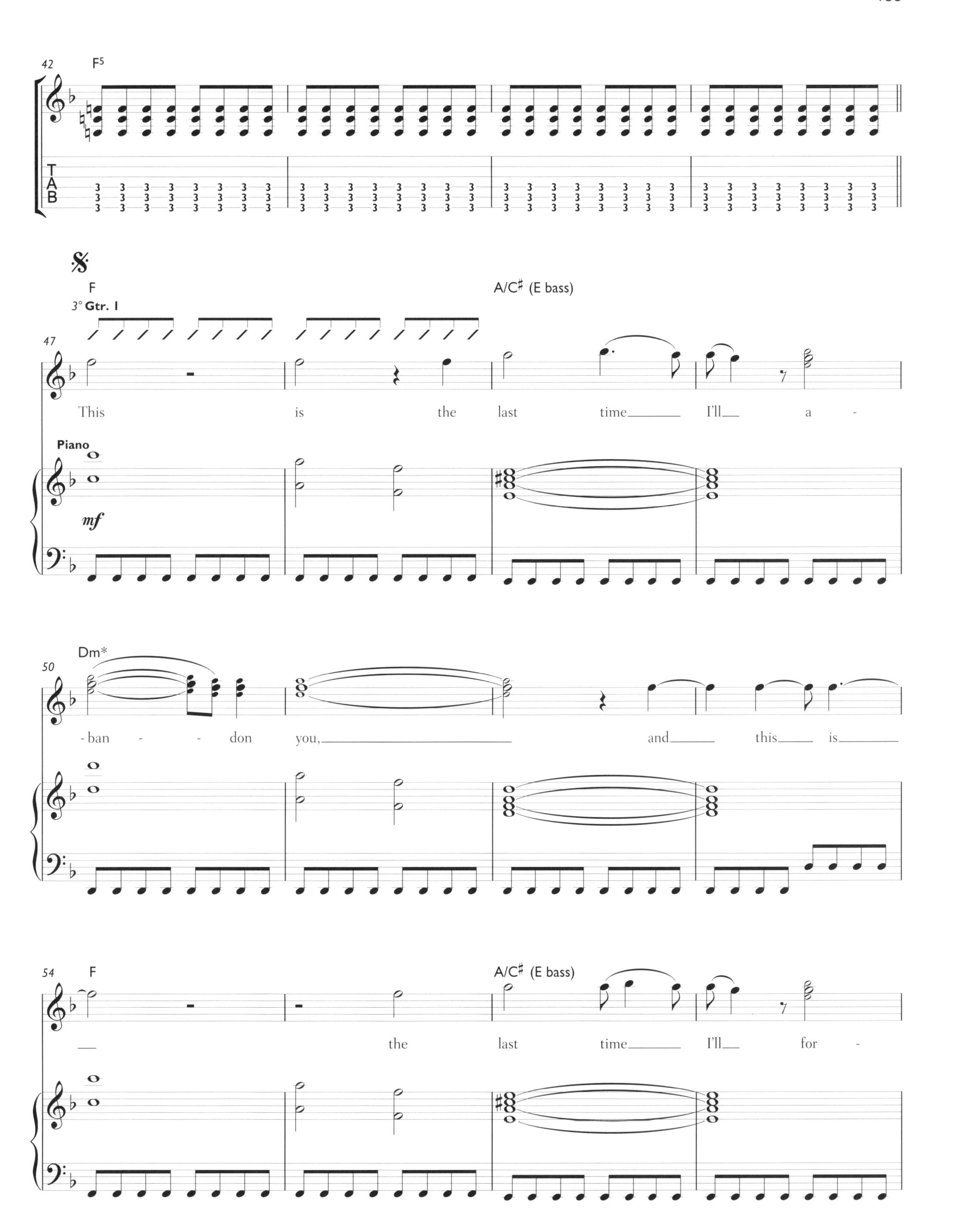
42
F5
T
A
B
47
F
A/C♯ (E bass)
3° Gtr. I
This is the last time I'll a -
Piano
mf
50
Dm*
-ban - - don you, and this is
54
F
A/C♯ (E bass)
the last time I'll for -

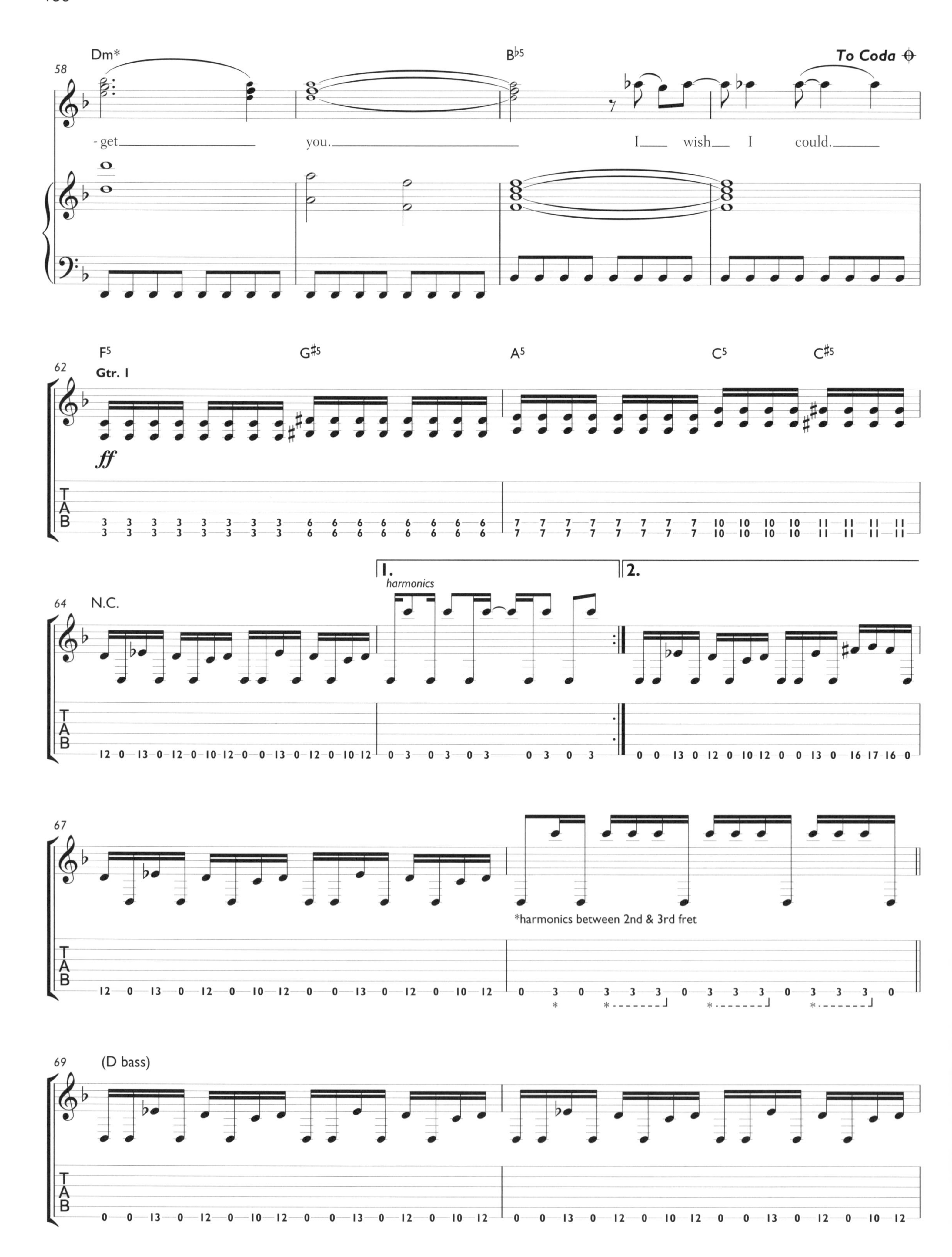

Dm*
B♭5
To Coda
- get
you.
I wish I could.
F5
G♯5
A5
C5
C♯5
Gtr. 1
ff
N.C.
1.
harmonics
2.
*harmonics between 2nd & 3rd fret
(D bass)

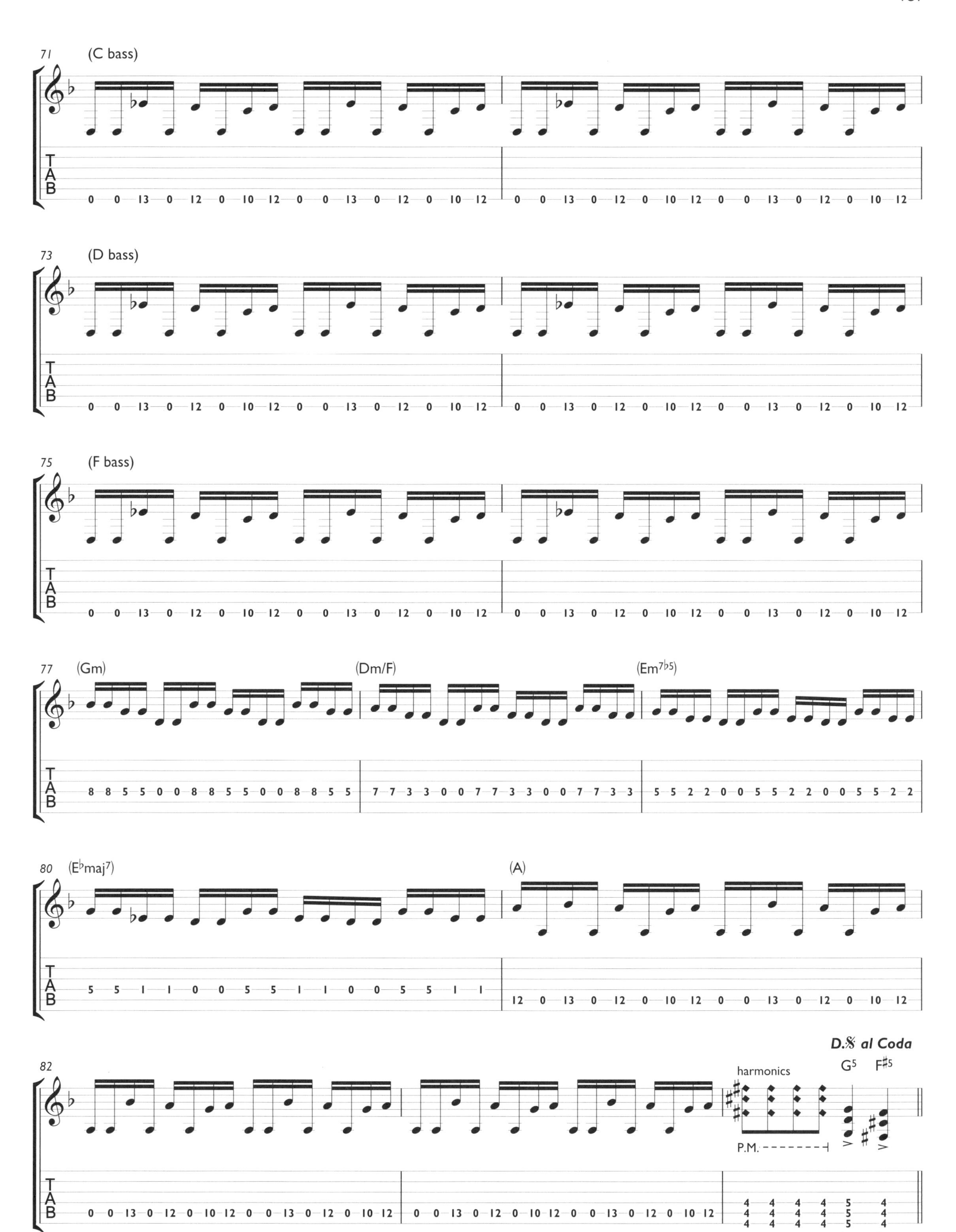
71
(C bass)
73
(D bass)
75
(F bass)
77
(Gm)
(Dm/F)
(Em7♭5)
80
(E♭maj7)
(A)
82
harmonics
P.M.
D.𝄋 al Coda
G5
F♯5
TAB

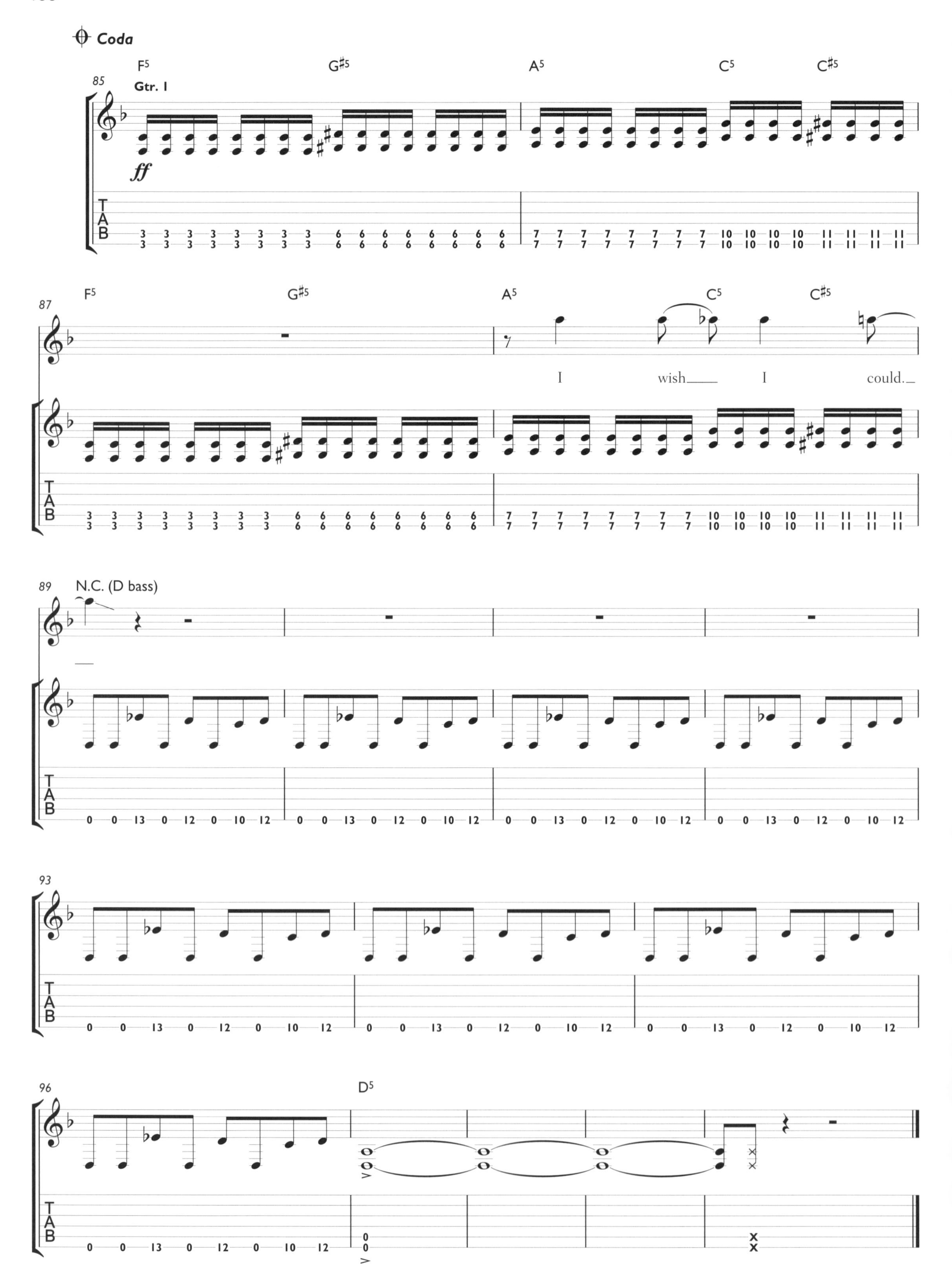
Coda
F5
G♯5
A5
C5
C♯5
Gtr. 1
ff
I wish I could.
N.C. (D bass)
D5

SUPERMASSIVE BLACK HOLE

Words and Music by Matthew Bellamy

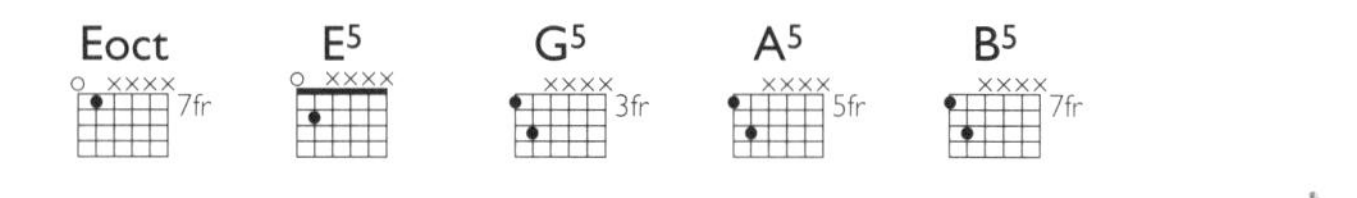

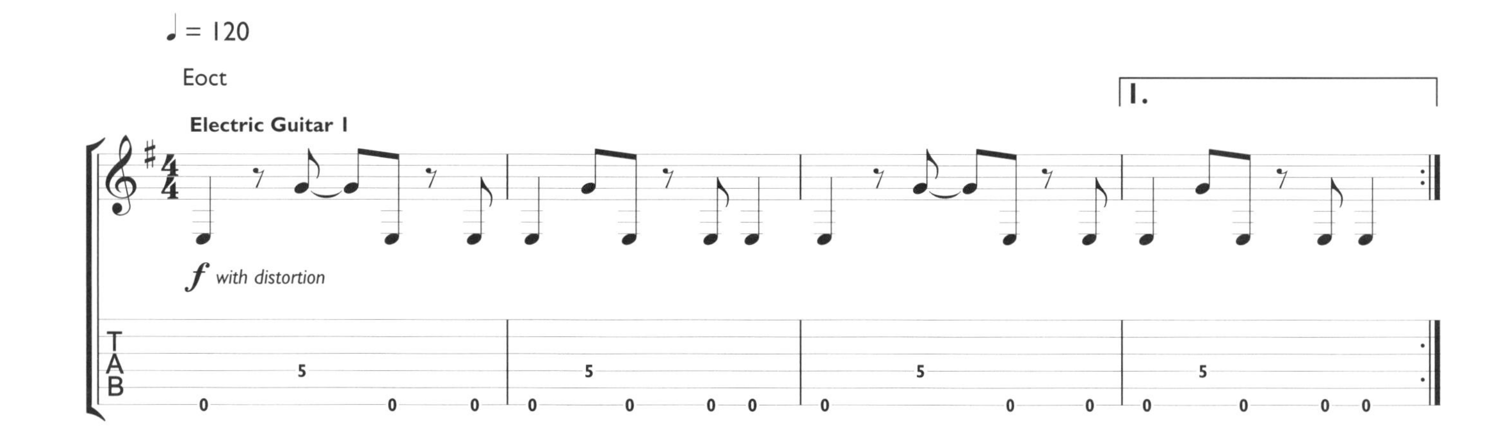

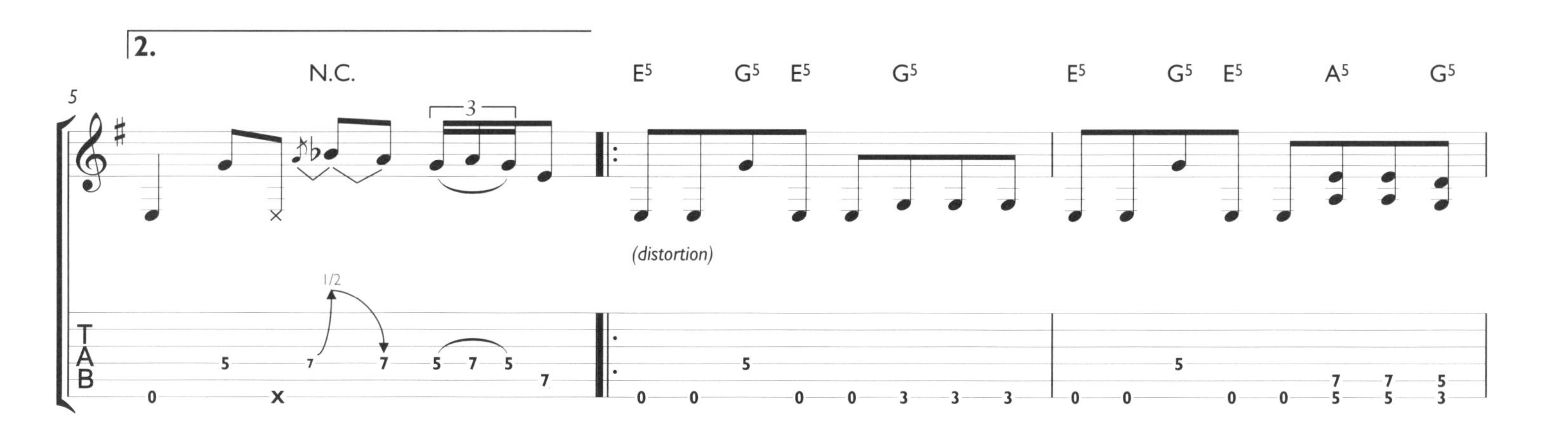

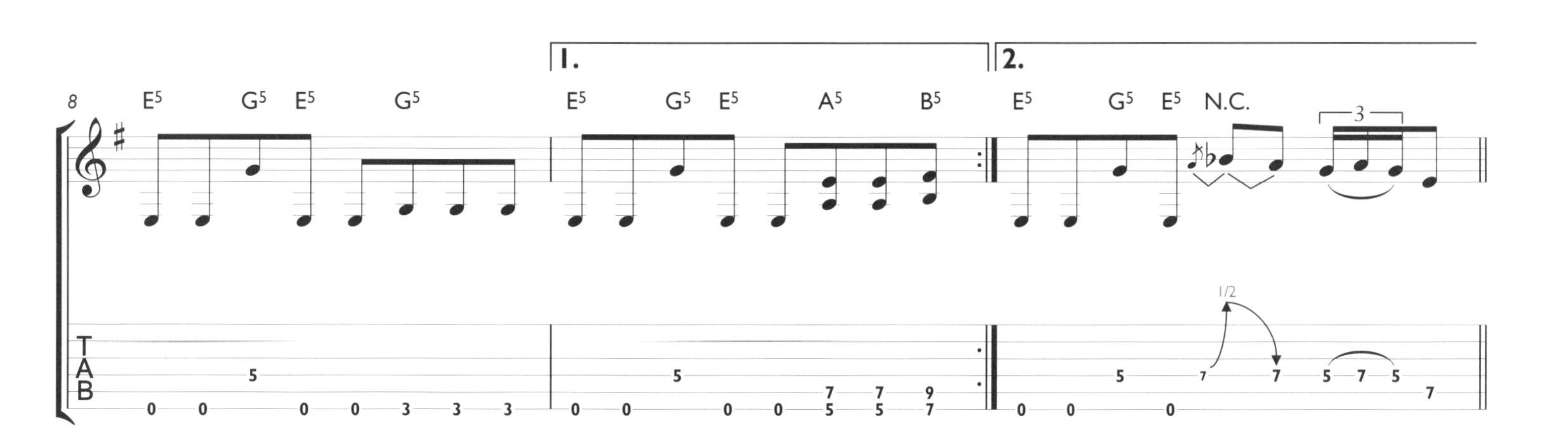

E5 G5 E5 G5 E5 G5 E5 A5 G5 E5 G5 G5
1. Oo ba - by don't you know I suf - fer, oo ba - by can't you
2. I thought I was a fool for no - one, oo ba - by I'm a
mf with crunch
Fig. 1
Tacet 2°
E5 G5 E5 A5 B5 E5 G5 E5 G5 E5 G5 E5 A5 G5
hear me moan? You caught me un - der false pre - ten - ces,
fool for you. You're the queen of the su - per - fi - cial,
E5 G5 G5 E5 G5 E5 N.C. A5
how long be - fore you let me go?
how long be - fore you tell the truth?
Oo
f
G5 B5 E5
you set my soul a - light,

A5 G5 B5
oo you set my soul
N.C. E5 A5 G5
a - light. Oo
(Gla - ciers melt - ing in the dead of night, and the
B5 E5 A5
you set my soul a - light, oo
su - per - stars sucked in - to the su - per - mas - sive. Gla - ciers melt - ing in the
G5 B5 N.C.
you set my soul...
dead of night, and the su - per - stars sucked in - to the...)

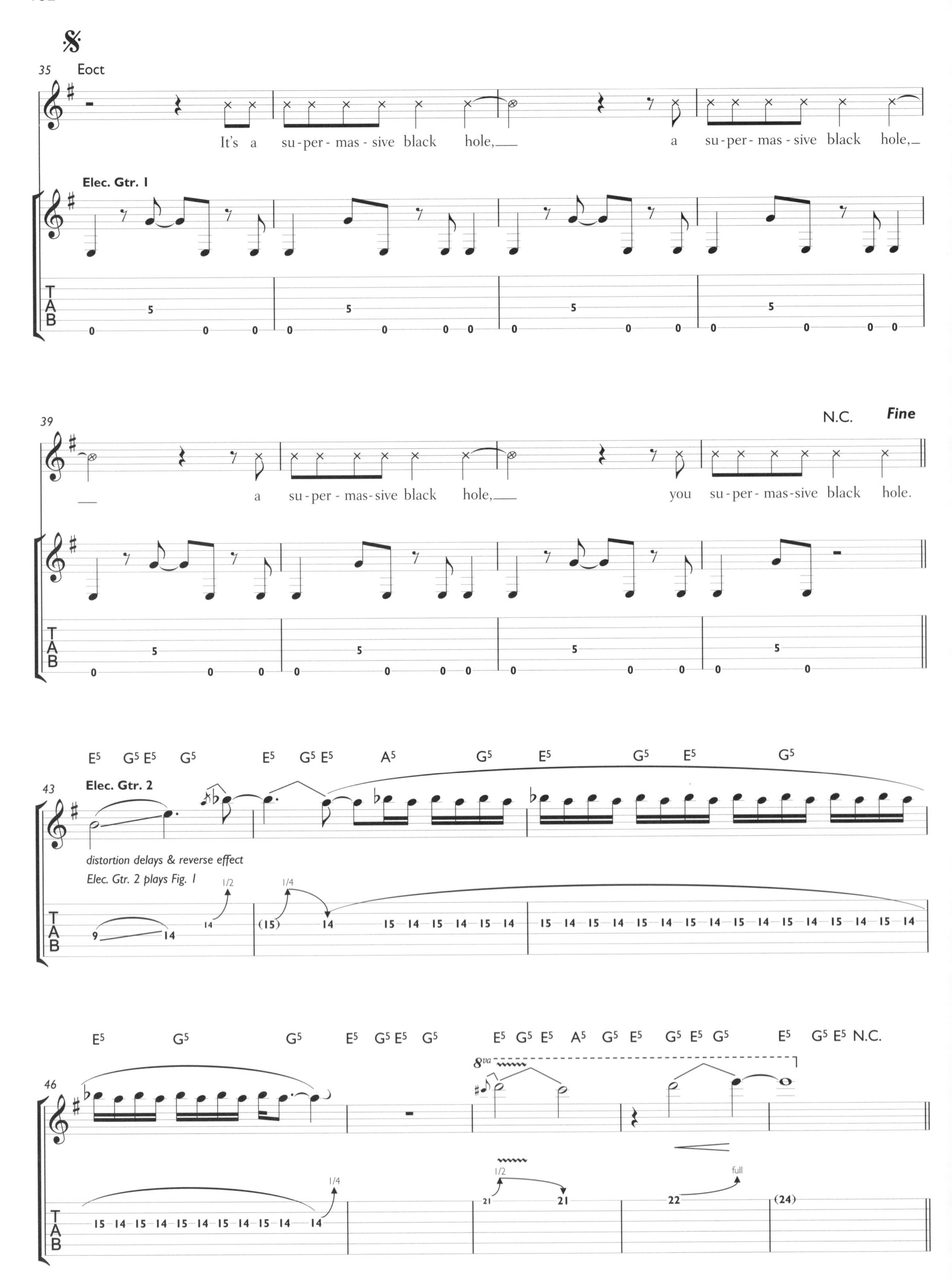

35 Eoct
It's a su-per-mas-sive black hole, a su-per-mas-sive black hole,
Elec. Gtr. 1
39
N.C. Fine
a su-per-mas-sive black hole, you su-per-mas-sive black hole.
E5 G5 E5 G5 E5 G5 E5 A5 G5 E5 G5 E5 G5
43 Elec. Gtr. 2
distortion delays & reverse effect
Elec. Gtr. 2 plays Fig. 1
E5 G5 G5 E5 G5 E5 G5 E5 G5 E5 A5 G5 E5 G5 E5 G5 E5 G5 E5 N.C.
46
8va

51
A5
G5
B5
(Gla - ciers melt - ing in the dead of night, and the su - per - stars sucked in - to the
TAB

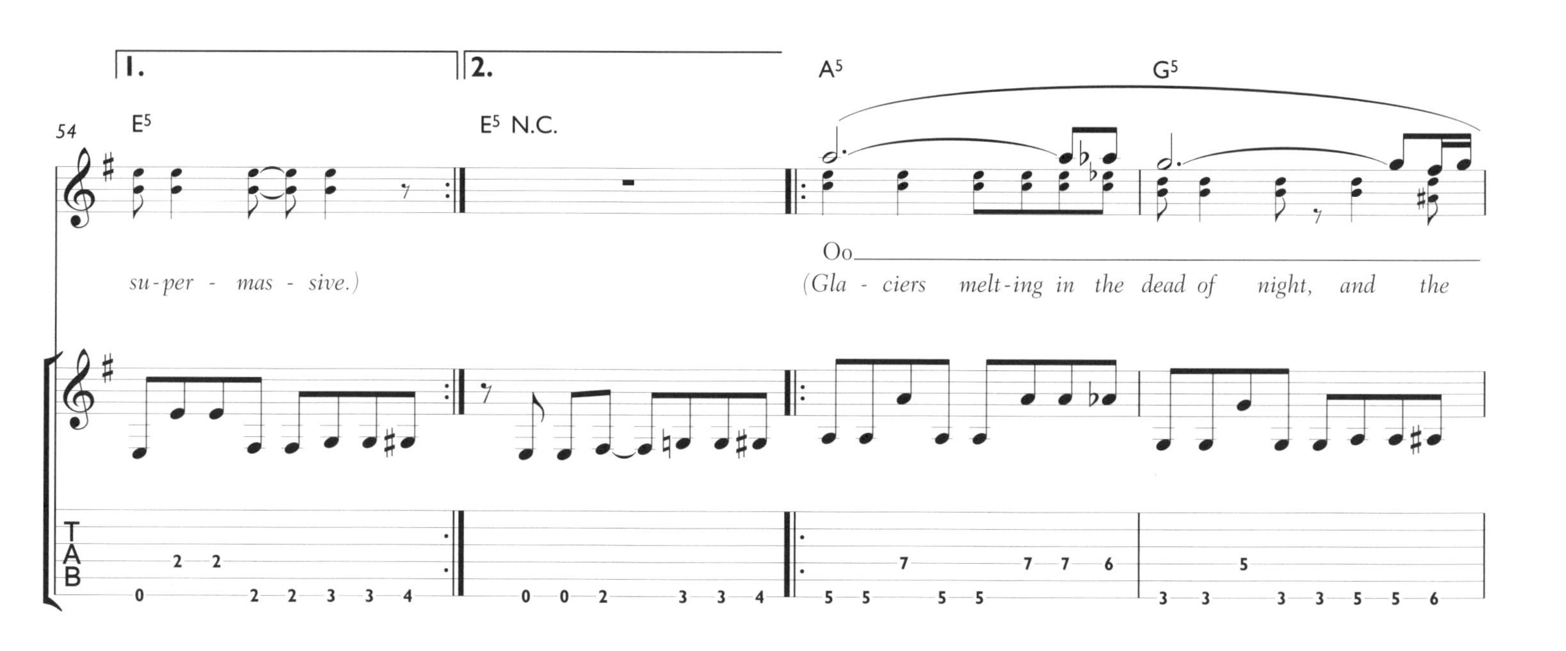
1.
2.
54
E5
E5 N.C.
A5
G5
Oo
su - per - mas - sive.)
(Gla - ciers melt - ing in the dead of night, and the
TAB

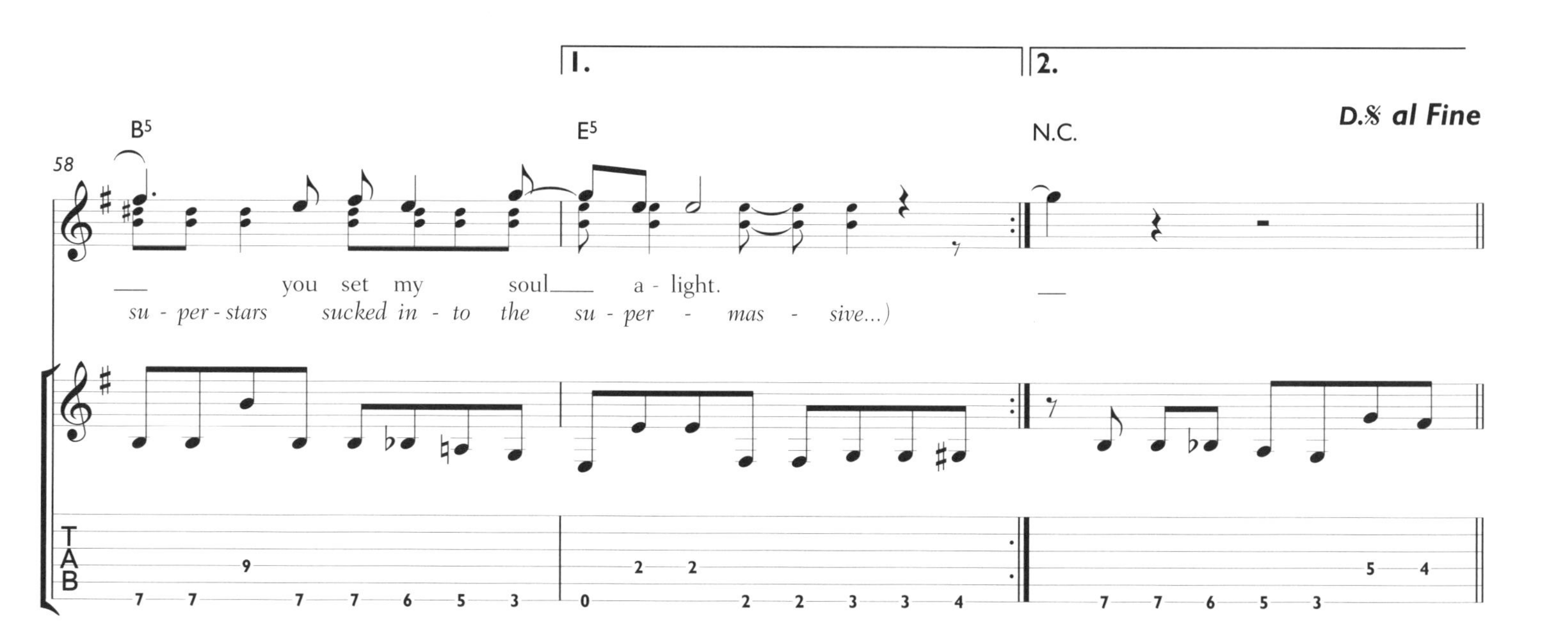
1.
2.
D.% al Fine
58
B5
E5
N.C.
you set my soul a - light.
su - per - stars sucked in - to the su - per - mas - sive...)
TAB

SUPREMACY

Words and Music by Matthew Bellamy

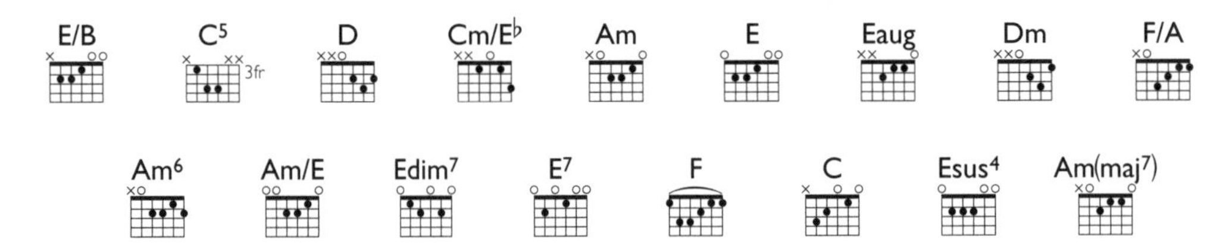

Tune Electric Guitar to drop A tuning:
6 = low A (7 steps below E)
Or if playing on 7-string guitar, tune:
7 = low A (a whole tone below low B string)

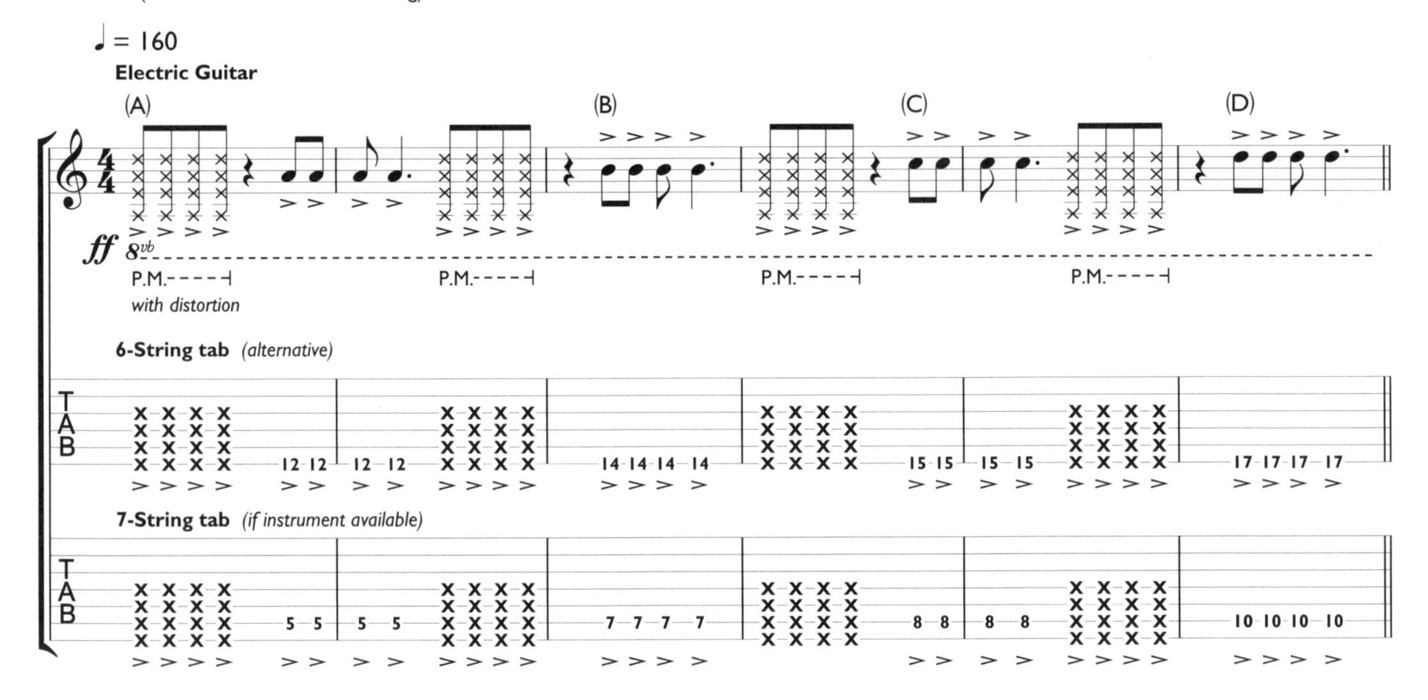

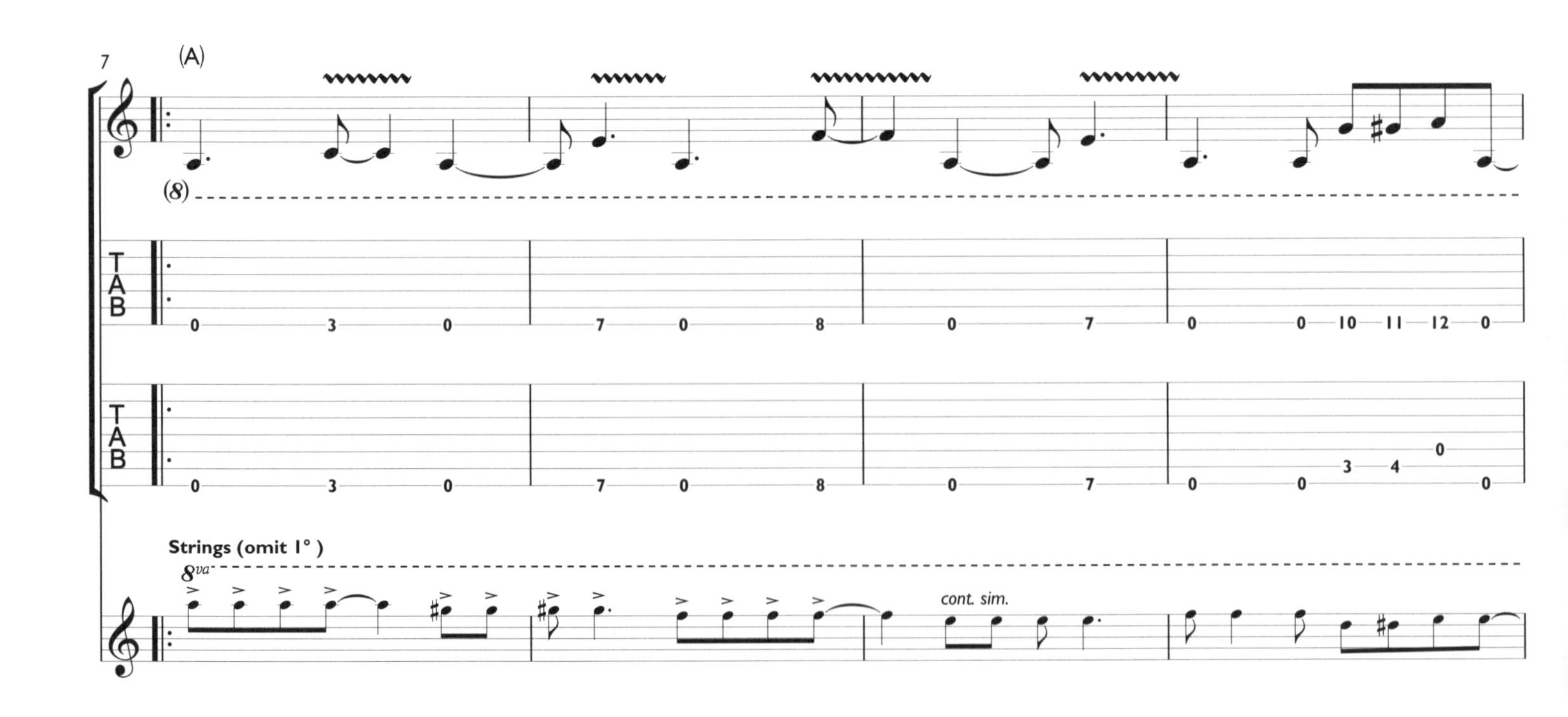

1, 2.
(8)
T
A
B
3 0 7 0 8 0 7 0 10 11 12 15
3 0 7 0 8 0 7 0 10 11 12 15
(8)

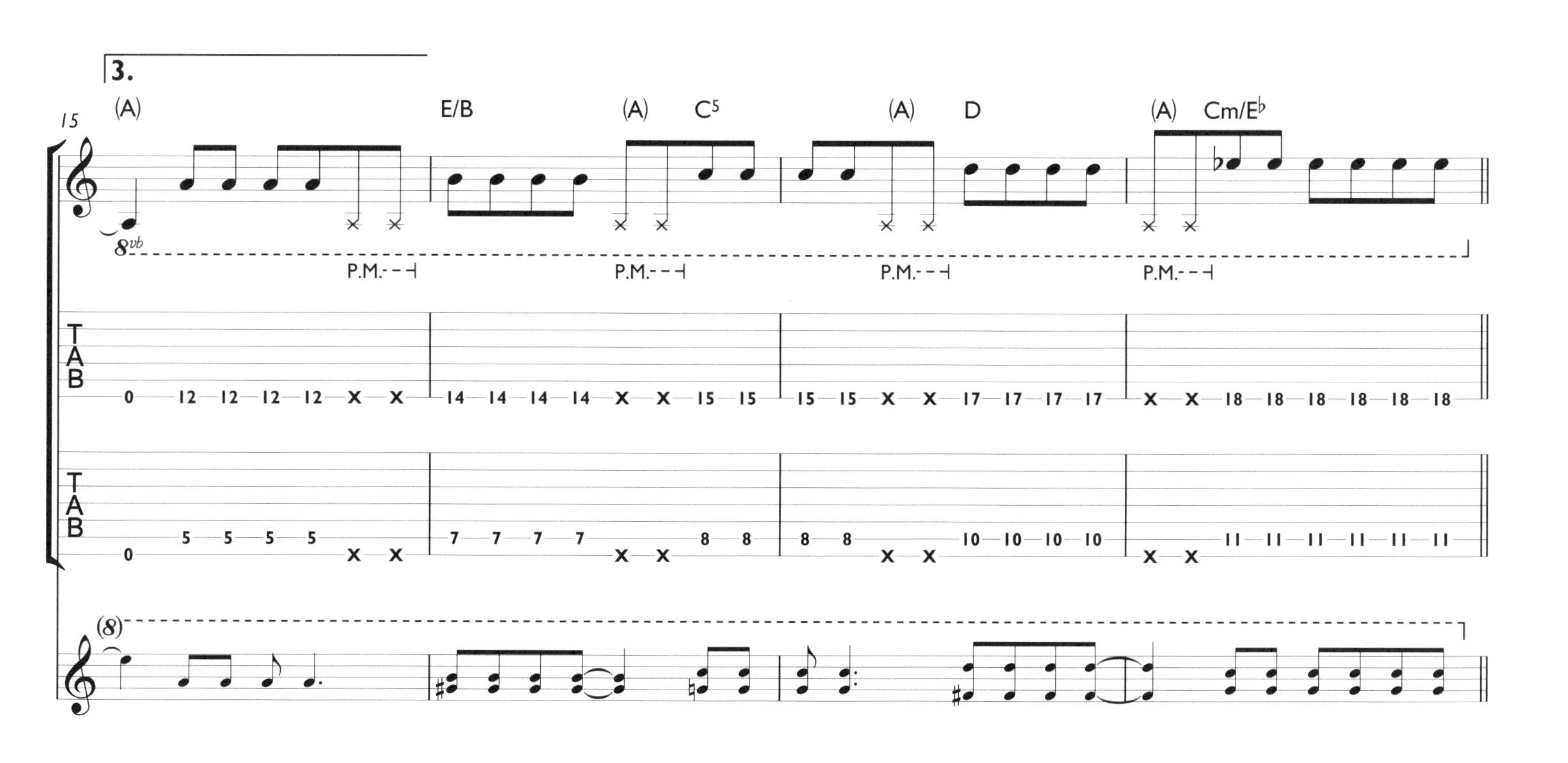
3.
(A)
E/B
(A) C5
(A) D
(A) Cm/E♭
8vb
P.M.
0 12 12 12 12 X X 14 14 14 14 X X 15 15 15 15 X X 17 17 17 17 X X 18 18 18 18 18 18
0 5 5 5 5 X X 7 7 7 7 X X 8 8 8 8 X X 10 10 10 10 X X 11 11 11 11 11 11
(8)

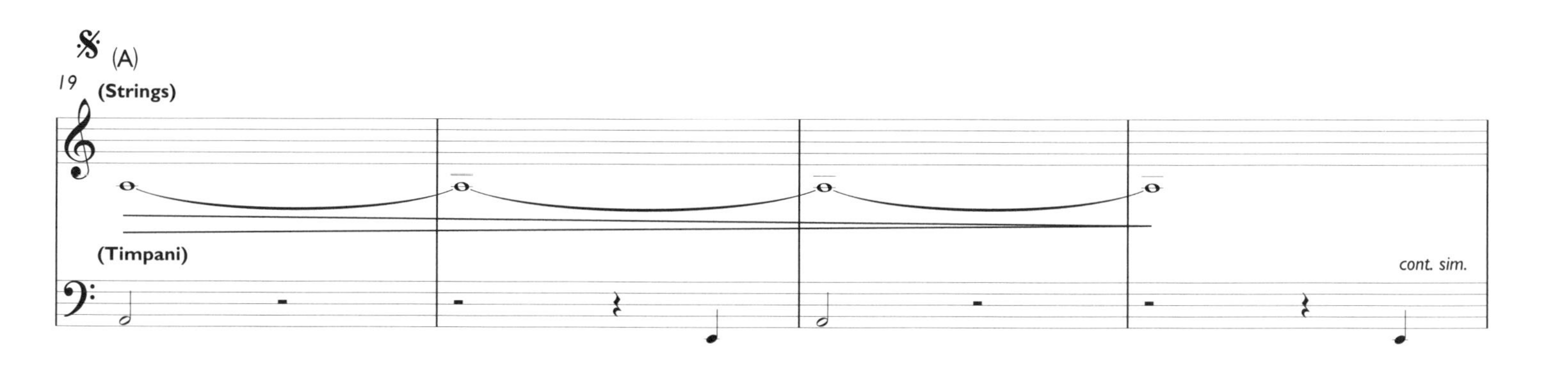
(A)
(Strings)
(Timpani)
cont. sim.

23
Am
E
Eaug
E
1. Wake to see, your true e-man-ci-pa-tion is a fan-ta-sy.
𝄋. (Instrumental)
Elec. Gtr. (on 𝄋 only)
rake
(Strings)
31
Dm
Am
F/A
Am6
F/A
Po-li-cies have ris-en up and o-ver-come the brave.
rake
39
Am
E
Am/E
Edim7
E7
Great-ness dies, un-sung and lost in-vi-si-ble to his-to-ry.
Em-
rake

47
Dm
Am
F/A
Am6
F/A
- bed - ded spies, brain-wash-ing our child-ren to be mean.
rake
rake
3
55
F
C
Am
E
(1, 𝄋.) You don't have long, I am on to you. The
mp
63
F
Dm
Esus4
E
To Coda
time, it has come to des - troy your su - pre-ma - cy.
f

(A)
ff
Yeah, yeah, yeah, yeah, yeah, yeah, yeah, yeah, yeah, yeah, yeah, yeah, yeah.
(Strings)
8va
cont. sim.

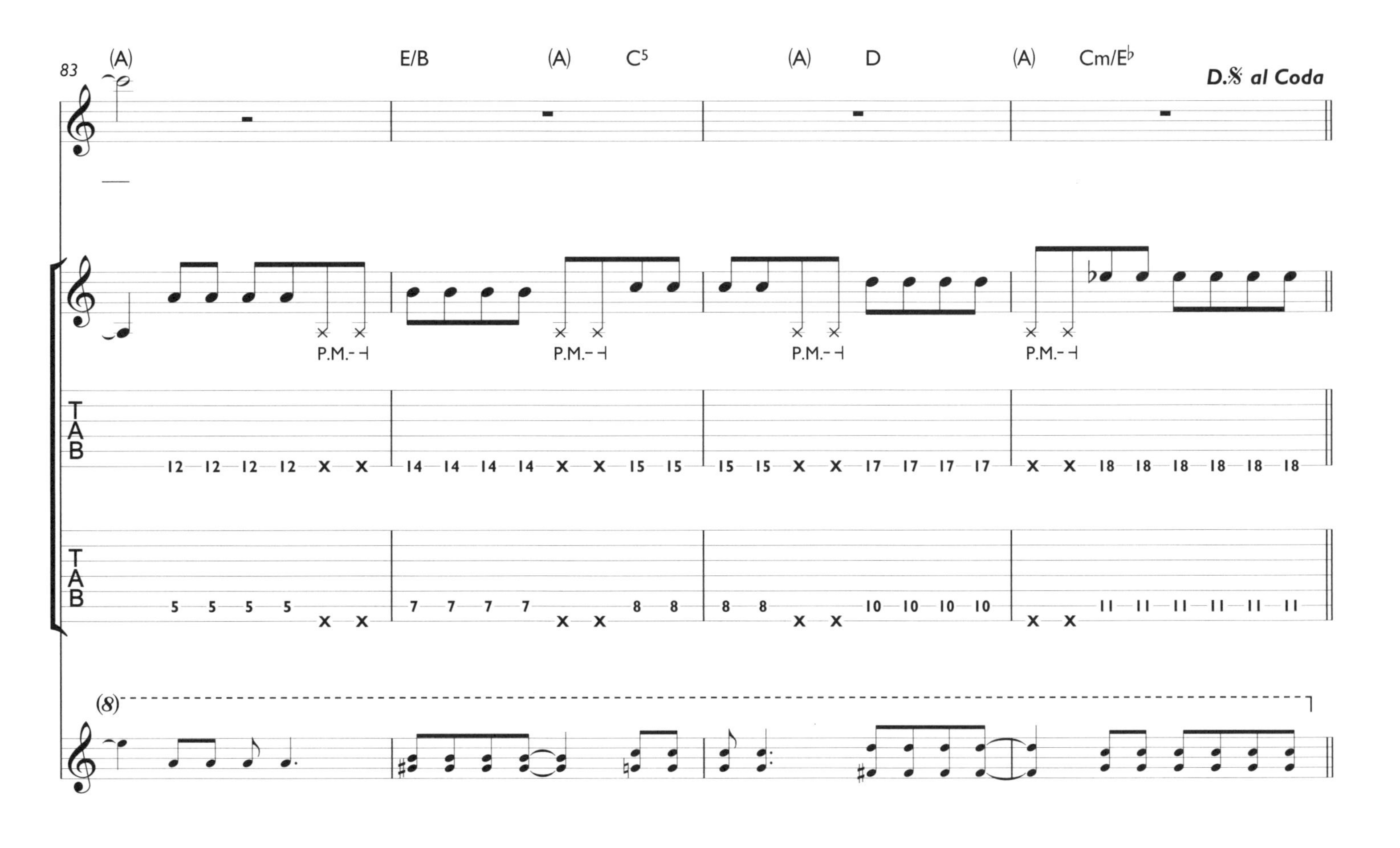
83
(A)
E/B
(A)
C5
(A)
D
(A)
Cm/E♭
D.𝄋 al Coda
P.M.
T
A
B
(8)

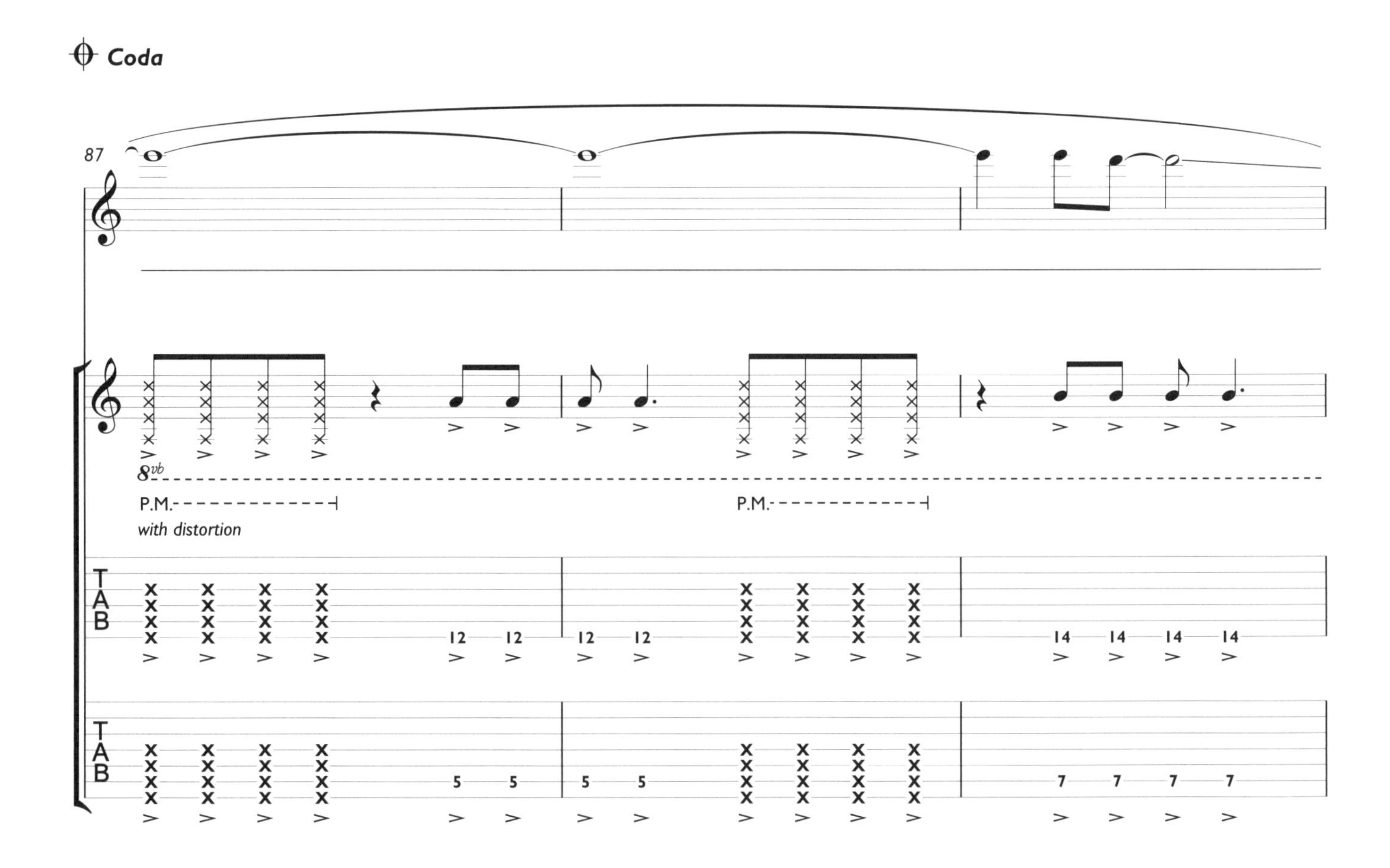
Coda
87
8vb
P.M.
with distortion
T
A
B

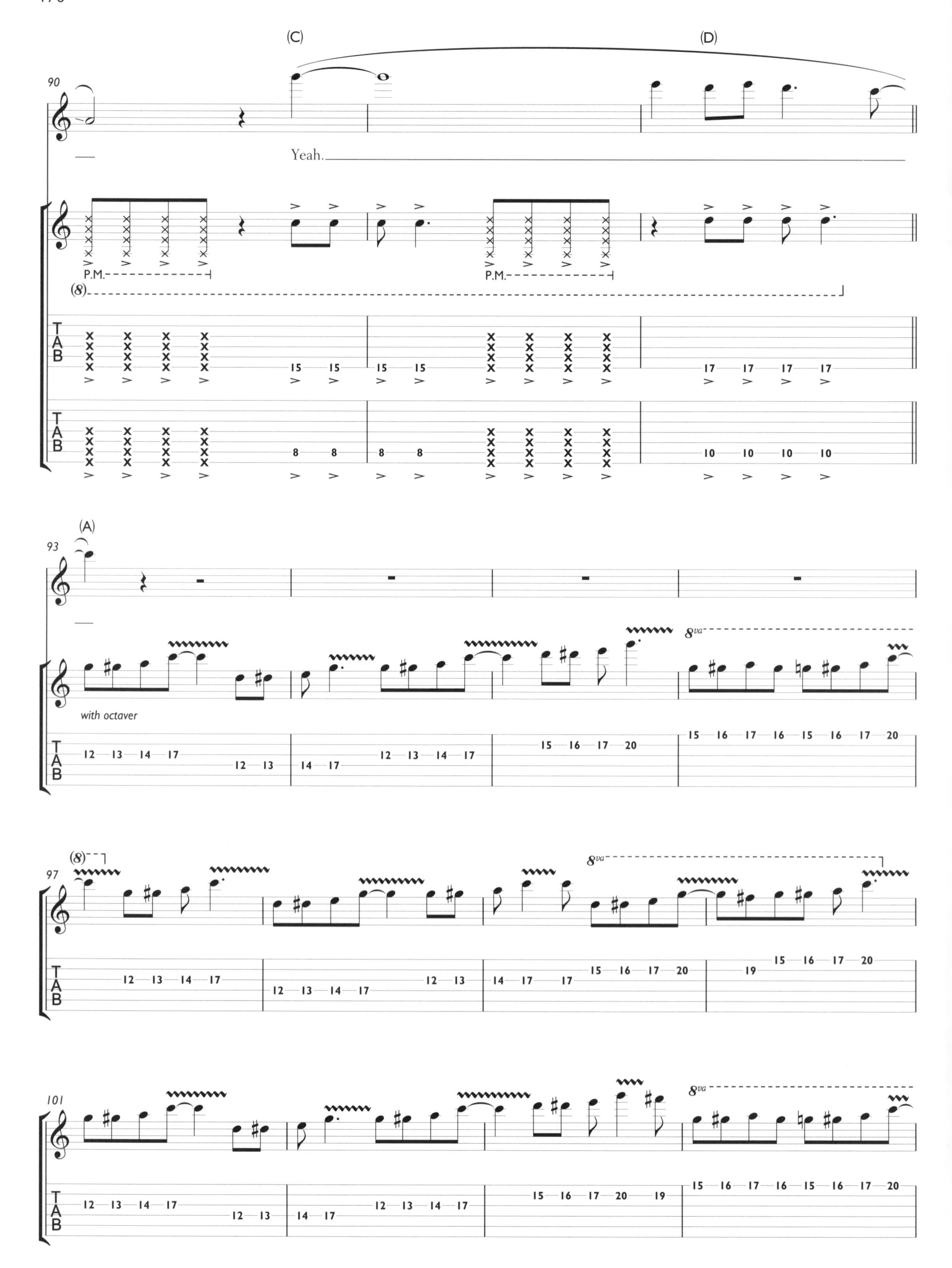
(C)
(D)
Yeah.
P.M.
(8)
with octaver
(A)
8va
T
A
B

105
Your su - pre-ma - cy.
(8)
T
A
B
12 13 14 17
12 13 14 17 12 13
14 17 14 17 14 17 14 17
14 17 14 17 14 17 14 17
(A)
109
0 3 0
7 0
8 0 7
0 0 10 11 12 0
0 3 0
7 0
8 0 7
0 0 3 4 0 0
(Strings)
8va
cont. sim.
1.
113
3 0 7 0 8 0 7 0 10 11 12 15
3 0 7 0 8 0 7 0 10 11 12 15
(8)

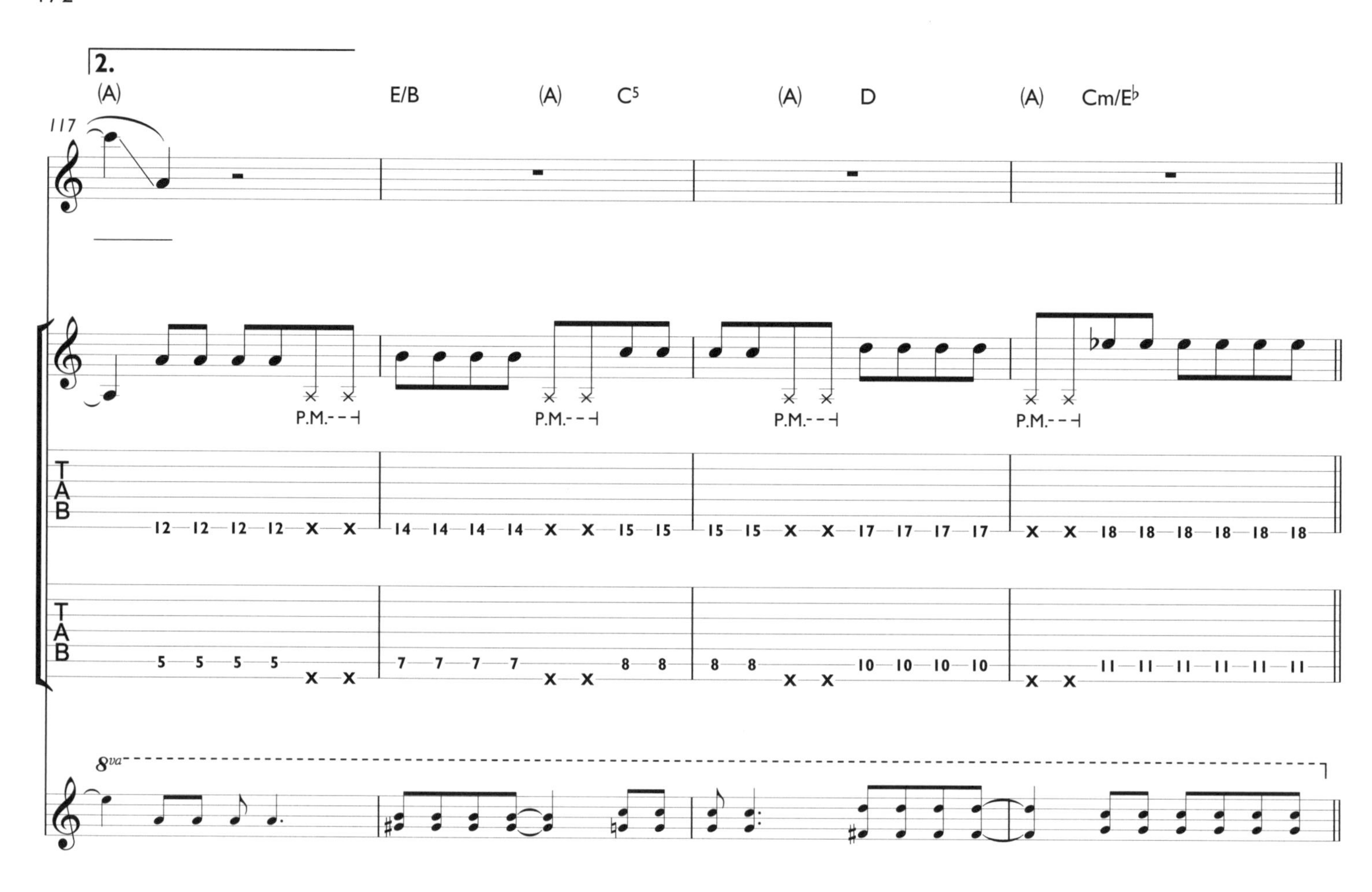
2.
(A)
E/B
(A)
C5
(A)
D
(A)
Cm/E♭
117
P.M.
P.M.
P.M.
P.M.
T
A
B
12 12 12 12 X X 14 14 14 14 X X 15 15 15 15 X X 17 17 17 17 X X 18 18 18 18 18 18
T
A
B
5 5 5 5 X X 7 7 7 7 X X 8 8 8 8 X X 10 10 10 10 X X 11 11 11 11 11 11
8va

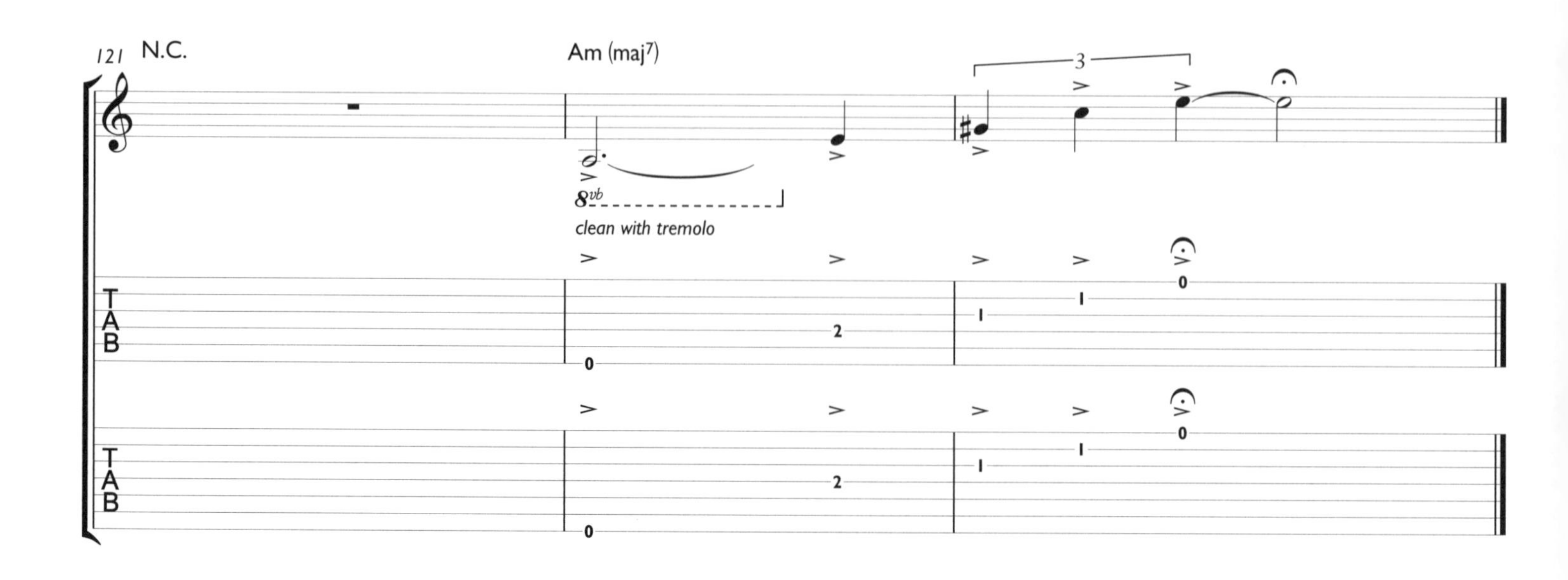
121
N.C.
Am (maj7)
3
8vb
clean with tremolo
T
A
B
0 2 1 1 0
T
A
B
0 2 1 1 0

TIME IS RUNNING OUT

Words and Music by Matthew Bellamy

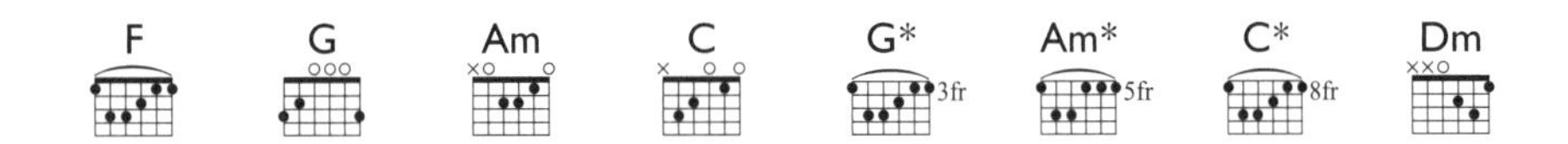

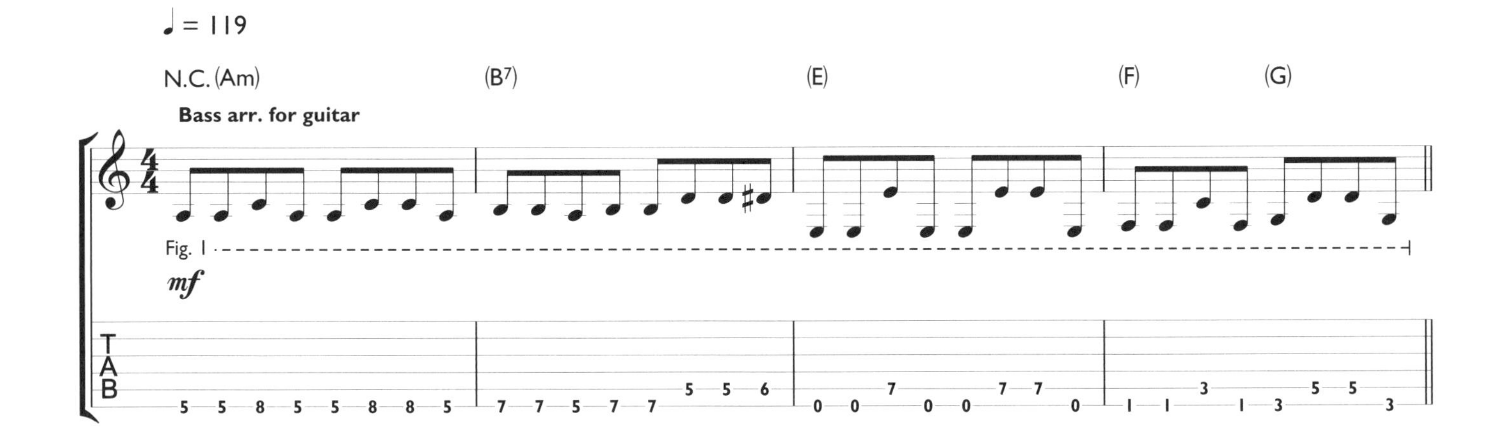

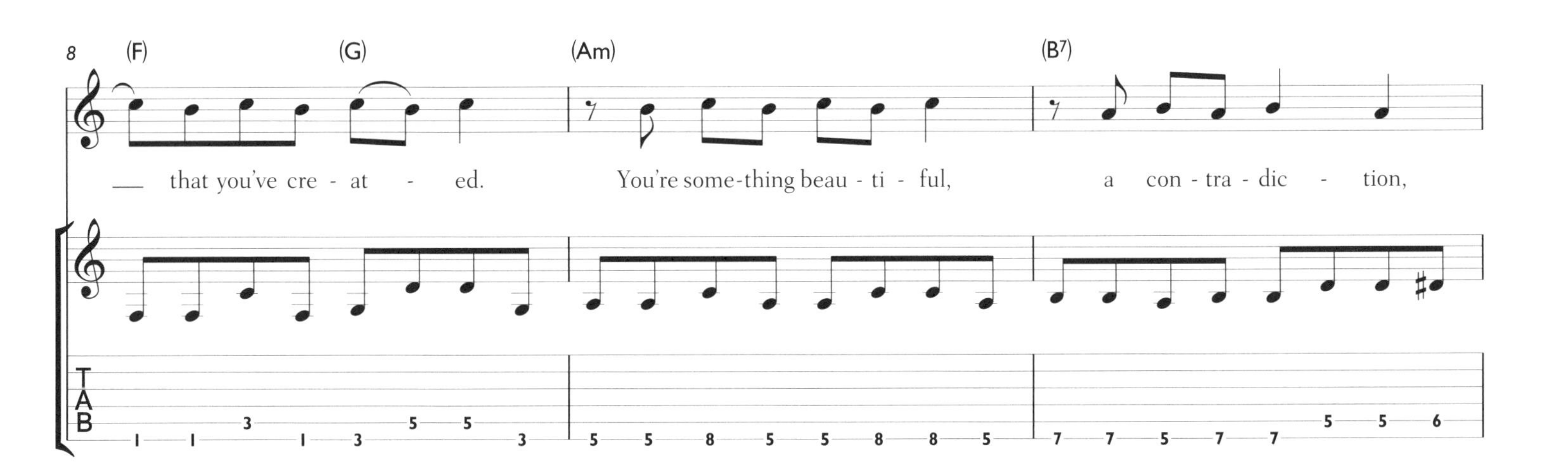

11
(E)
(F)
(G)
(Am)
I wan - na play the game, I want the fric - tion. You will
Piano arr. for guitar
Fig. 2
Bass arr. Gtr. plays Fig. 1
14
(B7♯5)
(E)
(F)
(G)
be the death of me. A - yeah,
Fig. 2
17
(Am)
(B7♯5)
(E)
(F)
(G)
you will be the death of me.
21
F
G
Am
C
Bu - ry it, I won't let you bu - ry it, I won't let you
Gtr. 1
P.M.

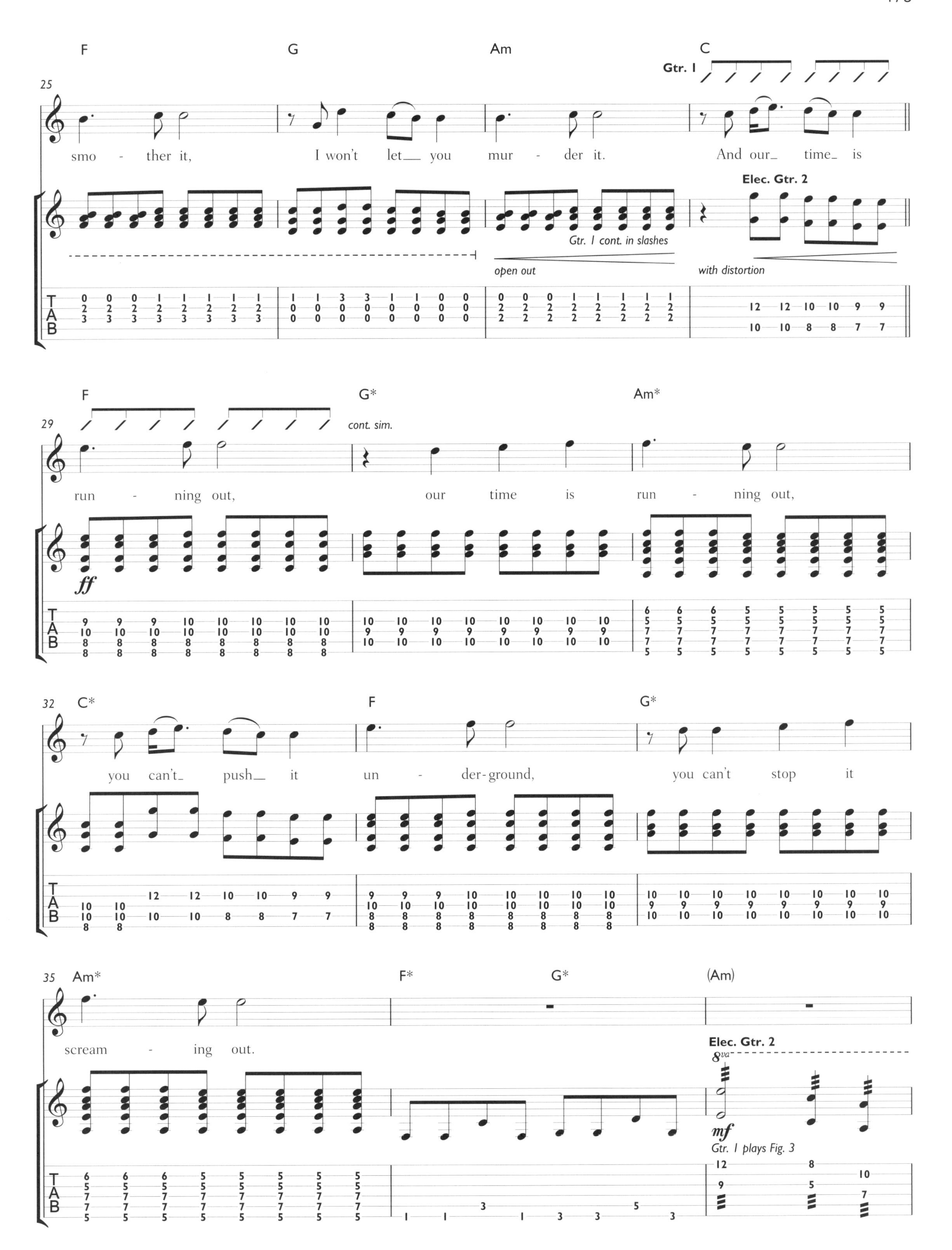
F G Am C
Gtr. 1
25
smo - ther it, I won't let you mur - der it. And our time is
Elec. Gtr. 2
Gtr. 1 cont. in slashes
open out
with distortion
F G* Am*
29
cont. sim.
run - ning out, our time is run - ning out,
ff
32 C* F G*
you can't push it un - der-ground, you can't stop it
35 Am* F* G* (Am)
scream - ing out.
Elec. Gtr. 2
8va
mf
Gtr. 1 plays Fig. 3

38
(B7♯5)
(E)
(F)
(G)
(8)
11
8
8
5
10
7
9
6
12
9
12
9
13
10
10
7
12
9
41
(Am)
(B7)
(E)
2. I want - ed free - dom, bound and re - strict - ed, I tried to give you up,
Gtr. 1
Fig. 3
mf double at 8ve with whammy pedal
44
(F)
(G)
(Am)
(B7)
but I'm ad - dic - ted. Now that you know I'm trapped, sense of e - la - tion,
Fig. 3
47
(E)
(F)
(G)
(Am)
(B7♯5)
you'd nev - er dream of breaking this fix - a - tion. You will squeeze the

51
(E)
(F)
(G)
F
G
life out of me. And bu - ry it, I won't let you
55
Am
C
F
G
bu - ry it, I won't let you smoth - er it, I won't let you
Am
C
F
cont. sim.
59
Gtr. 1
mur - der it. Our time is run - ning out,
Gtr. 2
Gtr. 1 cont. in slashes
f
62
G*
Am*
C*
our time is run - ning out, you can't push it

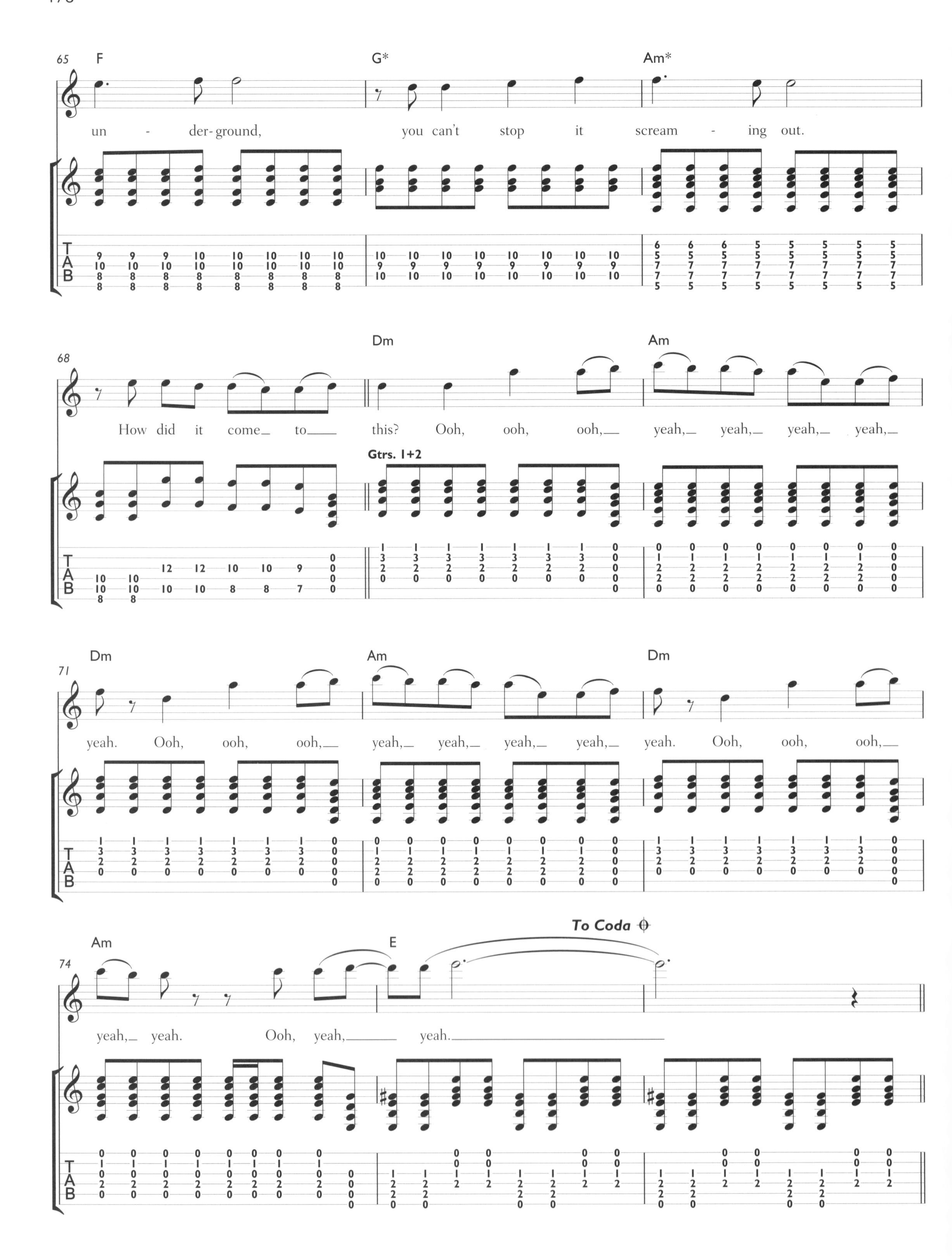
65
F
G*
Am*
un - der-ground, you can't stop it scream - ing out.
68
Dm
Am
How did it come_ to___ this? Ooh, ooh, ooh,__ yeah,_ yeah,_ yeah,_ yeah,_
Gtrs. 1+2
71
Dm
Am
Dm
yeah. Ooh, ooh, ooh,__ yeah,_ yeah,_ yeah,_ yeah,_ yeah. Ooh, ooh, ooh,__
To Coda
74
Am
E
yeah,_ yeah. Ooh, yeah,____ yeah.____

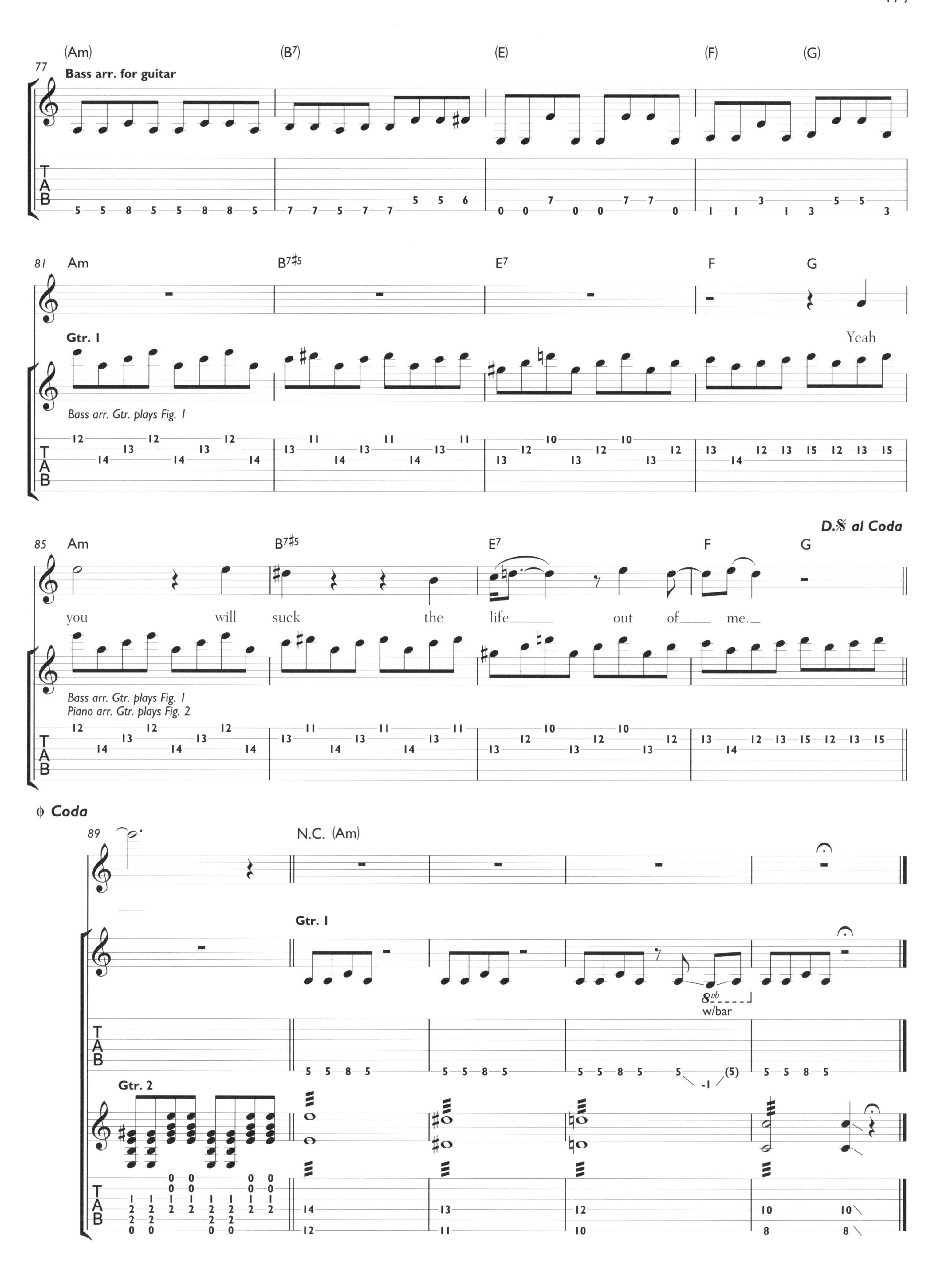
(Am)
Bass arr. for guitar
(B7)
(E)
(F)
(G)
Am
B7♯5
E7
F
G
Gtr. 1
Yeah
Bass arr. Gtr. plays Fig. 1
D.𝄋 al Coda
you will suck the life out of me.
Piano arr. Gtr. plays Fig. 2
Coda
N.C. (Am)
w/bar
Gtr. 2

UNINTENDED

Words and Music by Matthew Bellamy

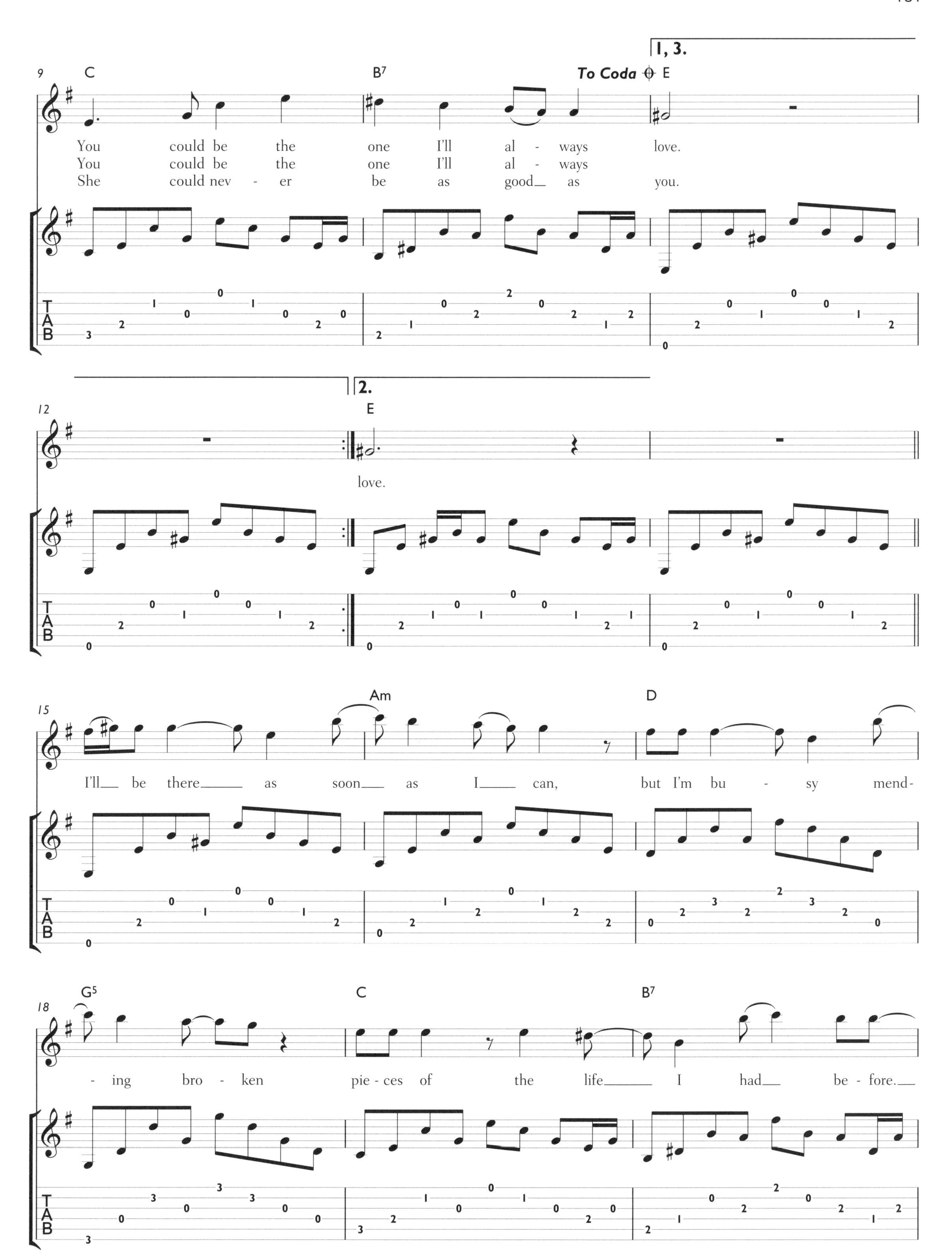
1, 3.
9
C
B7
To Coda
E
You could be the one I'll al - ways love.
You could be the one I'll al - ways
She could nev - er be as good as you.
TAB
2.
12
E
love.
15
Am
D
I'll be there as soon as I can, but I'm bu - sy mend-
18
G5
C
B7
- ing bro - ken pie - ces of the life I had be - fore.

21
E
D.𝄋 al Coda
with repeats
Coda
23
E
Em
B7
love.
25
E
Am
D
I'll be there as soon as I can, but I'm bu - sy mend -
28
G5
C
- ing bro - ken pie - ces of the life
T
A
B

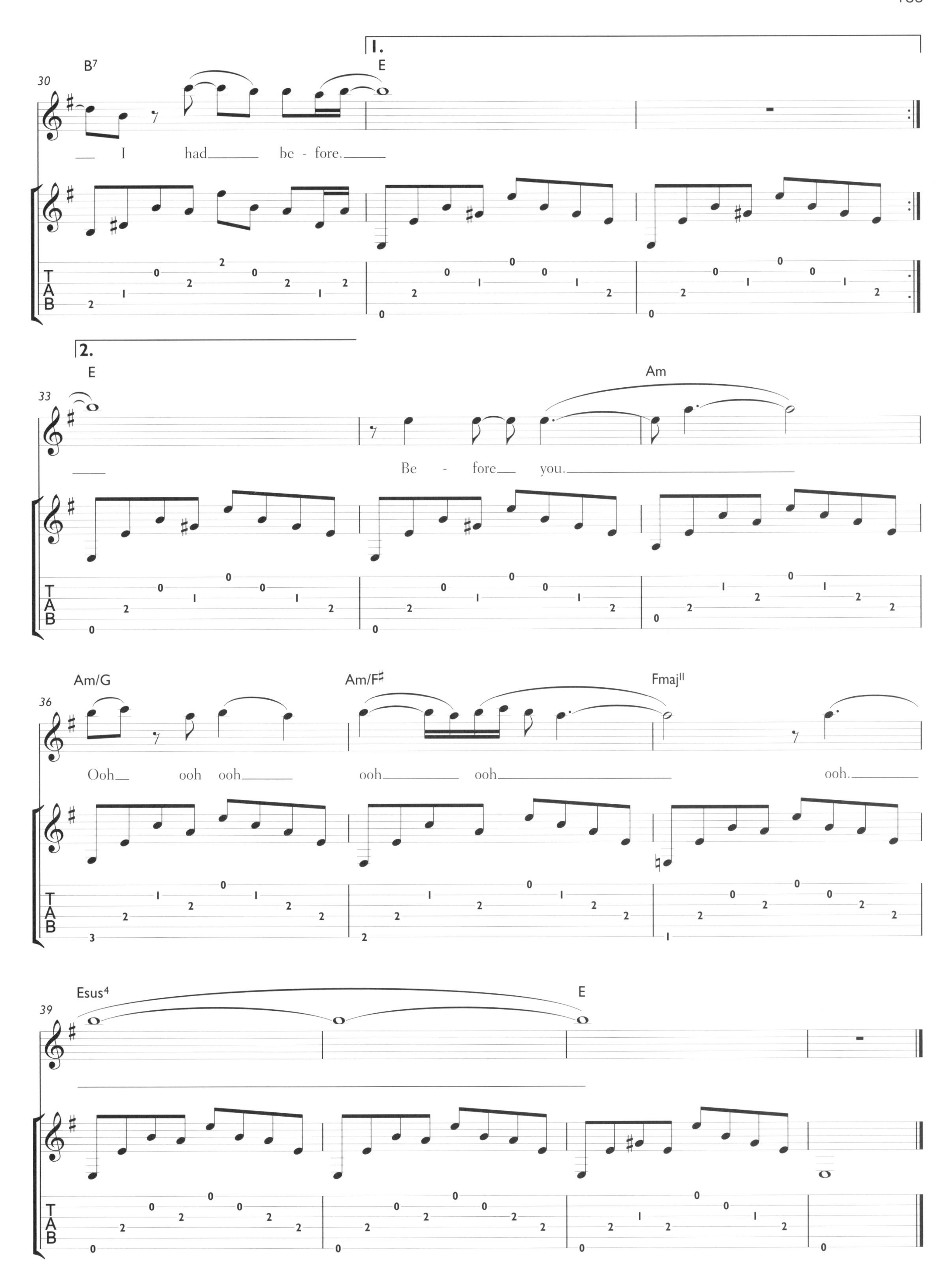
B7
1.
E
I
had
be - fore.
2.
E
Am
Be - fore
you.
Am/G
Am/F♯
Fmaj11
Ooh
ooh
ooh
ooh
ooh
ooh.
Esus4
E

UNNATURAL SELECTION

Words and Music by Matthew Bellamy

(G)
(B♭)
(C)
(D)
(F)
(F♯)
Fig. 1
1. I am hun - gry for some un - rest, I want to push this be - yond a peace-ful pro - test,
2. No re - li - gion or mind vi - rus, is there a hope that the facts will ev - er find us,
2º Elec. Gtr. 1
1º Elec. Gtr. 1 plays Fig. 1
I wan-na speak in a lang - uage that they'll un - der - stand.
just make sure that you are look - ing out for num - ber one.

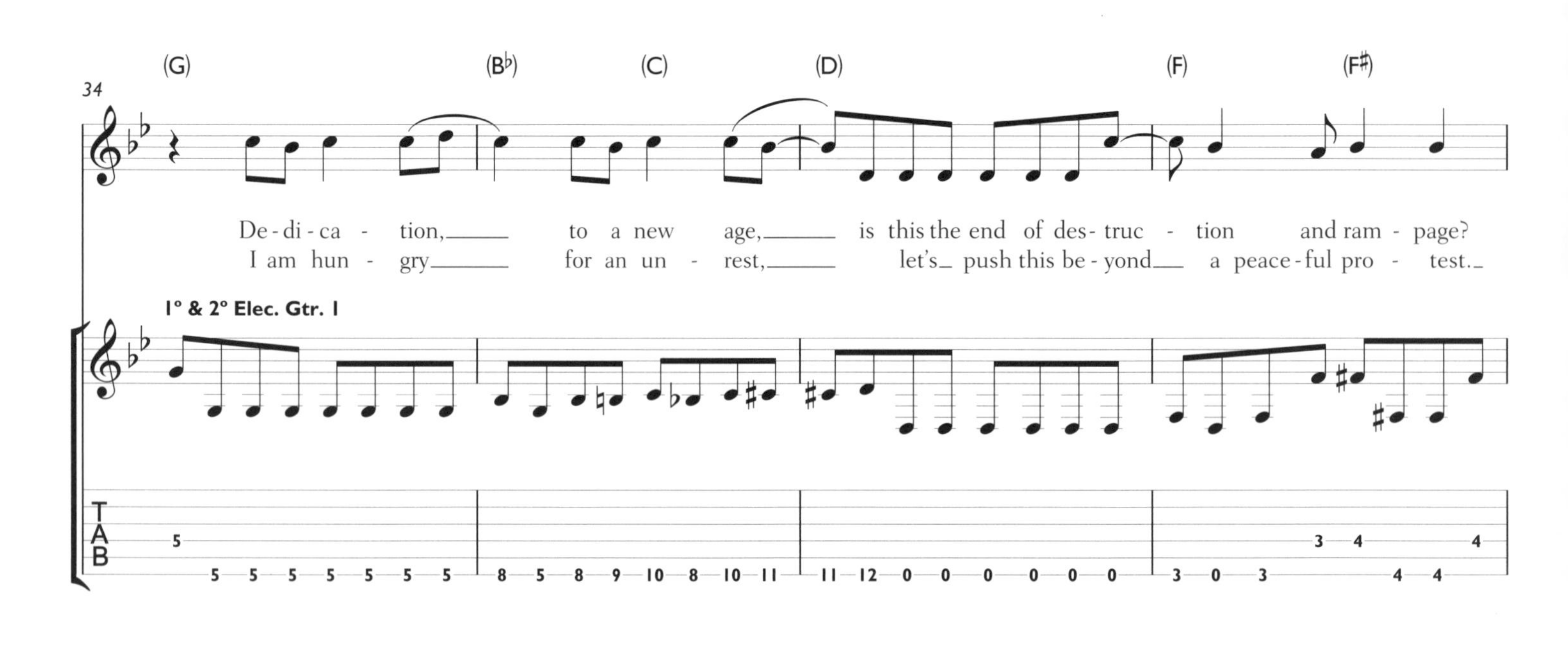
(G)
(B♭)
(C)
(D)
(F)
(F♯)
34
De - di - ca - tion, to a new age, is this the end of des - truc - tion and ram - page?
I am hun - gry for an un - rest, let's push this be - yond a peace - ful pro - test.
1° & 2° Elec. Gtr. 1
TAB

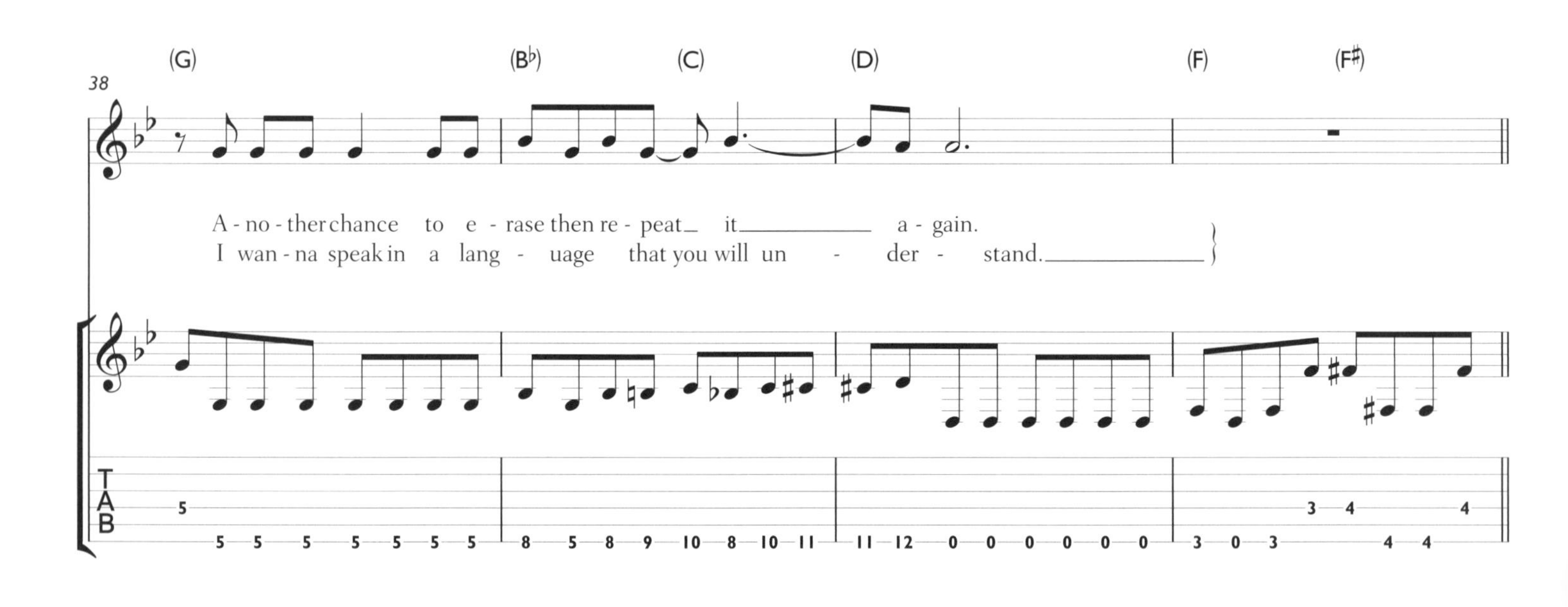
(G)
(B♭)
(C)
(D)
(F)
(F♯)
38
A - no - ther chance to e - rase then re - peat it a - gain.
I wan - na speak in a lang - uage that you will un - der - stand.
TAB

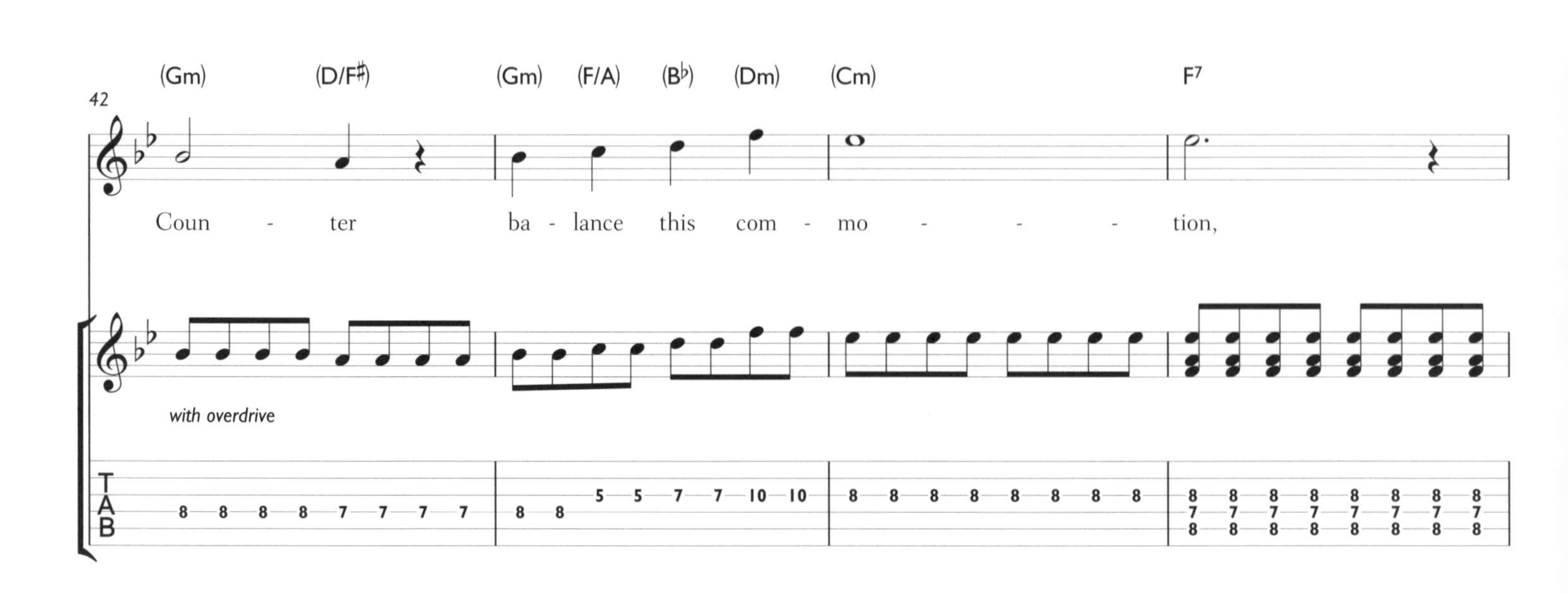
(Gm)
(D/F♯)
(Gm)
(F/A)
(B♭)
(Dm)
(Cm)
F7
42
Coun - ter ba - lance this com - mo - - - tion,
with overdrive
TAB

(B♭) (F/A) (B♭) (F/A) (Gm) (D/F♯) (Gm) (D5)
46
we're not drop - lets in the o - - - cean,
(Gm) (D) G5
50
o - - - cean.
1.3. They'll laugh as they watch
2. They'll laugh as they watch
Elec. Gtr. 1
let ring
ff P.M.
2° Elec. Gtr. 2
with overdrive
Cm C7 F5
54
us fall,
us crawl,
the luck - y don't care
the luck - y don't share
P.M.

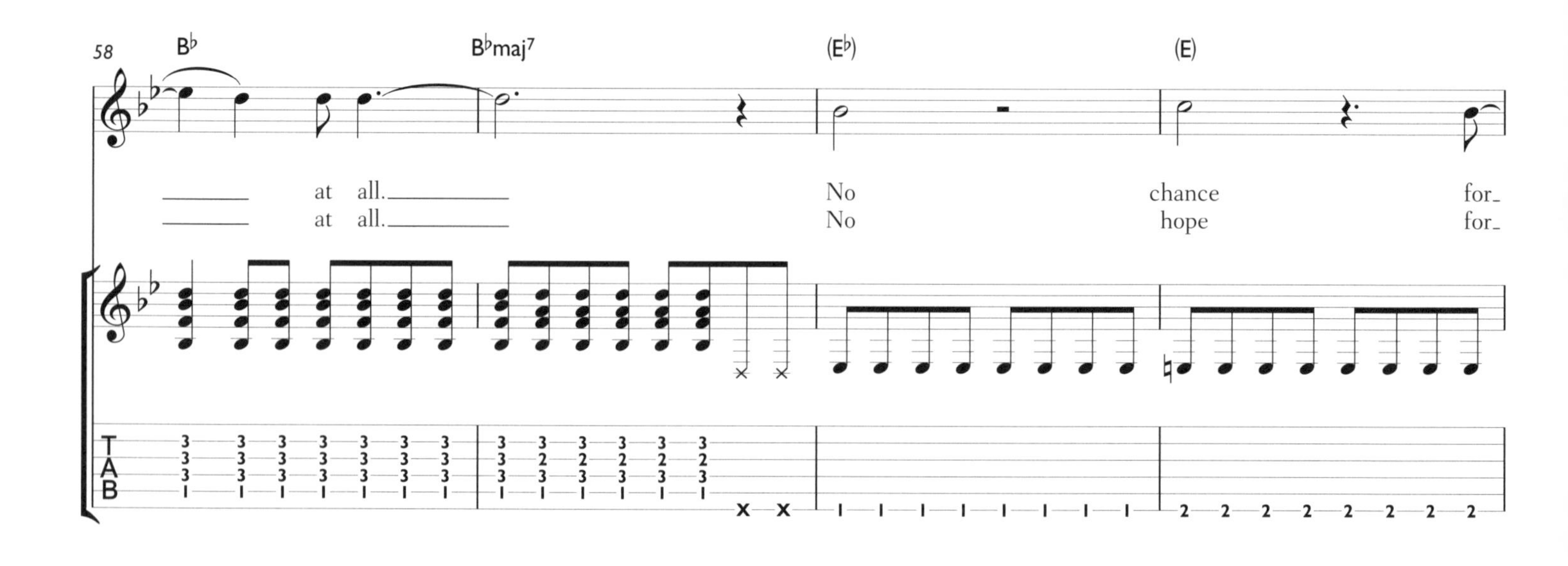
58
B♭
B♭maj7
(E♭)
(E)
at all.
at all.
No
No
chance
hope
for
for
T
A
B

To Coda
62
(F)
(F♯)
(G)
(E♭)
(F)
fate, it's un - na - tu - ral se - lec - tion, I want the
fate, it's a ran - dom chance se - lec - tion, I want the
T
A
B

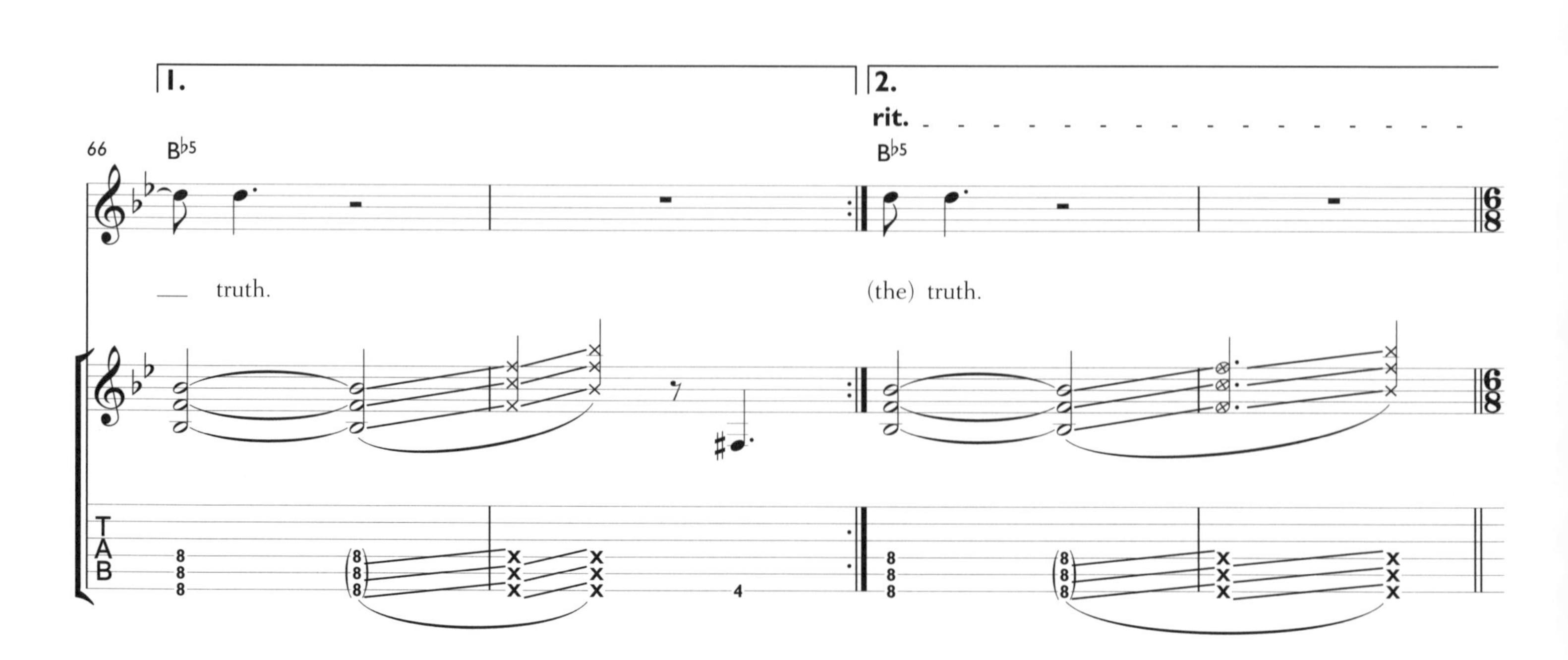
1.
2.
rit.
66
B♭5
B♭5
truth.
(the) truth.
T
A
B

♩ = 50 Shuffle feel

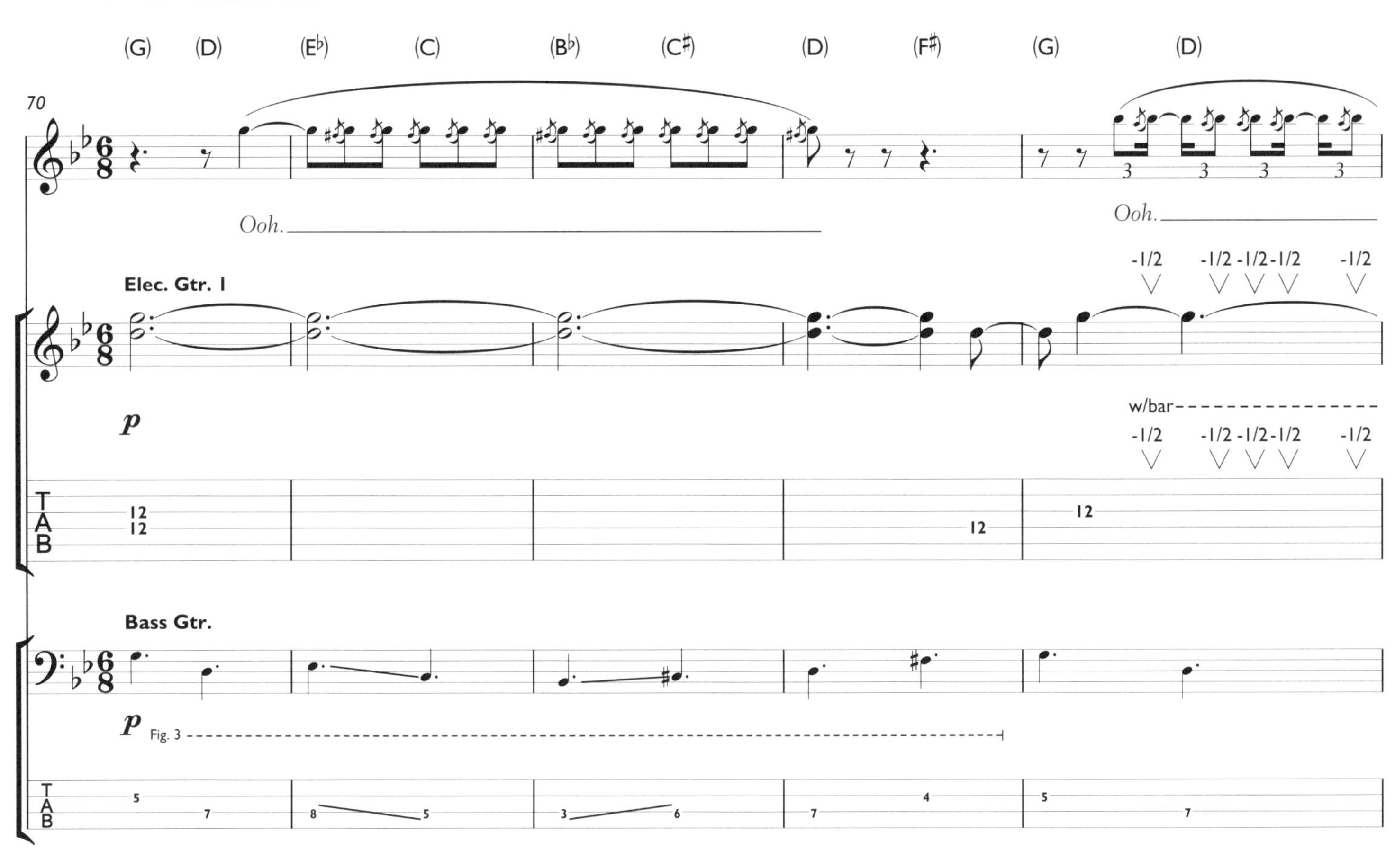
(G)
(D)
(E♭)
(C)
(B♭)
(C♯)
(D)
(F♯)
(G)
(D)
70
Ooh.
Ooh.
Elec. Gtr. 1
w/bar
-1/2
Bass Gtr.
Fig. 3

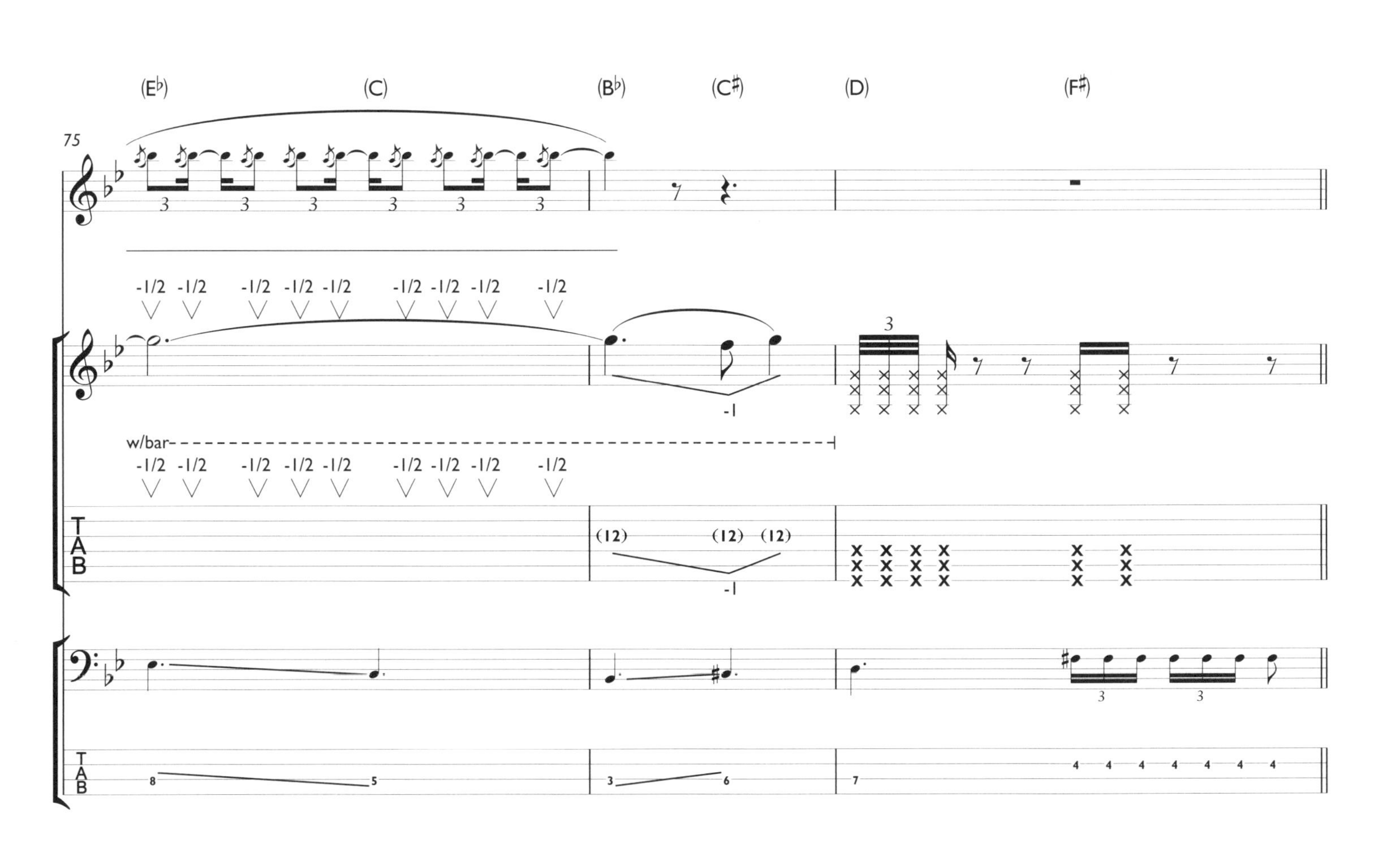
(E♭)
(C)
(B♭)
(C♯)
(D)
(F♯)
75
-1/2
w/bar

1.
2.
(G) (D) (E♭) (C) (B♭) (C♯) (D) (F♯) (D) (F♯)
Elec. Gtr. 1
mf
Try to ride out the storm, whilst they'll make you be-lieve
Bass guitar plays fig. 3
that they are the spe-cial ones.
(We have not been cho-sen.)
w/bar-

95
(G)
(D)
(E♭)
(C)
let ring
let ring
97
(B♭)
(C♯)
(D)
(F♯)
let ring
full
99
(G)
(D)
(E♭)
(C)
(B♭)
(C♯)
(D)
(F♯)
In - jus - tice is the norm, you are not the first,
tr
1/2
rit.
103
(G)
(D)
(E♭)
(C)
(B♭)
(C♯)
(D)
and you know you won't be the last.
trem dive.
1/2
trem dive.

♩ = 159
(Gm) (D/F♯) (Gm) (F/A) (B♭) (Dm) (Cm) F7 (B♭) (F/A)
Coun - ter ba - lance this com - mo - - - tion, we're not
(B♭) (F/A) (Gm) (D/F♯) (Gm) (D5) (Gm) (D5)
drop - lets in the o - - - cean, o - - - cean,
let ring
(Gm) (D) (Gm) (D)
D.𝄋 al Coda
o - - - cean, o - - - cean.
Elec. Gtr. 1
let ring
Elec. Gtr. 2
let ring

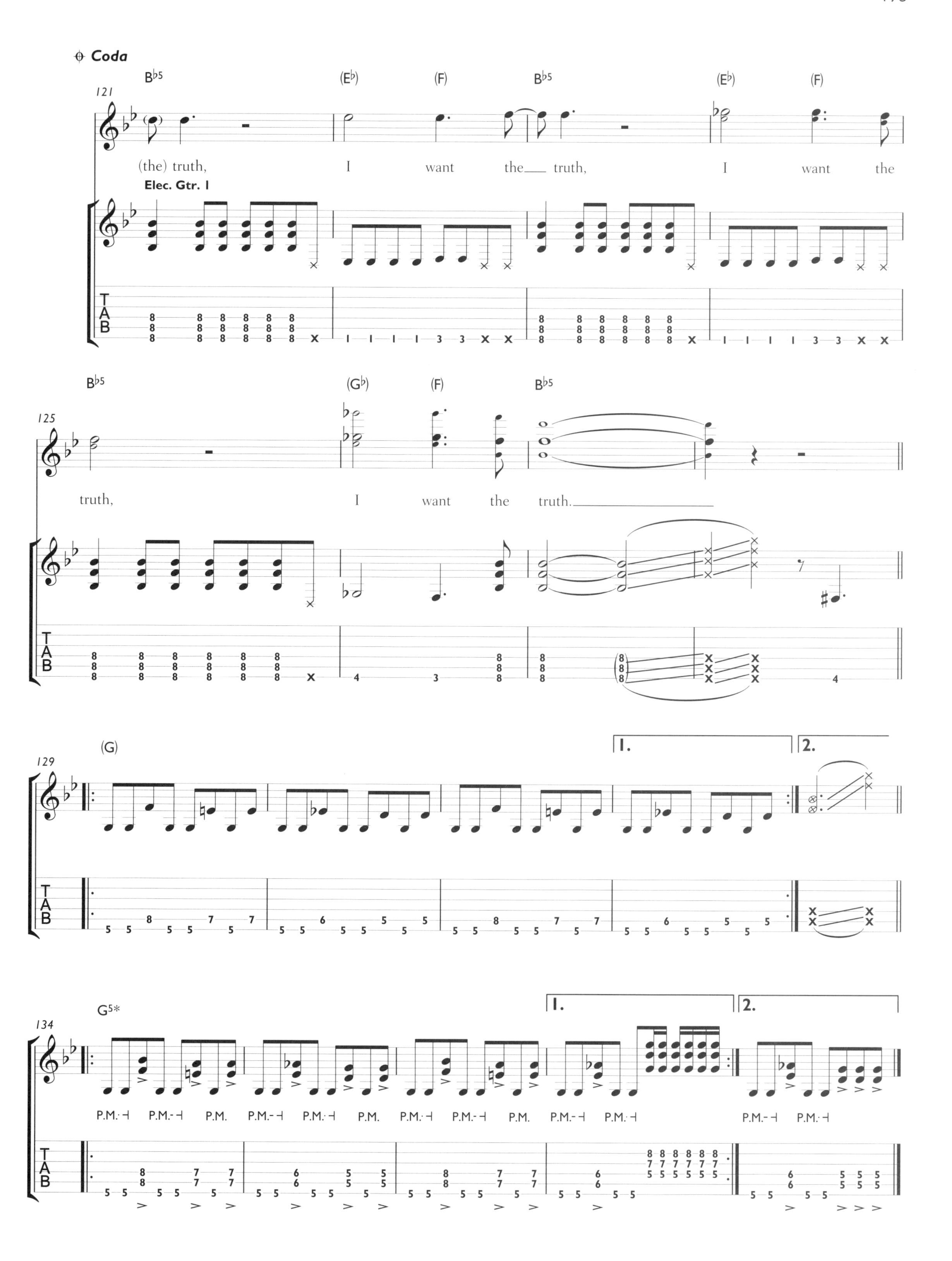
Coda
B♭5
(E♭)
(F)
121
(the) truth,
I
want
the
truth,
I
want
the
Elec. Gtr. 1
125
(G♭)
truth,
I
want
the
truth.
(G)
129
1.
2.
G5*
134
P.M.

UPRISING

Words and Music by Matthew Bellamy

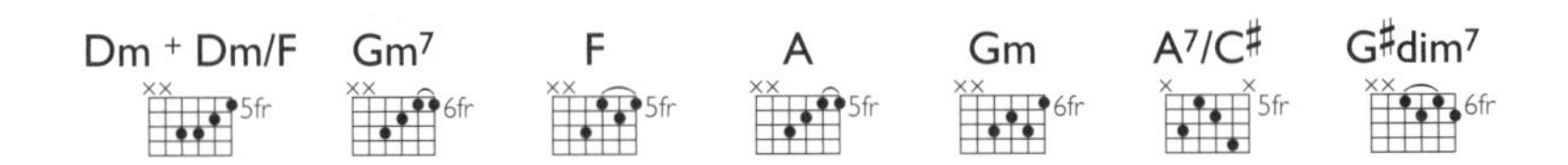

Electric Guitar in drop-D tuning

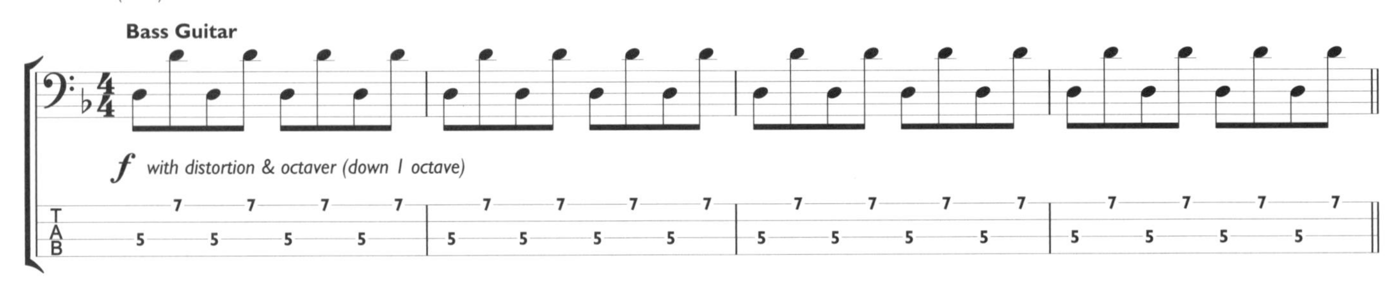

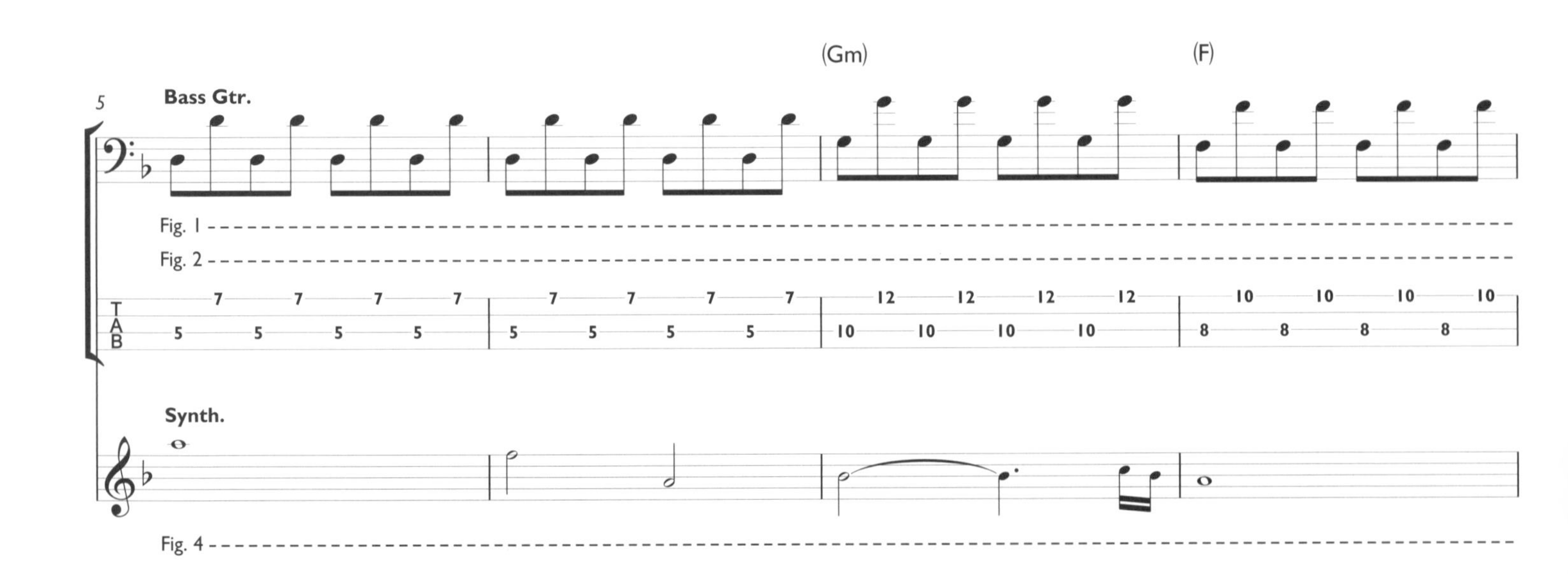

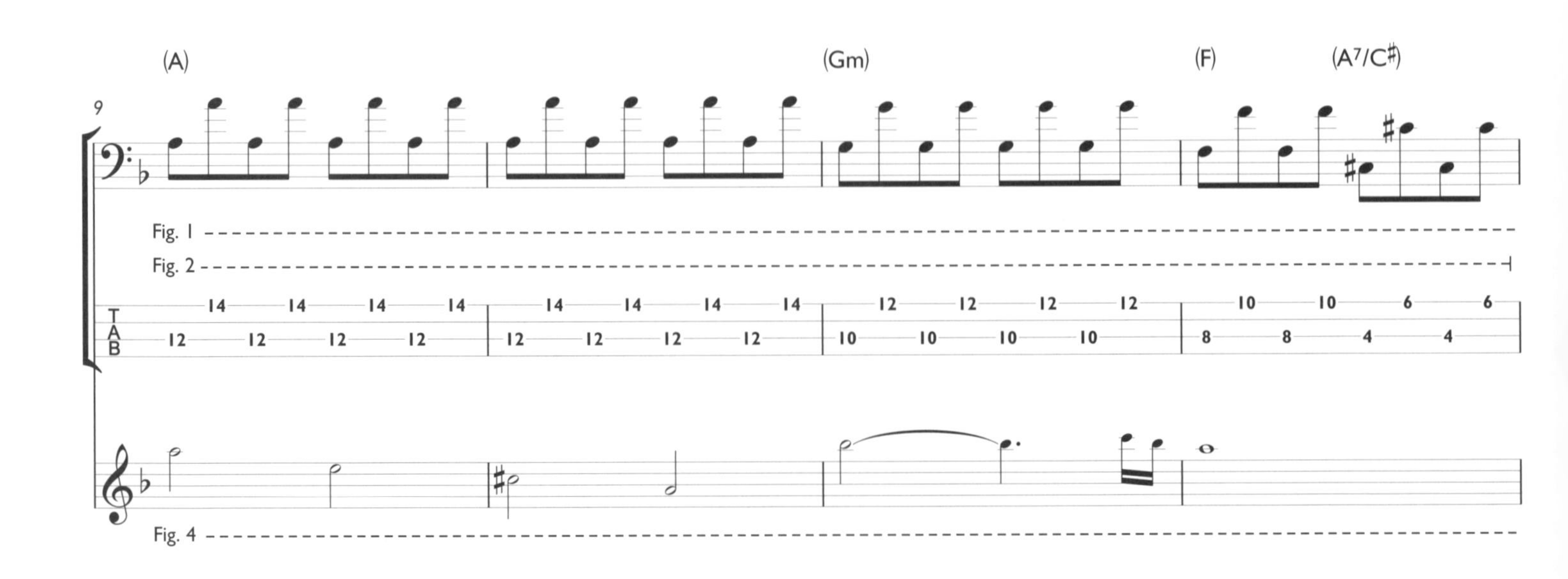

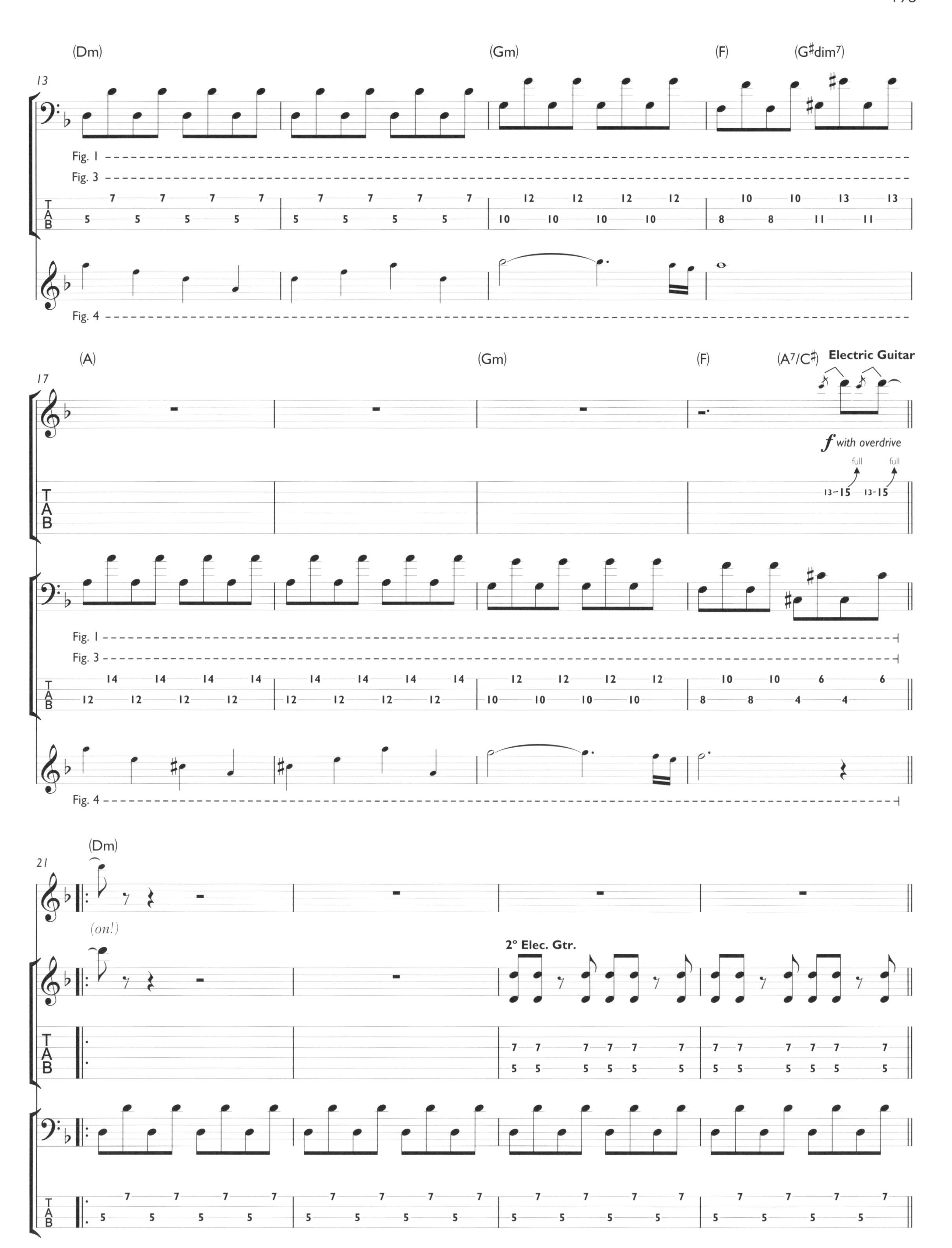
(Dm)
(Gm)
(F)
(G♯dim7)
13
Fig. 1
Fig. 3
Fig. 4
(A)
(Gm)
(F)
(A7/C♯)
Electric Guitar
17
f with overdrive
full
full
(Dm)
21
(on!)
2º Elec. Gtr.

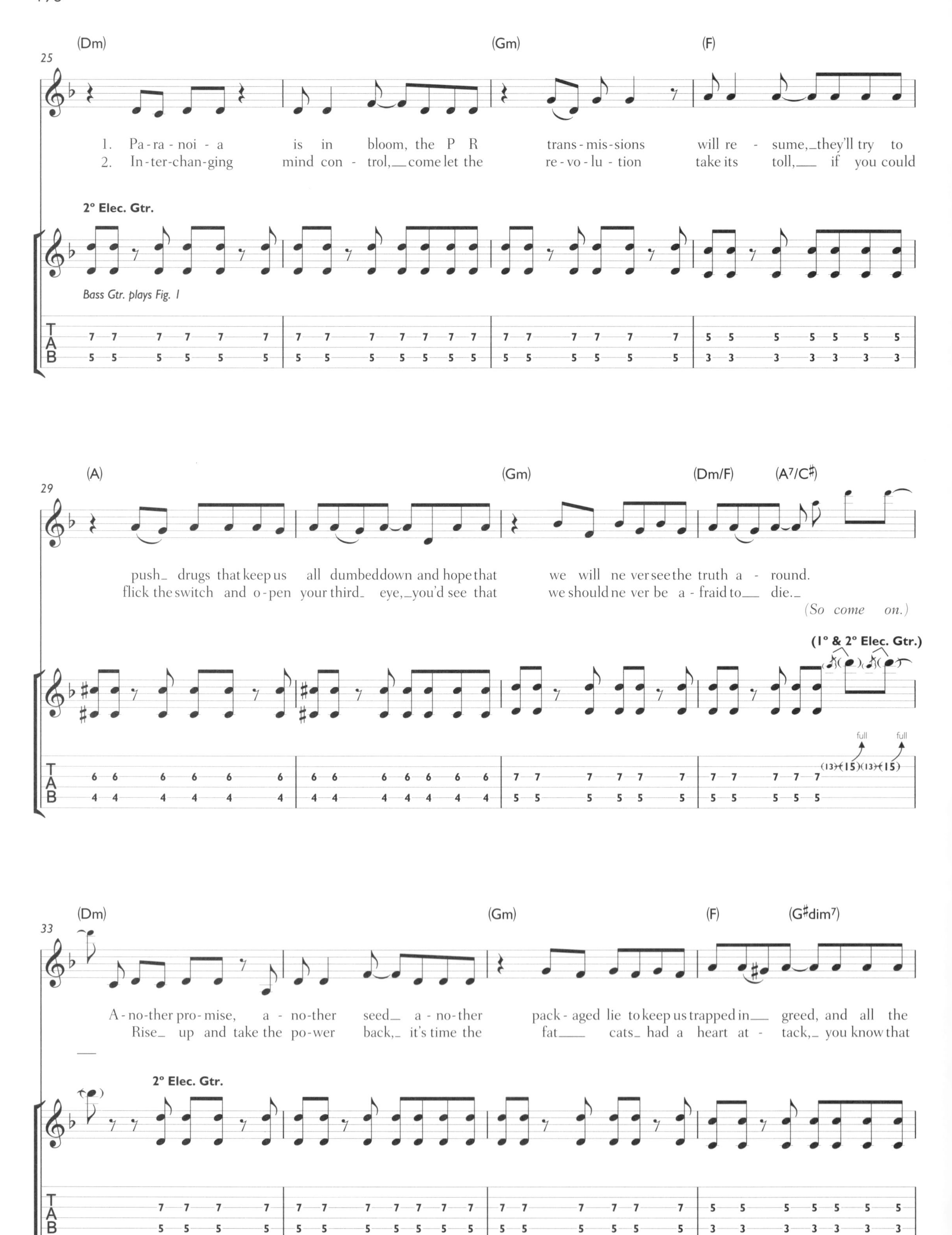
(Dm)
25
(Gm)
(F)
1. Pa-ra-noi-a is in bloom, the P R trans-mis-sions will re-sume, they'll try to
2. In-ter-chan-ging mind con-trol, come let the re-vo-lu-tion take its toll, if you could
2° Elec. Gtr.
Bass Gtr. plays Fig. 1
TAB
(A)
29
(Gm)
(Dm/F)
(A7/C♯)
push drugs that keep us all dumbed down and hope that we will ne ver see the truth a-round.
flick the switch and o-pen your third eye, you'd see that we should ne ver be a-fraid to die.
(So come on.)
(1° & 2° Elec. Gtr.)
full
full
(Dm)
33
(Gm)
(F)
(G♯dim7)
A-no-ther pro-mise, a-no-ther seed a-no-ther pack-aged lie to keep us trapped in greed, and all the
Rise up and take the po-wer back, it's time the fat cats had a heart at-tack, you know that
2° Elec. Gtr.

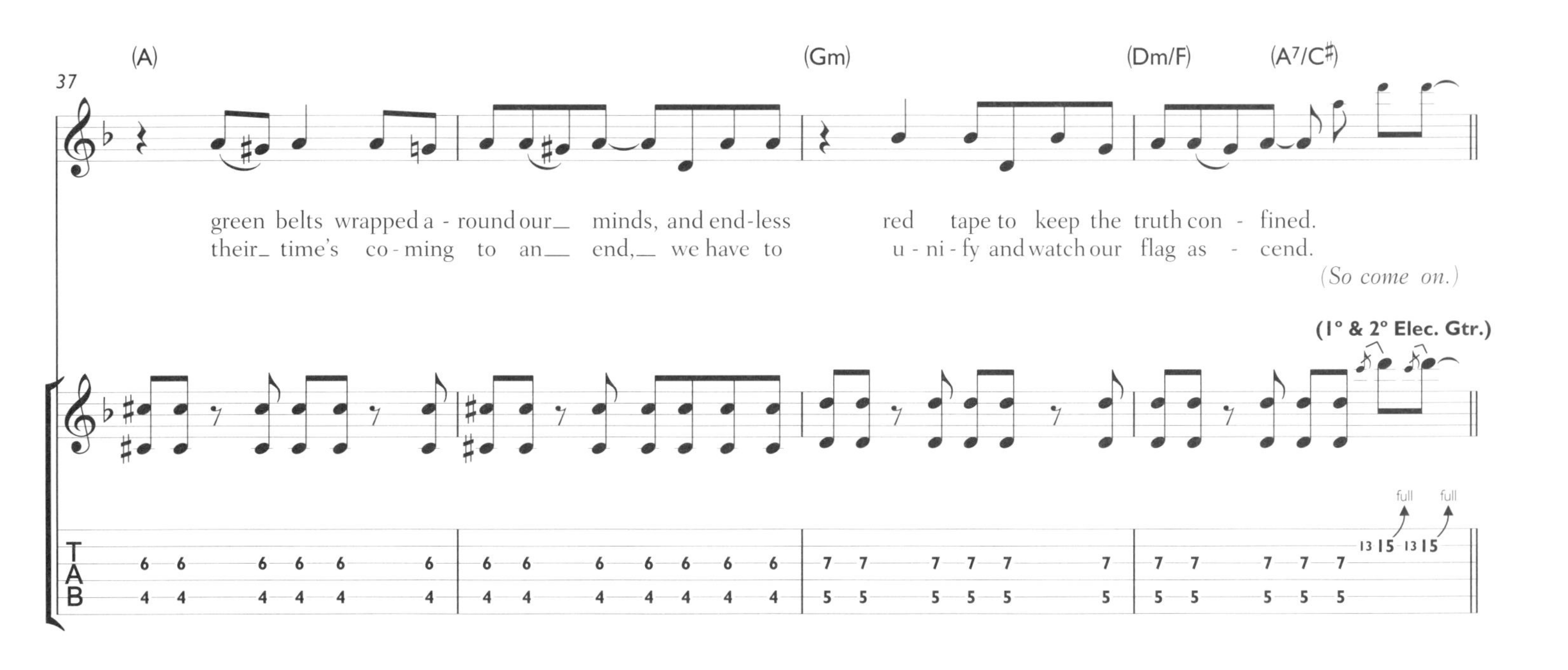
(A)
(Gm)
(Dm/F)
(A7/C♯)
37
green belts wrapped a - round our_ minds, and end-less red tape to keep the truth con - fined.
their_ time's co - ming to an_ end,_ we have to u - ni - fy and watch our flag as - cend.
(So come on.)
(1º & 2º Elec. Gtr.)
full
full
TAB

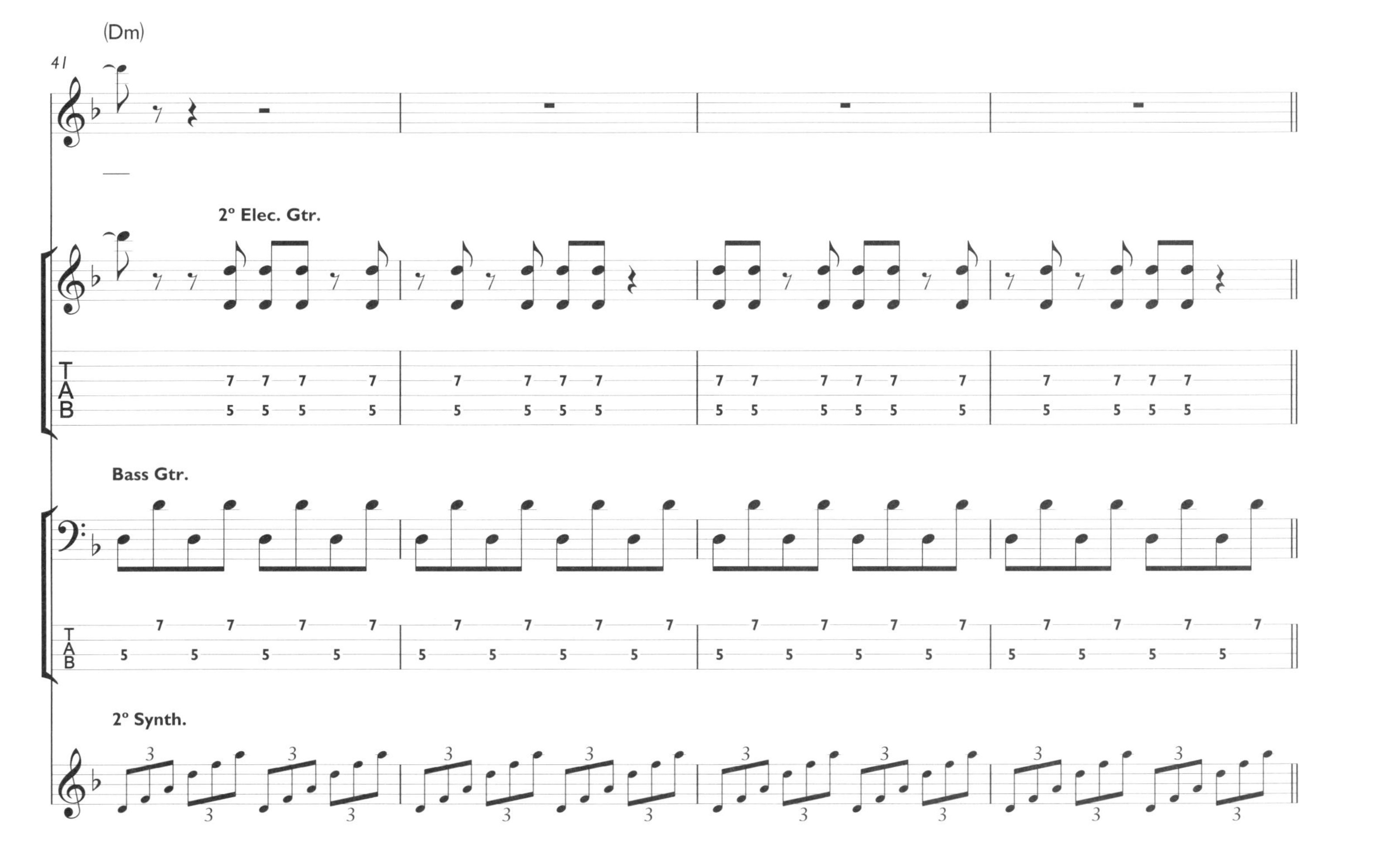
(Dm)
41
2º Elec. Gtr.
TAB
Bass Gtr.
TAB
2º Synth.

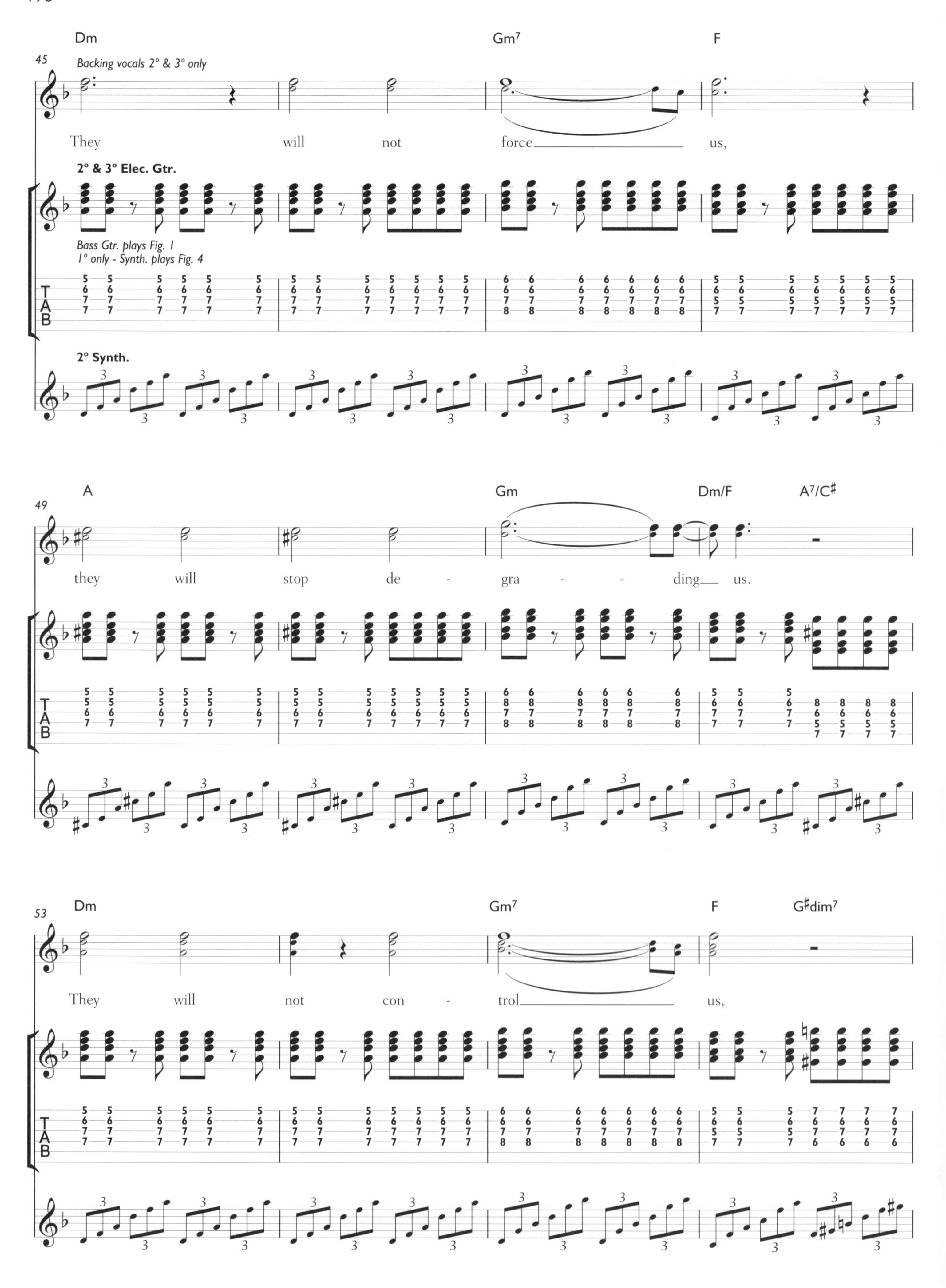
Dm
Gm7
F
45
Backing vocals 2° & 3° only
They will not force us,
2° & 3° Elec. Gtr.
Bass Gtr. plays Fig. 1
1° only - Synth. plays Fig. 4
TAB
2° Synth.
A
Gm
Dm/F
A7/C#
49
they will stop de - gra - - ding us.
Dm
Gm7
F
G#dim7
53
They will not con - trol us,

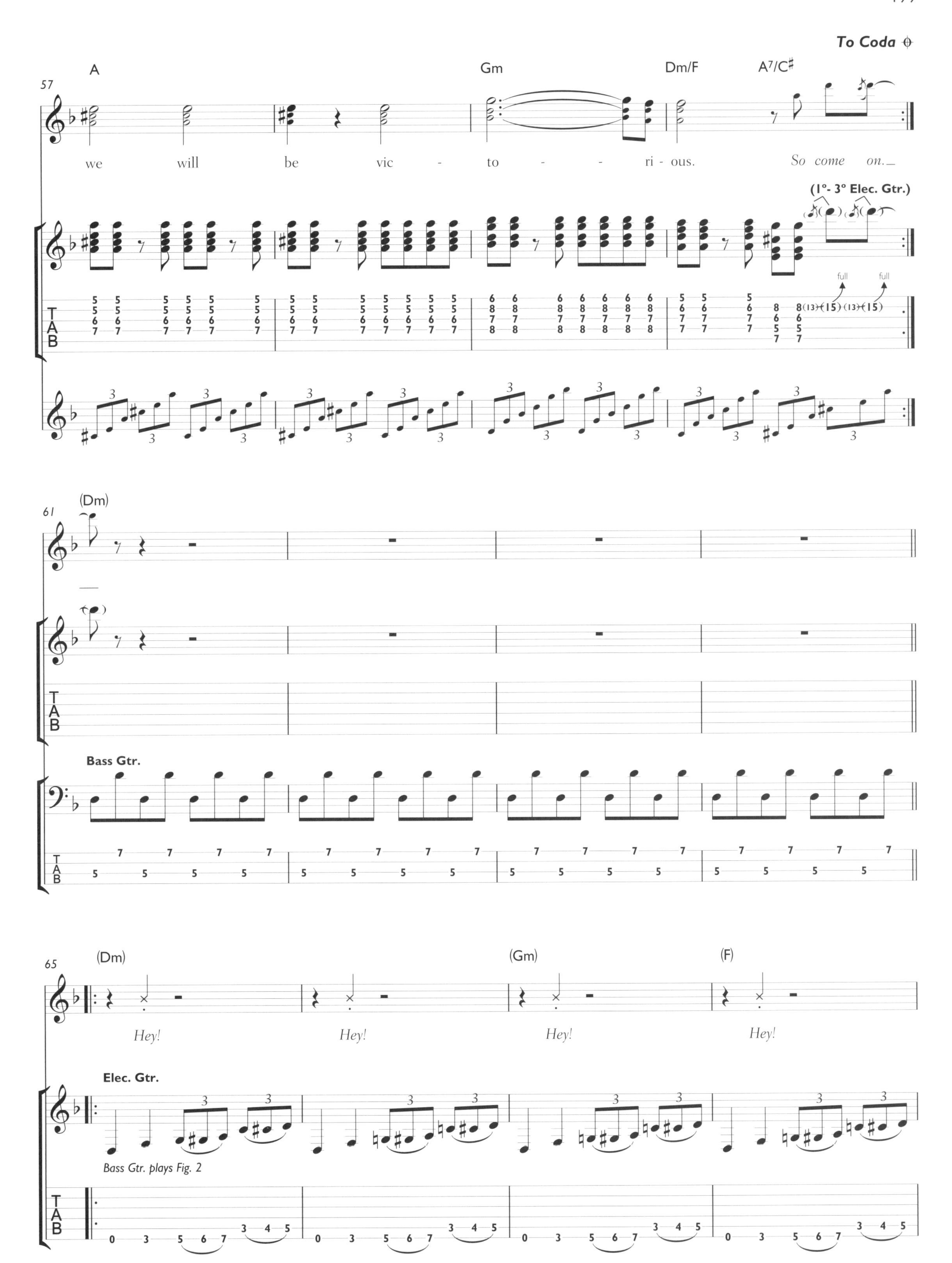
To Coda
A
Gm
Dm/F
A7/C#
we will be vic - to - - ri - ous. So come on.
(1º- 3º Elec. Gtr.)
full
full
(Dm)
Bass Gtr.
(Dm)
(Gm)
(F)
Hey! Hey! Hey! Hey!
Elec. Gtr.
Bass Gtr. plays Fig. 2

1.
(A)
(Gm)
(F)
(A7/C♯)
full
2.
(Dm)
(G♯dim7)
Hey!
Elec. Gtr.
Bass Gtr. plays Fig. 3
Synth.

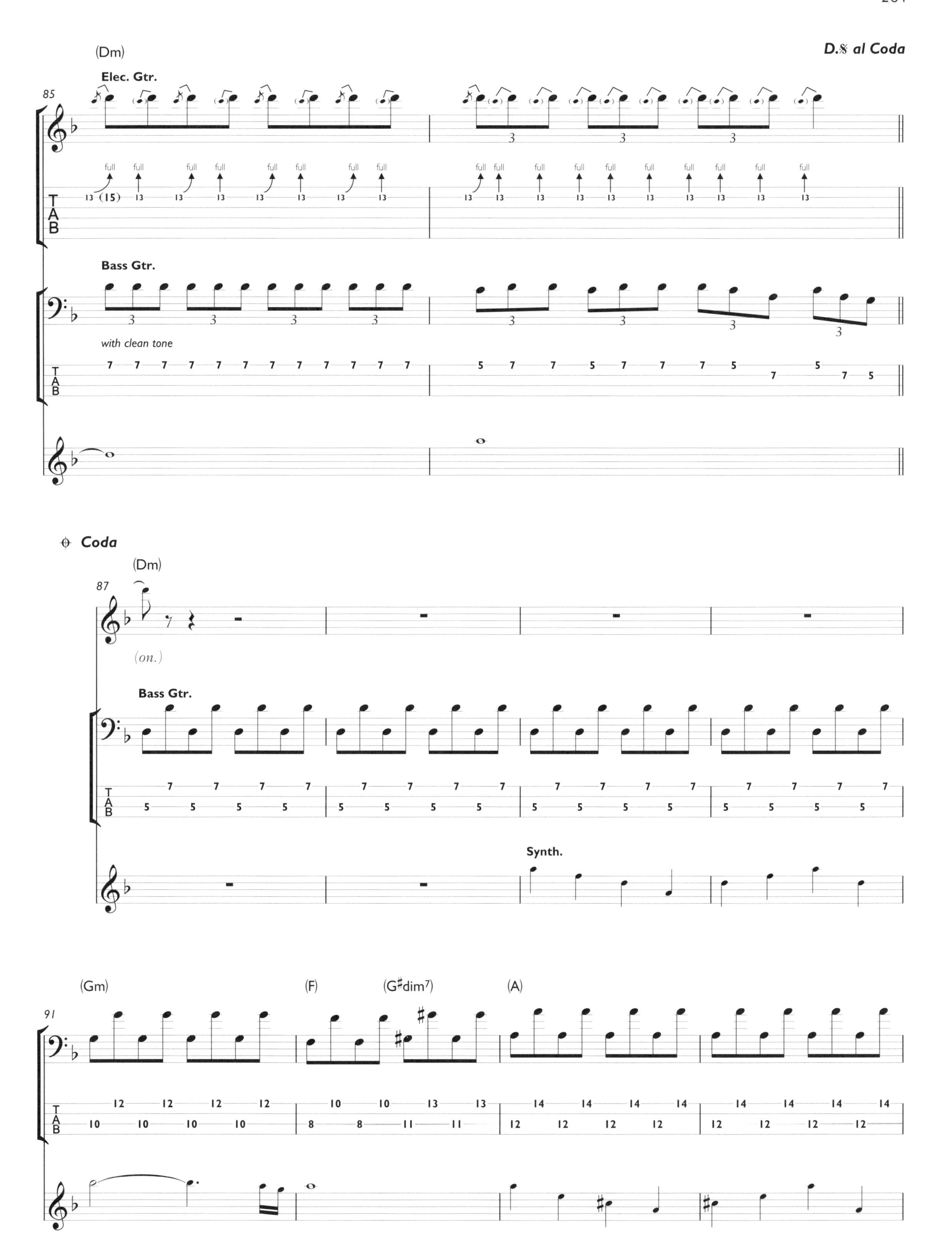
(Dm)
D.𝄋 al Coda
Elec. Gtr.
Bass Gtr.
with clean tone
Coda
(Dm)
(on.)
Bass Gtr.
Synth.
(Gm)
(F)
(G♯dim7)
(A)

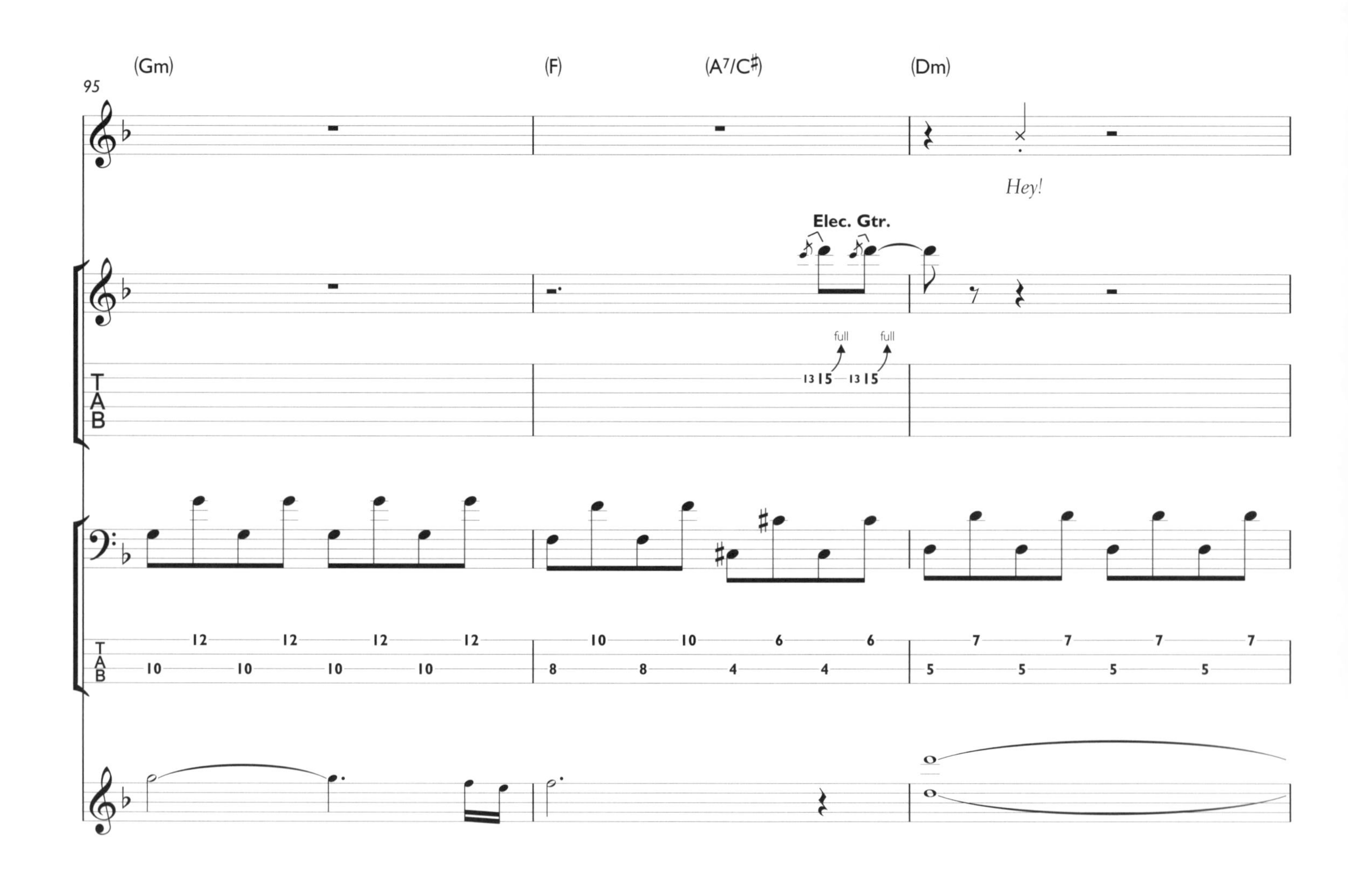
(Gm)
(F)
(A7/C♯)
(Dm)
95
Hey!
Elec. Gtr.
full
full
13 15 13 15
12 12 12 12
10 10 10 10
10 10 6 6
8 8 4 4
7 7 7 7
5 5 5 5

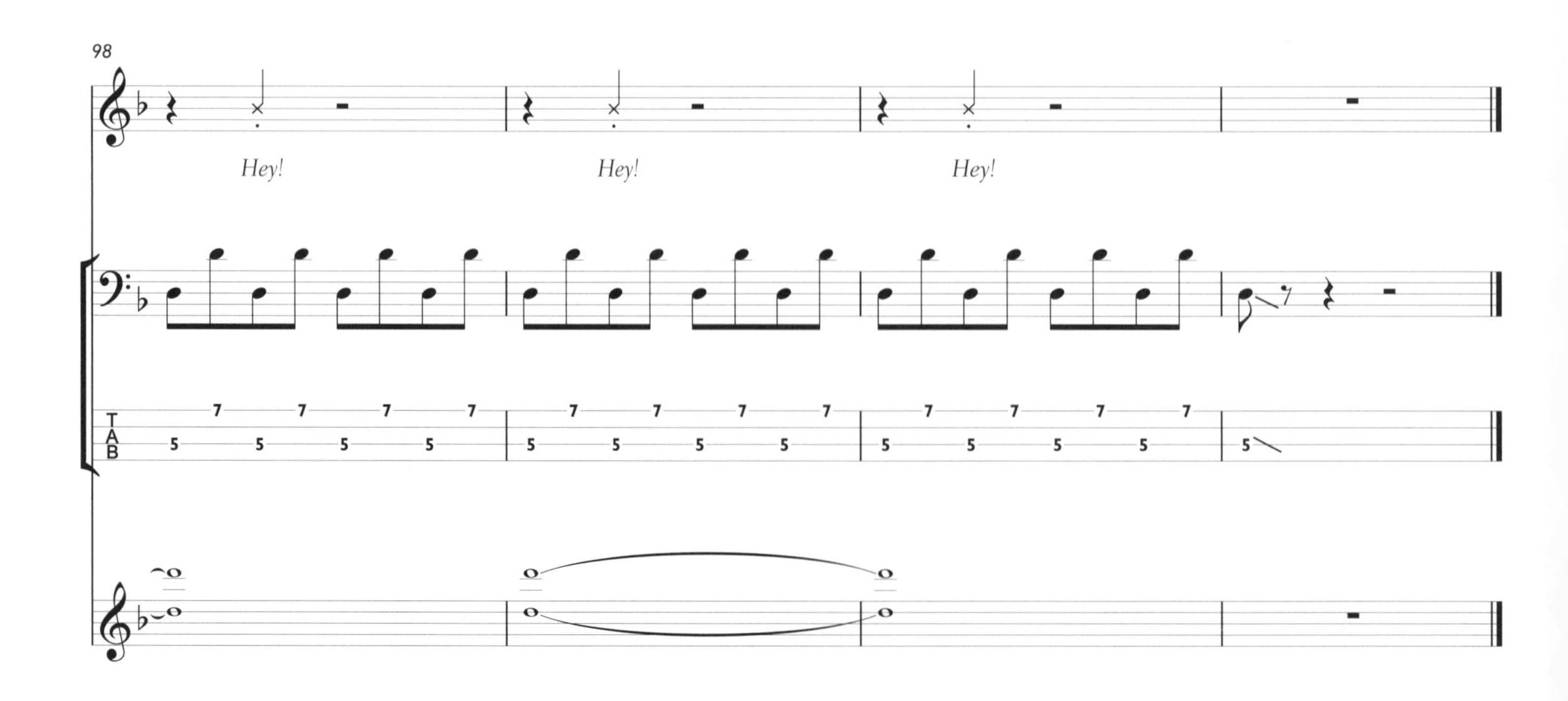
98
Hey!
Hey!
Hey!
7 7 7 7
5 5 5 5
7 7 7 7
5 5 5 5
7 7 7 7
5 5 5 5
5

Notation and Tablature explained

Understanding chord boxes

Chord boxes show the neck of your guitar as if viewed head on—the vertical lines represent the strings (low E to high E, from left to right), and the horizontal lines represent the frets.

An X above a string means 'don't play this string'.
An O above a string means 'play this open string'.
The black dots show you where to put your fingers.

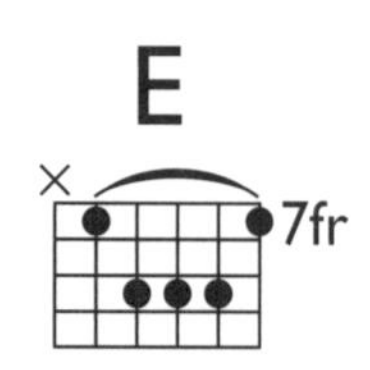

A curved line joining two dots on the fretboard represents a 'barre'. This means that you flatten one of your fingers (usually the first) so that you hold down all the strings between the two dots at the fret marked.

A fret marking at the side of the chord box shows you where chords that are played higher up the neck are located.

Tuning your guitar

The best way to tune your guitar is to use an electronic tuner. Alternatively, you can use relative tuning; this will ensure that your guitar is in tune with itself, but won't guarantee that you will be in tune with the original track (or any other musicians).

How to use relative tuning

Fret the low E string at the 5th fret and pluck; compare this with the sound of the open A string. The two notes should be in tune. If not, adjust the tuning of the A string until the two notes match.

Repeat this process for the other strings according to this diagram:

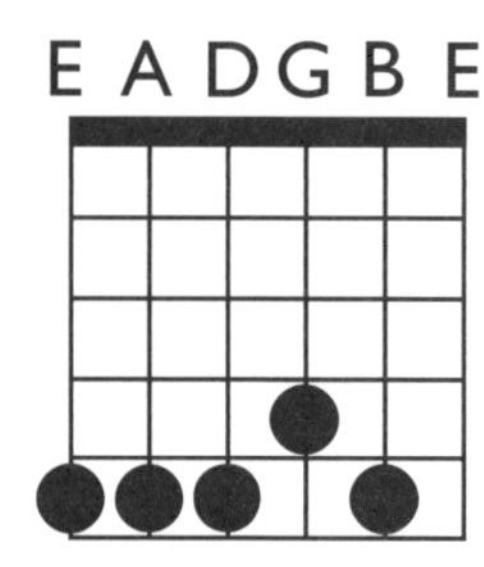

Note that the B string should match the note at the 4th fret of the G string, whereas all the other strings match the note at the 5th fret of the string below.

As a final check, ensure that the bottom E string and top E string are in tune with each other.

Detuning and Capo use

If the song uses an unconventional tuning, it will say so clearly at the top of the music, e.g. '6 = D' (tune string 6 to D) or 'detune guitar down by a semitone'. If a capo is used, it will tell you the fret number to which it must be attached. The standard notation will always be in the key at which the song sounds, but the guitar tab will take tuning changes into account. Just detune/add the capo and follow the fret numbers. The chord symbols will show the sounding chord above and the chord you actually play below in brackets.

Use of figures

In order to make the layout of scores clearer, figures that occur several times in a song will be numbered, e.g. 'Fig. 1', 'Fig. 2', etc.
A dotted line underneath shows the extent of the 'figure'. When a phrase is to be played, it will be marked clearly in the score, along with the instrument that should play it.

Reading Guitar Tab

Guitar tablature illustrates the six strings of the guitar graphically, showing you where you put your fingers for each note or chord. It is always shown with a stave in standard musical notation above it. The guitar tablature stave has six lines, each of them representing a different string. The top line is the high E string, the second line being the B string, and so on. Instead of using note heads, guitar tab uses numbers which show the fret number to be stopped by the left hand. The rhythm is indicated underneath the tab stave. Ex. 1 (below) shows four examples of single notes.

Ex. 2 shows four different chords. The 3rd one (Asus4) should be played as a barre chord at the 5th fret. The 4th chord (C9) is a half, or jazz chord shape. You have to mute the string marked with an 'x' (the A string in this case) with a finger of your fretting hand in order to obtain the correct voicing.

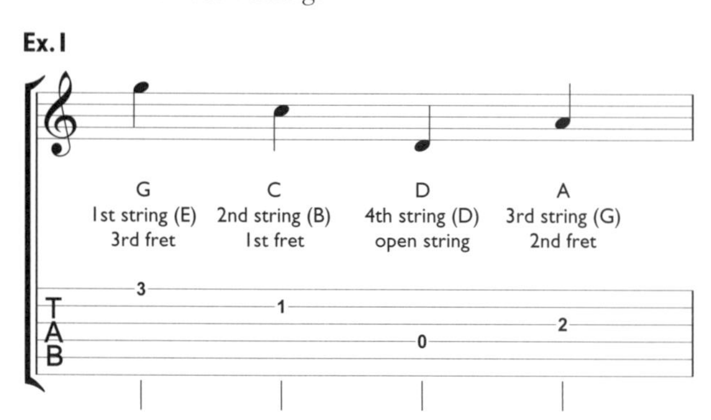

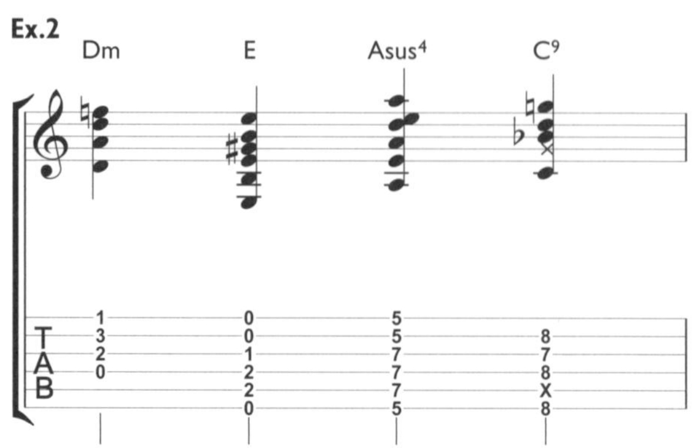

Notation of other guitar techniques

Picking hand techniques:

1. Down and up strokes
These symbols show that the first and third notes are to be played with a down stroke of the pick and the others up strokes.

2. Palm mute
Mute the notes with the palm of the picking hand by lightly touching the strings near the bridge.

3. Pick rake
Drag the pick across the indicated strings with a single sweep. The extra pressure will often mute the notes slightly and accentuate the final note.

4. Arpeggiated chords
Strum across the indicated strings in the direction of the arrow head of the wavy line.

5. Tremolo picking
Shown by the slashes on the stem of the note. Very fast alternate picking. Rapidly and continuously move the pick up and down on each note.

6. Pick scrape
Drag the edge of the pick up or down the lower strings to create a scraping sound.

7. Right hand tapping
'Tap' onto the note indicated by a '+' with a finger of the picking hand. It is nearly always followed by a pull-off to sound the note fretted below.

8. Tap slide
As with tapping, but the tapped note is slid randomly up the fretboard, then pulled off to the following note.

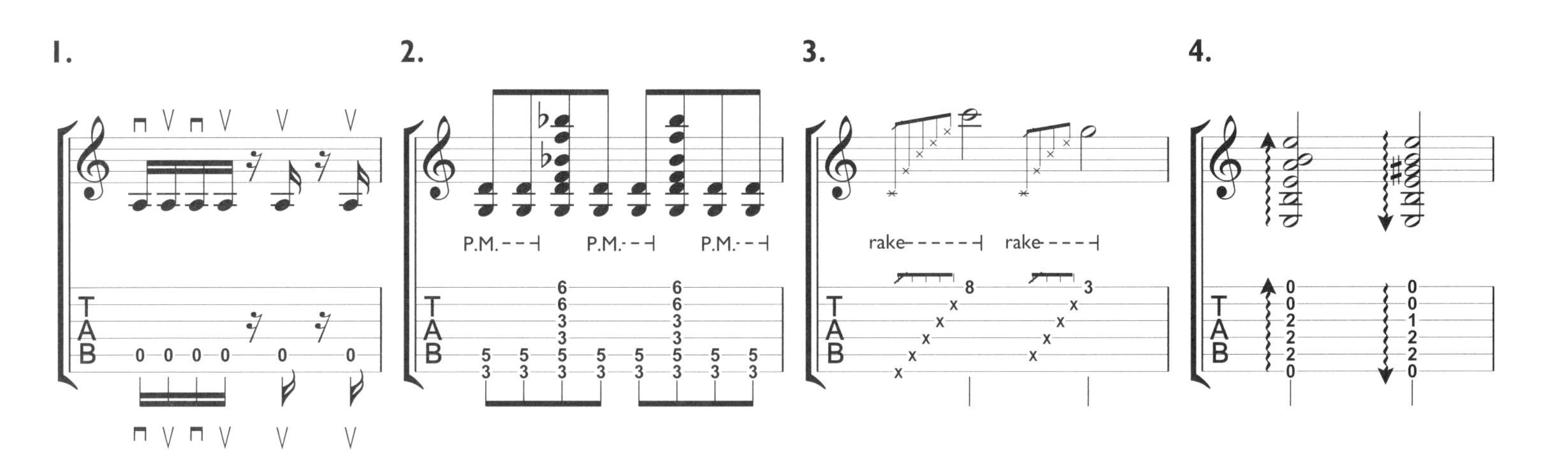

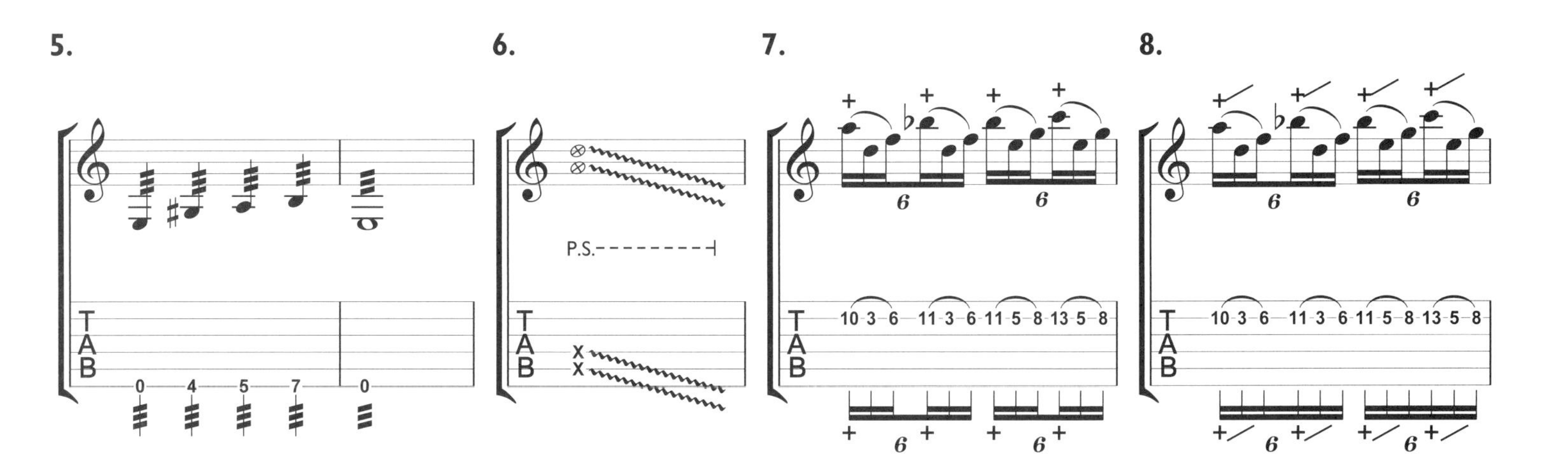

MUSE